**PERGAMON INTERNATIONAL LIBRARY**
**of Science, Technology, Engineering and Social Studies**
*The 1000-volume original paperback library in aid of education, industrial training and the enjoyment of leisure*
**Publisher: Robert Maxwell, M.C.**

# AIRCRAFT DYNAMIC STABILITY AND RESPONSE

## OTHER PERGAMON TITLES OF INTEREST

| | |
|---|---|
| CHERINGTON | Airline Price Policy |
| CURTIN | Trends in Communications Satellites |
| HEARN | Mechanics of Materials |
| KÜCHEMANN | The Aerodynamic Design of Aircraft |
| MANN & MILLIGAN | Aircraft Fatigue Design, Operation and Economic Aspects |
| MARSCHALL & MARINGER | Dimensional Instability |
| OPPENHEIM | Gasdynamics of Explosions and Reactive Systems |
| REAY | The History of Man Powered Flight |
| SARKAR | Wear of Metals |
| SCHURING | Scale Models in Engineering |

## RELATED JOURNALS PUBLISHED BY PERGAMON

Progress in Aerospace Sciences
Acta Astronautica
Vertica

Free specimen copies of
all journals are available on request
from your nearest Pergamon Office;
see addresses on page iv.

# AIRCRAFT DYNAMIC STABILITY AND RESPONSE

A. W. BABISTER
M.A., Ph.D., M.R.Ae.S.

Senior Lecturer in Aeronautical Engineering
University of Glasgow, Scotland

PERGAMON PRESS

OXFORD · NEW YORK · TORONTO · SYDNEY · PARIS · FRANKFURT

| | |
|---|---|
| U.K. | Pergamon Press Ltd., Headington Hill Hall,<br>Oxford OX3 0BW, England |
| U.S.A. | Pergamon Press Inc., Maxwell House, Fairview Park,<br>Elmsford, New York 10523, U.S.A. |
| CANADA | Pergamon of Canada, Suite 104, 150 Consumers Road,<br>Willowdale, Ontario M2J 1P9, Canada |
| AUSTRALIA | Pergamon Press (Aust.) Pty. Ltd., P.O. Box 544,<br>Potts Point, N.S.W. 2011, Australia |
| FRANCE | Pergamon Press SARL, 24 rue des Ecoles,<br>75240 Paris, Cedex 05, France |
| FEDERAL REPUBLIC<br>OF GERMANY | Pergamon Press GmbH, 6242 Kronberg-Taunus,<br>Pferdstrasse 1, Federal Republic of Germany |



First edition 1980
Reprinted 1985

**British Library Cataloguing in Publication Data**

Babister, Arthur William
Aircraft dynamic stability and response. - (Pergamon international library).
1. Stability of airplanes
2. Airplanes - Handling characteristics
I. Title
629.132'36 TL574.S7 79-41537

ISBN 0 08 024769 5 Hardcover
ISBN 0 08 024768 7 Flexicover

*In order to make this volume available as economically and as rapidly as possible the author's typescript has been reproduced in its original form. This method has its typographical limitations but it is hoped that they in no way distract the reader.*

*Printed and bound in Great Britain*
*by A. Wheaton & Co. Ltd, Exeter*

# CONTENTS

## PART II — LONGITUDINAL DYNAMIC STABILITY AND RESPONSE



## PART III — LATERAL DYNAMIC STABILITY AND RESPONSE

# PREFACE

This book is intended for undergraduate students of Aeronautical Engineering, and for newcomers to the aircraft industry. Its aim is thus more restricted than that of my earlier book, *Aircraft Stability and Control* (published in 1961), and its length has been correspondingly reduced. The fundamental basis of the subject has not, however, changed, and the best approach to Aircraft Dynamic Stability and Response is through a consideration of general underlying principles. There is still a great need for a *concise treatment of the fundamentals of the subject* — hence the present book.

In Part I, after an *introductory chapter on Aircraft Static Stability and Manoeuvrability, the theoretical basis of Flight Dynamics is given in full, together with an explanation of the technical terms used. The physical background for the estimation of Aerodynamic Derivatives* is discussed.

In Parts II and III, *the theory is applied to both the longitudinal and lateral motion of aircraft (including the effect of automatic control). Modern developments, such as the effects of aeroelasticity, dynamic coupling and high incidence are treated in Part IV, and the book concludes with an example of the estimation of dynamic stability characteristics.* Throughout the whole book, the aircraft and its behaviour are kept well to the fore.

In general, a non-dimensional system of notation is used, based on that approved by the British Standards Institution (and by the Engineering Sciences Data Unit). To cater for the needs of students, *problems are included at the end of chapters.*

The author wishes to thank Mrs. R. Young and Mrs. H.M. Todd for the preparation of the diagrams, and Pergamon Press for the final preparation of the typescript. The author must also record the great assistance given by his wife in reading the proofs.

Acknowledgement must also be made to the Controller of H.M. Stationery Office and the Institute of Aeronautics and Astronautics for permission to reproduce diagrams from the Aeronautical Research Council's Reports and Memoranda and from the Journal of Aero/Space Science. The committee of A.G.A.R.D. must also be thanked for permission to reproduce text from one of their Conference Proceedings.

A.W. Babister

# LIST OF SYMBOLS

The following is a list of symbols used in the text, together with the corresponding American symbol. It should be noted that the American symbols are not always equivalent to the British ones; the two may differ by some numerical factor. The relations between British and American non-dimensional aerodynamic derivatives are given at the end of this list of symbols (as well as at the ends of Chapters 3 and 4).

| Symbol | Meaning | Corresponding American symbol |
|---|---|---|
| $A$ | Aircraft attitude | |
| $A$ | Aspect ratio, $b^2/S$ | $A$ |
| $A_1$ | Coefficient of $\lambda^4$ in longitudinal stability quartic | $A$ |
| $A_2$ | Coefficient of $\lambda^4$ in lateral stability quartic | $A$ |
| $A_q$, $A_w$, $A_z$ | Frequency response functions | |
| $a$ | Aircraft lift curve slope, $dC_L/d\alpha$ | $C_{L\alpha}$ |
| $a_1$ | Tailplane (or fin) lift curve slope | |
| $a_2$ | Lift curve slope for a control | |
| $B_1$ | Coefficient of $\lambda^3$ in longitudinal stability quartic | $B$ |
| $B_2$ | Coefficient of $\lambda^3$ in lateral stability quartic | $B$ |
| $b$ | Wing span (tip to tip) | $b$ |
| $C_1$ | Coefficient of $\lambda^2$ in longitudinal stability quartic | $C$ |
| $C_2$ | Coefficient of $\lambda^2$ in lateral stability quartic | $C$ |
| $C_D$ | Drag/$\frac{1}{2}\rho V^2 S$ | $C_D$ |
| $C_L$ | Lift/$\frac{1}{2}\rho V^2 S$ | $C_L$ |
| $C_{LT}$ | Tailplane lift/$\frac{1}{2}\rho V^2 S_T$ | $C_{L_H}$ |
| $C_l$ | Rolling moment about $Ox/\frac{1}{2}\rho_e V_e{}^2 Sb$ | $C_l$ |
| $C_m$ | Pitching moment about $Oy/\frac{1}{2}\rho V^2 S\bar{\bar{c}}$ | $C_m$ |

| Symbol | Meaning | Corresponding American symbol |
|---|---|---|
| $C_n$ | Yawing moment about $Oz/\frac{1}{2}\rho_e V_e{}^2 Sb$ | $C_n$ |
| $C_X$, $C_Z$ | Non-dimensional force coefficients, $X/\frac{1}{2}\rho V^2 S$, $Z/\frac{1}{2}\rho V^2 S$ | $C_X$, $C_Z$ |
| $c$ | Wing chord | $c$ |
| $\bar{\bar{c}}$ | Mean aerodynamic chord of wing | $\bar{c}$ |
| $D$ | Drag | $D$ |
| $D$ | Differential operator, d/dt | $D$ |
| $\hat{D}$ | Differential operator, d/d$\hat{t}$ | |
| $D_1$ | Coefficient of $\lambda$ in longitudinal stability quartic | $D$ |
| $D_2$ | Coefficient of $\lambda$ in lateral stability quartic | $D$ |
| $E_1$ | Term independent of $\lambda$ in longitudinal stability quartic | $E$ |
| $E_2$ | Term independent of $\lambda$ in lateral stability quartic | $E$ |
| $e_x$ | $-I_{zx}/I_x$ | |
| $e_z$ | $-I_{zx}/I_z$ | |
| $G$ | Transfer function | |
| $g$ | Acceleration due to gravity | $g$ |
| $\hat{g}$ | $mg/\frac{1}{2}\rho_e V_e{}^2 S = C_L \sec \Theta_e$ | |
| $g_x$, $g_y$, $g_z$ | Components of gravitational acceleration | |
| $g_\theta$, $g_\psi$, ... | Non-dimensional autopilot parameters | |
| $g_1$ | $g \cos \Theta_e$ | |
| $\hat{g}_1$ | $\hat{g} \cos \Theta_e = C_L$ | |
| $g_2$ | $g \sin \Theta_e$ | |
| $\hat{g}_2$ | $\hat{g} \sin \Theta_e = C_L \tan \Theta_e$ | |
| $H$ | Gust gradient | |
| $H_m$ | Manoevre margin, stick fixed | |
| $h$ | Height above a given datum | |
| $h_F$ | Distance of aerodynamic centre of fin above $Ox$ | |
| $h\,\bar{\bar{c}}$ | Distance of c.g. aft of leading edge of mean aerodynamic chord of wing | |
| $h_m\bar{\bar{c}}$ | Distance of manoeuvre point, stick fixed, aft of leading edge of mean aerodynamic chord of wing | |
| $h_n\bar{\bar{c}}$ | Distance of aerodynamic centre of aircraft aft of leading edge of mean aerodynamic chord of wing | |

| Symbol | Meaning | Corresponding American symbol |
|---|---|---|
| $h_0\bar{\bar{c}}$ | Distance of aerodynamic centre of aircraft without tail aft of leading edge of mean aerodynamic chord of wing | |
| $I_x$ | Moment of inertia about longitudinal (rolling) axis $Ox$ | $I_X$ |
| $I_y$ | Moment of inertia about lateral (pitching) axis $Oy$ | $I_Y$ |
| $I_z$ | Moment of inertia about yawing axis $Oz$ | $I_Z$ |
| $I_{xy}$ | Product of inertia about $Ox$ and $Oy$ | $I_{XY}$ |
| $I_{yz}$ | Product of inertia about $Oy$ and $Oz$ | $I_{YZ}$ |
| $I_{zx}$ | Product of inertia about $Oz$ and $Ox$ | $I_{ZX}$ |
| $i_x$ | $I_x/mb^2$ | |
| $i_y$ | $I_y/m\bar{\bar{c}}^2$ | |
| $i_z$ | $I_z/mb^2$ | |
| $i_{zx}$ | $I_{zx}/mb^2$ | |
| $i_1$ | $(I_z - I_x)/I_y$ | |
| $i_2$ | $(I_y - I_x)/I_z$ | |
| $K$ | Gust alleviation factor | |
| $K_n$ | Static margin, stick fixed | |
| $L$ | Lift | $L$ |
| $L_W$, $L_T$ | Wing lift, tail lift | |
| $L$ | Rolling moment about $Ox$ | $L$ |
| $\mathring{L}_p$, $\mathring{L}_r$, $\mathring{L}_v$, $\mathring{L}_\xi$, $\mathring{L}_\zeta$ | Rolling moment derivatives, $\partial L/\partial p$, $\partial L/\partial r$, $\partial L/\partial v$, $\partial L/\partial \xi$, $\partial L/\partial \zeta$ | |
| $L_p$ | Non-dimensional rolling moment derivative due to rate of roll, $\mathring{L}_p/\frac{1}{2}\rho_e V_e S b^2$ | $C_{l_p}$ |
| $L_r$ | Non-dimensional rolling moment derivative due to rate of yaw, $\mathring{L}_r/\frac{1}{2}\rho_e V_e S b^2$ | $C_{l_r}$ |
| $L_v$ | Non-dimensional rolling moment derivative due to sideslip, $\mathring{L}_v/\frac{1}{2}\rho_e V_e S b$ | $C_{l_\beta}$ |
| $L_\xi$ | Non-dimensional rolling moment derivative due to ailerons, $\mathring{L}_\xi/\frac{1}{2}\rho_e {V_e}^2 S b$ | $C_{l_{\delta_a}}$ |
| $L_\zeta$ | Non-dimensional rolling moment derivative due to rudder, $\mathring{L}_\zeta/\frac{1}{2}\rho_e {V_e}^2 S b$ | $C_{l_{\delta_r}}$ |
| $l$ | Distance of aerodynamic centre of tailplane aft of aerodynamic centre of aircraft without tail | |
| $l_F$ | Distance of aerodynamic centre of fin aft of c.g. of aircraft | |

| Symbol | Meaning | Corresponding American symbol |
|---|---|---|
| $l_T$ | Distance of aerodynamic centre of tailplane aft of c.g. of aircraft | |
| $l_p$ | $-L_p/i_x$ | |
| $l_r$ | $-L_r/i_x$ | |
| $l_v$ | $-\mu_2 L_v/i_x$ | |
| $l_\xi$ | $-\mu_2 L_\xi/i_x$ | |
| $l_\zeta$ | $-\mu_2 L_\zeta/i_x$ | |
| $M$ | Pitching moment about $Oy$ | $M$ |
| $\mathring{M}_q$, $\mathring{M}_u$, $\mathring{M}_w$, $\mathring{M}_{\dot{w}}$, $\mathring{M}_\eta$ | Pitching moment derivatives, $\partial M/\partial q$, $\partial M/\partial u$, $\partial M/\partial w$, $\partial M/\partial \dot{w}$, $\partial M/\partial \eta$ | |
| $M_q$ | Non-dimensional pitching moment derivative due to rate of pitch, $\mathring{M}_q/\frac{1}{2}\rho_e V_e S\bar{\bar{c}}^2$ | $C_{m_q}$ |
| $M_u$ | Non-dimensional pitching moment derivative due to velocity increment along $Ox$, $\mathring{M}_u/\frac{1}{2}\rho_e V_e S\bar{\bar{c}}$ | $C_{m_u}$ |
| $M_w$ | Non-dimensional pitching moment derivative due to velocity increment along $Oz$, $\mathring{M}_w/\frac{1}{2}\rho_e V_e S\bar{\bar{c}}$ | $C_{m_\alpha}$ |
| $M_{\dot{w}}$ | Non-dimensional pitching moment derivative due to rate of change of $w$, $\mathring{M}_{\dot{w}}/\frac{1}{2}\rho_e S\bar{\bar{c}}^2$ | $C_{m_{D\alpha}}$ |
| $M_\eta$ | Non-dimensional pitching moment derivative due to elevator, $\mathring{M}_\eta/\frac{1}{2}\rho_e V_e^2 S\bar{\bar{c}}$ | $C_{m_{\delta_e}}$ |
| $m$ | Aircraft mass | $m$ |
| $m_{DYN}$ | Acceleration in pitch | |
| $m_{\alpha DYN}$, $m_{\beta DYN}$ | $\partial m_{DYN}/\partial\alpha$, $\partial m_{DYN}/\partial\beta$ | |
| $m_q$ | $-M_q/i_y$ | |
| $m_u$ | $-\mu_1 M_u/i_y$ | |
| $m_w$ | $-\mu_1 M_w/i_y$ | |
| $m_{\dot{w}}$ | $-M_{\dot{w}}/i_y$ | |
| $m_\eta$ | $-\mu_1 M_\eta/i_y$ | |
| $N$ | Yawing moment about $Oz$ | $N$ |
| $\mathring{N}_p$, $\mathring{N}_r$, $\mathring{N}_v$, $\mathring{N}_\xi$, $\mathring{N}_\zeta$ | Yawing moment derivatives, $\partial N/\partial p$, $\partial N/\partial r$, $\partial N/\partial v$, $\partial N/\partial \xi$, $\partial N/\partial \zeta$ | |
| $N_p$ | Non-dimensional yawing moment derivative due to rate of roll, $\mathring{N}_p/\frac{1}{2}\rho_e V_e S b^2$ | $C_{n_p}$ |
| $N_r$ | Non-dimensional yawing moment derivative due to rate of yaw, $\mathring{N}_r/\frac{1}{2}\rho_e V_e S b^2$ | $C_{n_r}$ |
| $N_v$ | Non-dimensional yawing moment derivative due to sideslip, $\mathring{N}_v/\frac{1}{2}\rho_e V_e S b$ | $C_{n_\beta}$ |
| $N_\xi$ | Non-dimensional yawing moment derivative due to ailerons, $\mathring{N}_\xi/\frac{1}{2}\rho_e V_e^2 S b$ | $C_{n_{\delta_a}}$ |

| Symbol | Meaning | Corresponding American symbol |
|---|---|---|
| $N_\zeta$ | Non-dimensional yawing moment derivative due to rudder, $\mathring{N}_\zeta/\frac{1}{2}\rho_e V_e^2 Sb$ | $C_{n_{\delta_r}}$ |
| $n$ | Normal acceleration (in units of g) = normal load factor -1 | |
| $\Delta n$ | Increment in load factor | |
| $-n_{DYN}$ | Acceleration in yaw | |
| $n_{\alpha DYN}$, $n_{\beta DYN}$ | $\partial n_{DYN}/\partial\alpha$, $\partial n_{DYN}/\partial\beta$ | |
| $n_p$ | $-N_p/i_z$ | |
| $n_r$ | $-N_r/i_z$ | |
| $n_v$ | $-\mu_2 N_v/i_z$ | |
| $n_\xi$ | $-\mu_2 N_\xi/i_z$ | |
| $n_\zeta$ | $-\mu_2 N_\zeta/i_z$ | |
| $p$ | Aircraft angular velocity in roll | $p$ |
| $\hat{p}$ | $\tau p$ | |
| $p$ | Laplace operator | |
| $q$ | Aircraft angular velocity in pitch | $q$ |
| $\hat{q}$ | $\tau q$ | |
| $R$ | Routh's discriminant | |
| $R$ | Radius of turn | |
| $r$ | Aircraft angular velocity in yaw | $r$ |
| $\hat{r}$ | $\tau r$ | |
| $r$ | Non-dimensional damping (negative real part of $\lambda$) | |
| $S$ | Wing area | $S$ |
| $S_F$ | Fin area (vertical tail area) | $S_V$ |
| $S_T$ | Tailplane area | $S_H$ |
| $s$ | Wing semi-span, $\frac{1}{2}b$ | |
| $s$ | Non-dimensional frequency (imaginary part of $\lambda$) | |
| $T$ | Periodic time of oscillation | |
| $T$ | Propulsive thrust | $T$ |
| $T_{\theta\eta}$, $T_{\phi\zeta}$, ... | Aircraft transfer functions | |
| $t$ | Time | $t$ |
| $\hat{t}$ | Non-dimensional time, $t/\tau$ | |
| $t_{\frac{1}{2}}$ | Time to half amplitude | $t_{\frac{1}{2}}$ |
| $t_d$ | Time to double amplitude | |
| $t/c$ | Thickness/chord ratio of aerofoil | |

| Symbol | Meaning | Corresponding American symbol |
|---|---|---|
| $U$ | Velocity component of c.g. along $Ox$ in disturbed flight | |
| $U_e$ | Velocity component of c.g. along $Ox$ in datum steady flight | $U$ |
| $u$ | $U - U_e$ | |
| $\hat{u}$ | $u/V_e$ | |
| $V$ | Velocity component of c.g. along $Oy$ in disturbed flight [used in this sense in Chapters 2 and 12 and in Appendix 1] | |
| $V$ | Resultant velocity of c.g. in disturbed longitudinal flight | |
| $V_e$ | Resultant velocity of aircraft c.g. in datum steady flight | $V$ |
| $\bar{V}$ | Volume ratio, $S_T l/S\bar{\bar{c}}$ | |
| $\bar{V}_F$ | Fin volume ratio, $S_F l_F/Sb$ | |
| $\bar{V}_T$ | Tailplane volume ratio, $S_T l_T/S\bar{\bar{c}}$ | |
| $v$ | Component of velocity increment of c.g. along $Oy$ in disturbed flight | |
| $\hat{v}$ | $v/V_e$ (=$\beta$, for small angles of sideslip) | |
| $W$ | Aircraft weight, mg | $W$ |
| $W$ | Velocity component of c.g. along $Oz$ in disturbed flight | |
| $W_e$ | Velocity component of c.g. along $Oz$ in datum steady flight | $W$ |
| $w$ | $W - W_e$ | |
| $\hat{w}$ | $w/V_e$ | |
| $X$ | Force component along $Ox$ | |
| $\mathring{X}_q$, $\mathring{X}_u$, $\mathring{X}_w$, $\mathring{X}_{\dot{w}}$, $\mathring{X}_\eta$ | Force component derivatives, $\partial X/\partial q$, $\partial X/\partial u$, $\partial X/\partial w$, $\partial X/\partial \dot{w}$, $\partial X/\partial \eta$ | |
| $X_q$ | Non-dimensional force derivative due to rate of pitch, $\mathring{X}_q/\frac{1}{2}\rho_e V_e S\bar{\bar{c}}$ | $C_{X_q}$ |
| $X_u$ | Non-dimensional force derivative due to velocity increment along $Ox$, $\mathring{X}_u/\frac{1}{2}\rho_e V_e S$ | $C_{X_u}$ |
| $X_w$ | Non-dimensional force derivative due to velocity increment along $Oz$, $\mathring{X}_w/\frac{1}{2}\rho_e V_e S$ | $C_{X_\alpha}$ |
| $X_{\dot{w}}$ | Non-dimensional force derivative due to rate of change of $w$, $\mathring{X}_{\dot{w}}/\frac{1}{2}\rho_e S\bar{\bar{c}}$ | $C_{X_{D\alpha}}$ |
| $X_\eta$ | Non-dimensional force derivative due to elevator, $\mathring{X}_\eta/\frac{1}{2}\rho_e V_e^2 S$ | $C_{X_{\delta_e}}$ |

| Symbol | Meaning | Corresponding American symbol |
|---|---|---|
| $Ox$ | Axis through aircraft c.g. fixed in the aircraft in the forward direction in the plane of symmetry. (For wind axes, in the steady state, $Ox$ coincides with direction of motion of c.g.). | |
| $x_q$ | $-X_q/\mu_1$ | |
| $x_u$ | $-X_u$ | |
| $x_w$ | $-X_w$ | |
| $x_{\dot{w}}$ | $-X_{\dot{w}}/\mu_1$ | |
| $x_\eta$ | $-X_\eta$ | |
| $Y$ | Force component along $Oy$ | $Y$ |
| $\mathring{Y}_p$, $\mathring{Y}_r$, $\mathring{Y}_v$, $\mathring{Y}_\xi$, $\mathring{Y}_\zeta$ | Force component derivatives, $\partial Y/\partial p$, $\partial Y/\partial r$, $\partial Y/\partial v$, $\partial Y/\partial \xi$, $\partial Y/\partial \zeta$ | |
| $Y_p$ | Non-dimensional force derivative due to rate of roll, $\mathring{Y}_p/\frac{1}{2}\rho_e V_e S b$ | $C_{Y_p}$ |
| $Y_r$ | Non-dimensional force derivative due to rate of yaw, $\mathring{Y}_r/\frac{1}{2}\rho_e V_e S b$ | $C_{Y_r}$ |
| $Y_v$ | Non-dimensional force derivative due to sideslip, $\mathring{Y}_v/\frac{1}{2}\rho_e V_e S$ | $C_{Y_\beta}$ |
| $Y_\xi$ | Non-dimensional force derivative due to ailerons, $\mathring{Y}_\xi/\frac{1}{2}\rho_e V_e{}^2 S$ | $C_{Y_{\delta_a}}$ |
| $Y_\zeta$ | Non-dimensional force derivative due to rudder, $\mathring{Y}_\zeta/\frac{1}{2}\rho_e V_e{}^2 S$ | $C_{Y_{\delta_r}}$ |
| $Oy$ | Axis through aircraft c.g. fixed in the aircraft in the lateral direction, perpendicular to the plane of symmetry and positive to starboard | |
| $y_p$ | $-Y_p/\mu_2$ | |
| $y_r$ | $-Y_r/\mu_2$ | |
| $y_v$ | $-Y_v$ | |
| $y_\xi$ | $-Y_\xi$ | |
| $y_\zeta$ | $-Y_\zeta$ | |
| $Z$ | Force component along $Oz$ | $Z$ |
| $\mathring{Z}_q$, $\mathring{Z}_u$, $\mathring{Z}_w$, $\mathring{Z}_{\dot{w}}$, $\mathring{Z}_\eta$ | Force component derivatives, $\partial Z/\partial q$, $\partial Z/\partial u$, $\partial Z/\partial w$, $\partial Z/\partial \dot{w}$, $\partial Z/\partial \eta$ | |
| $Z_q$ | Non-dimensional force derivative due to rate of pitch, $\mathring{Z}_q/\frac{1}{2}\rho_e V_e S\bar{\bar{c}}$ | $C_{Z_q}$ |
| $Z_u$ | Non-dimensional force derivative due to velocity increment along $Ox$, $\mathring{Z}_u/\frac{1}{2}\rho_e V_e S$ | $C_{Z_u}$ |
| $Z_w$ | Non-dimensional force derivative due to velocity increment along $Oz$, $\mathring{Z}_w/\frac{1}{2}\rho_e V_e S$ | $C_{Z_\alpha}$ |

| Symbol | Meaning | Corresponding American symbol |
|---|---|---|
| $z_{\dot{w}}$ | Non-dimensional force derivative due to rate of change of $w$, $\mathring{Z}_{\dot{w}}/\frac{1}{2}\rho_e S\bar{\bar{c}}$ | $C_{Z_{D\alpha}}$ |
| $Z_\eta$ | Non-dimensional force derivative due to elevator, $\mathring{Z}_\eta/\frac{1}{2}\rho_e V_e{}^2 S$ | $C_{Z_{\delta_e}}$ |
| $Oz$ | Axis through aircraft c.g. fixed in the aircraft in the downward direction and perpendicular to $Ox$ and $Oy$ | |
| $z_q$ | $-Z_q/\mu_1$ | |
| $z_u$ | $-Z_u$ | |
| $z_w$ | $-Z_w$ | |
| $z_{\dot{w}}$ | $-Z_{\dot{w}}/\mu_1$ | |
| $z_\eta$ | $-Z_\eta$ | |
| $\alpha$ | Incidence (angle of attack) of mean aerodynamic chord of wing | $\alpha$ |
| $\alpha_e$ | Incidence of $Ox$ to the flight path in the steady state (positive upwards) ($\alpha_e = 0$ for wind axes) | |
| $\alpha_T$ | Tailplane incidence | $\alpha_H$ |
| $\beta$ | Angle of sideslip (the angle the direction of motion of the aircraft c.g. makes with the plane of symmetry $Oxz$) | $\beta$ |
| $\Gamma$ | Dihedral angle | |
| $\gamma$ | Angle of bank (Chapter 12) | |
| $\delta$ | Displacement | |
| $\Delta$ | Stability polynomial | |
| $\Delta$ | Natural mode shape | |
| $\Delta_{1\eta}, \Delta_{1\zeta}, \ldots$ | Response polynomials | |
| $\varepsilon$ | Angle of downwash at tailplane | $\varepsilon$ |
| $\varepsilon_q, \varepsilon_w$ | Phase differences in $q$ and $w$ in aircraft response to gusts | |
| $\xi, \eta, \zeta$ | Angular displacements of ailerons, elevator and rudder, respectively | $\delta_a, \delta_e, \delta_r$ |
| $\bar{\eta}$ | Elevator angle to trim | |
| $\eta'$ | Increment in elevator angle from trimmed position | |
| $\Theta_e$ | Inclination of $Ox$ to the horizontal in the datum steady flight (positive upwards) | |
| $\theta$ | Angle of pitch | $\theta$ |
| $\Lambda$ | Angle of sweepback | $\Lambda$ |
| $\lambda$ | Root of stability quartic ($= -r + is$) | |

| Symbol | Meaning | Corresponding American symbol |
|---|---|---|
| $\mu_1$ | Longitudinal relative density parameter, $m/\frac{1}{2}\rho_e S\bar{\bar{c}}$ | $\mu = m/\rho_e S\bar{\bar{c}}$ |
| $\mu_2$ | Lateral relative density parameter, $m/\frac{1}{2}\rho_e Sb$ | $\mu = m/\rho_e Sb$ |
| $\mu_g$ | Aircraft gust parameter, $m/\frac{1}{2}\rho_e Sa\ \bar{\bar{c}}$ | |
| $\rho$ | Air density | |
| $\rho_e$ | Air density in datum steady flight | |
| $\tau$ | Magnitude of time unit, $m/\frac{1}{2}\rho_e V_e S$ | |
| $\phi$ | Angle of bank | $\phi$ |
| $\psi$ | Angle of yaw | $\psi$ |
| $\Omega$ | Gust space frequency (wavelength $2\pi/\Omega$) | |
| $\omega_g$ | Non-dimensional gust frequency, $\Omega\mu_1\bar{\bar{c}}$ | |

# NON-DIMENSIONAL FORMS OF THE AERODYNAMIC DERIVATIVES USED IN AMERICA

We give here the commonly accepted definitions of the American derivatives, together with formulae relating them to the corresponding British derivatives.

NON-DIMENSIONAL LONGITUDINAL STABILITY DERIVATIVES (see Chapter 3)

$$C_{X_u} = \frac{\partial C_X}{\partial(u/V_e)} = X_u - 2C_X , \qquad C_{Z_u} = \frac{\partial C_Z}{\partial(u/V_e)} = Z_u - 2C_Z ,$$

$$C_{X_\alpha} = \frac{\partial C_X}{\partial\alpha} = X_w , \qquad C_{Z_\alpha} = \frac{\partial C_Z}{\partial\alpha} = Z_w ,$$

$$C_{X_{D\alpha}} = \frac{\partial C_X}{\partial(\dot{\alpha}\bar{\bar{c}}/2V_e)} = 2X_{\dot{w}} , \qquad C_{Z_{D\alpha}} = \frac{\partial C_Z}{\partial(\dot{\alpha}\bar{\bar{c}}/2V_e)} = 2Z_{\dot{w}} ,$$

$$C_{X_q} = \frac{\partial C_X}{\partial(q\bar{\bar{c}}/2V_e)} = 2X_q , \qquad C_{Z_q} = \frac{\partial C_Z}{\partial(q\bar{\bar{c}}/2V_e)} = 2Z_q ,$$

$$C_{X_{\delta_e}} = \frac{\partial C_X}{\partial\delta_e} = X_\eta , \qquad C_{Z_{\delta_e}} = \frac{\partial C_Z}{\partial\delta_e} = Z_\eta ,$$

$$C_{m_u} = \frac{\partial C_m}{\partial(u/V_e)} = M_u , \qquad C_{m_\alpha} = \frac{\partial C_m}{\partial\alpha} = M_w , \qquad C_{m_{D\alpha}} = \frac{\partial C_m}{\partial(\dot{\alpha}\bar{\bar{c}}/2V_e)} = 2M_{\dot{w}} ,$$

$$C_{m_q} = \frac{\partial C_m}{\partial(q\bar{\bar{c}}/2V_e)} = 2M_q , \qquad C_{m_{\delta_e}} = \frac{\partial C_m}{\partial\delta_e} = M_\eta .$$

NON-DIMENSIONAL LATERAL STABILITY DERIVATIVES (see Chapter 4)

$$C_{l_\beta} = \frac{\partial C_l}{\partial\beta} = L_v , \qquad C_{l_p} = \frac{\partial C_l}{\partial(pb/2V_e)} = 2L_p , \qquad C_{l_r} = \frac{\partial C_l}{\partial(rb/2V_e)} = 2L_r ,$$

$$C_{l_{\delta_a}} = \frac{\partial C_l}{\partial\delta_a} = L_\xi , \qquad C_{l_{\delta_r}} = \frac{\partial C_l}{\partial\delta_r} = L_\zeta ,$$

$$C_{n_\beta} = \frac{\partial C_n}{\partial\beta} = N_v , \qquad C_{n_p} = \frac{\partial C_n}{\partial(pb/2V_e)} = 2N_p , \qquad C_{n_r} = \frac{\partial C_n}{\partial(rb/2V_e)} = 2N_r ,$$

$$C_{n_{\delta_a}} = \frac{\partial C_n}{\partial \delta_a} = N_\xi \ , \qquad C_{n_{\delta_r}} = \frac{\partial C_n}{\partial \delta_r} = N_\zeta \ ,$$

$$C_{Y_\beta} = \frac{\partial C_Y}{\partial \beta} = Y_v \ , \qquad C_{Y_p} = \frac{\partial C_Y}{\partial (pb/2V_e)} = 2Y_p \ , \qquad C_{Y_r} = \frac{\partial C_Y}{\partial (rb/2V_e)} = 2Y_r \ ,$$

$$C_{Y_{\delta_a}} = \frac{\partial C_Y}{\partial \delta_a} = Y_\xi \ , \qquad C_{Y_{\delta_r}} = \frac{\partial C_Y}{\partial \delta_r} = Y_\zeta \ .$$

# UNITS

In developing the theory of aircraft stability we have used non-dimensional parameters wherever possible. In the determination of the numerical values of these parameters and in the final determination of motion and response for a given aircraft we have, of course, to use a consistent set of units. In the International System of Units (SI), the kilogramme is the unit of mass M, the metre is the unit of length L, and the second is the unit of time T. The following table gives the dimensions and the units of a number of terms used in the theory of aircraft stability.

| Quantity | Dimensions | Units |
|---|---|---|
| Length (chord $c$, tail arm $l_T$) | L | m |
| Area (wing area $S$, tailplane area $S_T$) | $L^2$ | $m^2$ |
| Speed (resultant velocity $V$) | L/T | m/s |
| Acceleration | $L/T^2$ | $m/s^2$ |
| Angle (incidence $\alpha$, pitch $\theta$) | - | radians |
| Air density $\rho$ | $M/L^3$ | $kg/m^3$ |
| Kinematic viscosity $\nu$ | $L^2/T$ | $m^2/s$ |
| Mass (aircraft mass $m$) | M | kg |
| Force (lift, drag, weight) | $ML/T^2$ | newtons |
| Moment of inertia | $ML^2$ | $kg.m^2$ |

It may be more useful (or more usual) to express the final result in some other units, e.g. to express the aircraft speed in knots, but it will be found easiest first to solve the equations in terms of the above units and after that to effect any further change in units.

# Part I

# FLIGHT DYNAMICS

# Chapter 1
# INTRODUCTION

Flight dynamics deals with the motion of an aircraft under the influence of forces. These are of six types:

(i) inertia forces, arising from the mass distribution and linear and angular acceleration of the aircraft;

(ii) aerodynamic damping forces and moments, depending on the angular velocities of the aircraft (sometimes called rotary forces and moments);

(iii) aerodynamic forces and moments depending on the linear velocities of the aircraft (sometimes called static forces and moments, since they depend on the attitude of the aircraft relative to the airstream and not on its angular velocities);

(iv) aerodynamic forces and moments due to application of controls (usually only the forces and moments due to control deflection are of importance; these are sometimes called static forces and moments due to controls);

(v) gravitational forces; and

(vi) propulsive forces.

The motion of an aircraft and its stability and response can be determined completely by dynamical principles. In this respect the problem does not differ fundamentally from that of investigating the stability of any other body. An aircraft, however, is in general free to move in any direction. Another complicating factor is the estimation of the aerodynamic forces.

In this book we consider aeroplanes only, although many of our remarks apply also to helicopters. It is assumed that the aeroplane has a longitudinal plane of symmetry, this being the vertical plane through the centre line of the fuselage in the steady state with wings level. The aircraft is taken to behave like a rigid body (unless stated otherwise); as shown in part IV, distortion or 'aeroelastic' effects can be of importance at high speeds.

## THE GENERAL MEANING OF STABILITY

Before proceeding further we shall consider the general meaning of stability. A dynamical system is said to be stable, or to possess stability, if, when slightly disturbed from a state of equilibrium (or steady motion), it tends to return to and remain in that state, the disturbance acting only for a finite time.

In subsequent chapters we shall consider the motion of an aircraft undergoing certain disturbances (for example, due to gusts, small changes in speed or incidence), the aircraft being initially in equilibrium (i.e. in trim). The resulting rather complicated motion will in general be composed of a number of modes of different frequency and damping, and the dependence of the motion of the basic characteristics of the aircraft is not easily seen. For this reason it is sometimes simpler to consider only the effect of the static forces and moments, no account being taken of the other forces acting on the aircraft. The stability then considered is known as static stability. An aircraft is said to be statically stable if the static moments tend to restore the aircraft to its equilibrium state.

In general an aircraft must be both dynamically and statically stable. However, if the deviation from steady flight increases so slowly that the pilot has time to take counter action (such as applying the appropriate controls) before any dangerous departure from the equilibrium state has occurred, the aircraft may still be acceptable.

As implied by the title, in this book we are mainly concerned with aircraft dynamic stability and response. However, it is of interest to set down briefly the elements of the theory of static stability and manoeuvrability, as they will be referred to in subsequent chapters. A more detailed account (including the effects of compressibility and distortion) is given in references 1 and 2.

## LONGITUDINAL STATIC STABILITY

Consider an aircraft, initially in a steady trimmed glide at speed $V$, undergoing a small symmetric disturbance (for example, due to a gust) in which both the speed and attitude of the aircraft (and hence the wing incidence) are changed. The attitude can be measured by the angle $A$ between an axis $Ox$ fixed in the aircraft in the plane of symmetry and the direction of motion of the centre of gravity $O$ of the aircraft (as in Fig. 1.1). We see that the wing incidence $\alpha$ (measured from the zero lift line of the wing) is given by

$$\alpha = A + \text{constant}.$$

The pitching moment $M$ about the centre of gravity $O$ is taken to be positive when acting in the nose-up direction (as in Fig. 1.1).

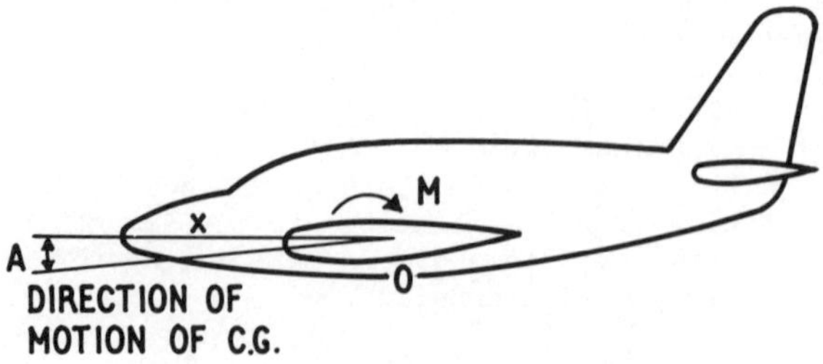


Fig. 1.1 Moment acting on the aircraft

In the steady trimmed flight, $A = A_0$ and the pitching moment $M_0$ about $O$ is zero. For a small disturbance we can write

$$M = M_0 + dM = dM \qquad (1.1)$$
$$A = A_0 + dA = A_0 + d\alpha$$

Thus if the incidence $\alpha$ is changed by $d\alpha$ there is a pitching moment $dM$ about $O$.

The aircraft is said to be statically stable if the pitching moment $dM$ tends to restore the aircraft to its original attitude, i.e. if $dM$ and $d\alpha$ have opposite signs. Thus the condition for static stability is

$$dM/d\alpha < 0. \qquad (1.2)$$

Put $$M = \tfrac{1}{2}\rho V^2 S\bar{\bar{c}}\ C_m \qquad (1.3)$$

where $V$ = forward speed of the aircraft,
$\rho$ = air density at the given height of flight,
$S$ = wing area,
$\bar{\bar{c}}$ = mean aerodynamic chord of the wing,
$C_m$ = pitching moment coefficient about the c.g.

In this simple theory we neglect the variation of $C_m$ with speed (due to compressibility or slipstream effects).

Then $$dM = \tfrac{1}{2}\rho V^2 S\bar{\bar{c}}\ dC_m + \rho V S\bar{\bar{c}}\ C_m\ dV$$
$$= \tfrac{1}{2}\rho V^2 S\bar{\bar{c}}\ dC_m \qquad \text{(since } C_m = 0 \text{ initially).}$$

Thus the condition for static stability is

$$dC_m/d\alpha < 0. \qquad (1.4)$$

We shall now derive another static stability criterion. Let $C$ be the aerodynamic centre of the whole aircraft (that is, that point about which the pitching moment does not change with incidence). It follows that any additional lift force $dL$ on the aircraft due to change in incidence will act upwards through $C$ (as shown in

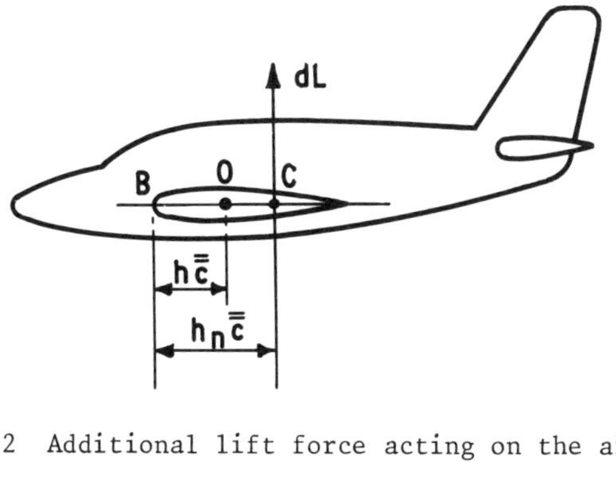


Fig. 1.2 Additional lift force acting on the aircraft

Fig. 1.2). Let $B$ be the leading edge of the mean aerodynamic chord (length $\bar{\bar{c}}$) of the wing. We denote the distances of the centre of gravity $O$ and the aerodynamic centre $C$ aft of $B$ by $h\bar{\bar{c}}$ and $h_n\bar{\bar{c}}$ respectively ($h_n$ will not vary with incidence, provided the disturbance is small). The elevator is kept at a constant setting (i.e. the pilot's control stick is kept fixed).

Considering the nose-up moment about $O$, and using Eq. (1.1), we obtain

$$dM = -(h_n - h)\,\bar{\bar{c}}\,dL \tag{1.5}$$

Put $$L = \tfrac{1}{2}\rho V^2 S C_L \tag{1.6}$$

where $C_L$ = lift coefficient.

Then Eq. (1.5) becomes

$$-\,dC_m/dC_L = h_n - h. \tag{1.7}$$

From Eq. (1.4), since $dC_L/d\alpha$ is positive at incidences below the stall, $(-dC_m/dC_L)$ must be positive for static stability, that is, $h_n > h$. We see that static stability is achieved by having the centre of gravity of the aircraft ahead of its aerodynamic centre.

## STATIC MARGIN

The *static margin with stick fixed*, $K_n$, is defined by

$$K_n = -(dC_m/dC_L)_{\text{stick fixed}}\,. \tag{1.8}$$

In this simplified theory (in which compressibility and distortion are neglected) we see that

$$K_n = h_n - h. \tag{1.9}$$

An aircraft is statically stable with stick fixed when the static margin $K_n$ is positive. Moving the centre of gravity aft increases $h$ and hence decreases the static margin. Moving the centre of gravity forward increases the static margin.

The position of the aerodynamic centre $C$ depends on the additional loads carried by the wing and tailplane, and their relative contributions to the pitching moment about $O$.

Consider first an aircraft without a tailplane; for such an aircraft the position of the aerodynamic centre $C_O$ will depend on both the wing planform and also the shape of the wing section. There will be a constant pitching moment $M_{C_O}$ about this point. Let $h_O\bar{\bar{c}}$ be the distance of $C_O$ aft of the leading edge of the mean aerodynamic chord of the wing. For unswept wings at low incidence, $C_O$ is usually close to the quarter-chord point; however, there can be a considerable forward movement of the aerodynamic centre of sweptback wings if there is a tip stall.

Consider next the contribution due to the tailplane. As shown in Fig. 1.3, the total lift $L$ on the aircraft is made up of the wing (and body) lift $L_W$ (acting through $C_O$) and the tailplane lift $L_T$ (acting through the aerodynamic centre $C_T$ of the tailplane).

Thus $$L = L_W + L_T. \tag{1.10}$$

The pitching moment $M$ about the c.g. $O$ is given by

$$M = M_{C_O} + L_W \times OC_O - L_T \times OC_T\,,$$

i.e., using Eq. (1.10),

$$M = M_{C_O} + L \times OC_O - L_T \times C_O C_T\,. \tag{1.11}$$

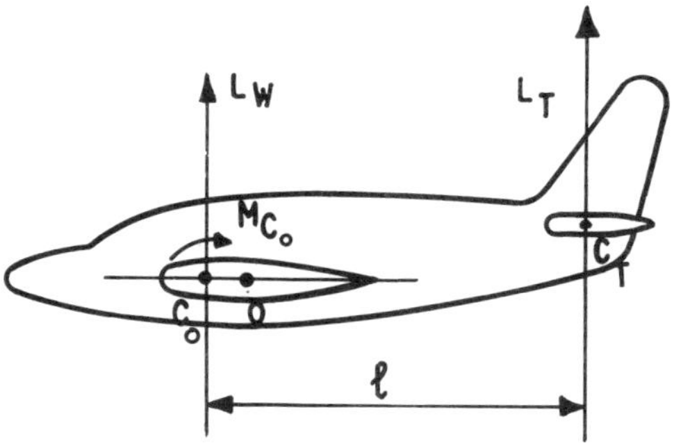


Fig. 1.3 Aerodynamic lift forces and moments acting on the aircraft

The tailplane lift will be proportional both to the tailplane area $S_T$ and the tailplane lift coefficient (which will depend upon the incidence at the tailplane). We define the non-dimensional volume ratio $\bar{V}$ by the equation

$$\bar{V} = S_T l / S\,\bar{\bar{c}} \tag{1.12}$$

where $l$ = distance of the aerodynamic centre $C_T$ of the tailplane aft of the aerodynamic centre $C_O$ of the aircraft without tail.

It is shown in references 1 and 2 that the rearward shift of the aerodynamic centre $C$ of the aircraft due to the tailplane is

$$\bar{V}\,\frac{a_1}{a}\left(1 - \frac{d\varepsilon}{d\alpha}\right),$$

where $a$ = aircraft wing lift curve slope
$a_1$ = tailplane lift curve slope
and $\varepsilon$ = angle of downwash at the tailplane.

Thus
$$h_n = h_O + \bar{V}\,\frac{a_1}{a}\left(1 - \frac{d\varepsilon}{d\alpha}\right). \tag{1.13}$$

We see that $h_n > h_O$; in general we find that $h_n > h > h_O$, i.e. the aircraft c.g. lies between the aerodynamic centre of the whole aircraft and that of the aircraft less tail.

From Eqs. (1.9) and (1.13), the static margin with stick fixed $K_n$ is given by

$$K_n = -(h - h_O) + \bar{V}\,\frac{a_1}{a}\left(1 - \frac{d\varepsilon}{d\alpha}\right). \tag{1.14}$$

From Eqs. (1.12) and (1.14), we see that, for a given c.g. position, increase in tailplane area increases the static margin.

Figure 1.4, which is based on Eq. (1.14), shows the effect of both forward and aft c.g. positions on the tailplane area required for a given static margin. If the aircraft c.g. coincides with its aerodynamic centre, the aircraft is neutrally stable (zero static margin). In general the tailplane should be designed to give at least neutral static stability in cruising flight with the c.g. at the aft limit.

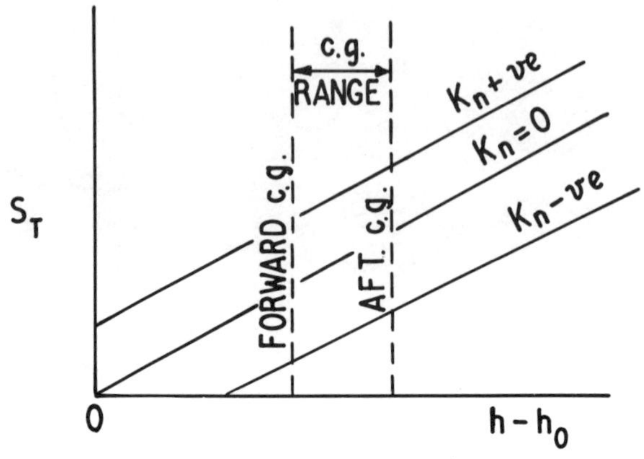


Fig. 1.4 Effect of c.g. range on tailplane area required for a given static margin

## STABILITY AND TRIM

So far we have assumed that the elevator is kept at a constant setting. Consider now the effect of changing the elevator angle. If the elevator is deflected downwards, there will be an additional lift force $L_E$ on the tailplane. Thus, *at a given overall lift of the aircraft*, from Eq. (1.11), the increment in pitching moment due to elevator deflection $\eta$ is seen to be

$$- L_E \times C_O C_T = - \tfrac{1}{2}\rho V^2 S_T l a_2 \eta$$

where $a_2 = dC_{LT}/d\eta$.

Thus Eq. (1.11) becomes, in terms of non-dimensional coefficients,

$$C_m = (C_m)_{(\text{stick fixed, } \eta=0)} - a_2 \bar{V} \eta \; .$$

Therefore $\bar{\eta}$, the elevator angle to trim (i.e. to make $C_m = 0$), is given by

$$a_2 \bar{V} \bar{\eta} = (C_m)_{(\text{stick fixed, } \eta=0)}$$

and, from Eq. (1.8),

$$a_2 \bar{V} \frac{d\bar{\eta}}{dC_L} = \left(\frac{dC_m}{dC_L}\right)_{\text{stick fixed}} = - K_n \; . \quad (1.15)$$

From Eq. (1.15) we see that the slope of the elevator trim curve is proportional to the static margin, and will thus vary with the c.g. position (as shown in Fig. 1.5).

If the c.g. is very far forward, the elevator angle needed to trim can become excessive at high $C_L$. If the aerodynamic centre $C$ and the c.g. $O$ coincide, $dC_m/dC_L = 0$ and the pitching moment does not change with incidence. It follows that the aircraft remains in trim, i.e. there is no change in elevator angle to trim with change of speed in level flight for a neutrally stable aircraft. Thus both static stability and trim play an important part in determining the range of c.g. positions for which an aircraft can be safely operated.

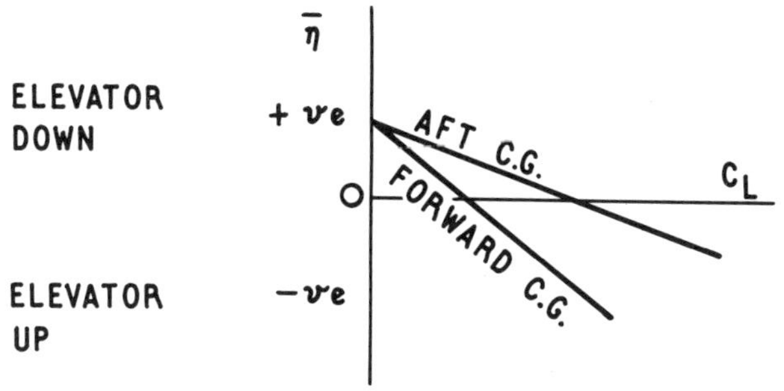


Fig. 1.5 Elevator angle to trim

MANOEUVRABILITY AND MANOEUVRE MARGIN

In Part II of this book we shall be concerned with the longitudinal response of an aircraft to application of controls. The response to elevator control in the pull-out from a dive is of importance in the estimation of the manoeuvrability of an aircraft. In such a manoeuvre, in general, both the speed and the attitude of the aircraft will vary. However, as a first approximation, we shall assume that the aircraft speed and incidence have settled down to constant values. We shall here obtain a simple formula for the elevator movement needed to maintain a constant normal acceleration $ng$ (perpendicular to the flight path) in steady flight at constant speed $V$ in an arc of a circle in the vertical plane. The aircraft thus has a constant rate of pitch, and is in trimmed flight at a constant elevator setting (i.e. stick fixed).

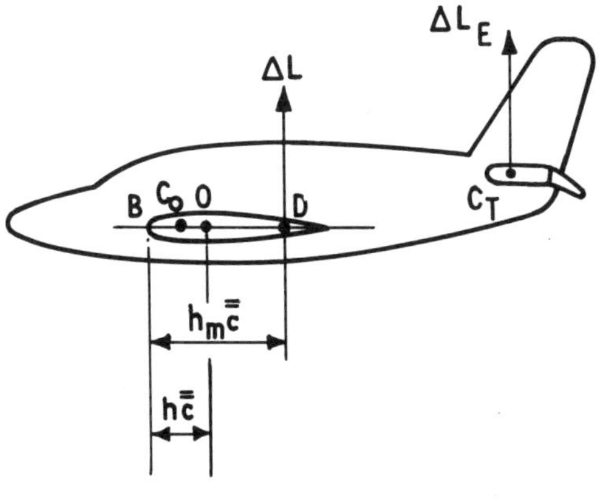


Fig. 1.6 Additional forces acting on the aircraft

As shown in Fig. 1.6, the addition lift $\Delta L$ (which need not be small) to provide the normal acceleration acts through some point $D$, distance $h_m\bar{\bar{c}}$ aft of the leading edge of the mean aerodynamic chord of the wing. The point $D$ does not coincide with the aerodynamic centre $C$, since the rate of pitch of the aircraft alters the tail-plane incidence and loading (in low speed flight, $D$ is aft of $C$). Trim is restored by changing the elevator angle, thus giving an upward force $\Delta L_E$ on the tailplane.

As above, *at a given overall lift*, the increase in the pitching moment due to the change in elevator angle is $(-\ \Delta L_E \times C_0C_T)$. There is also a moment $(-\ \Delta L \times OD)$ about

$O$ due to the additional lift force. Thus, since the aircraft is in trim,

$$l\,\Delta L_E + (h_m - h)\bar{\bar{c}}\,\Delta L = 0. \tag{1.16}$$

Now, for an aircraft mass $m$ with a normal acceleration $ng$,

$$\Delta L = mng = nL$$

where $L\ (= \tfrac{1}{2}\rho V^2 S C_L)$ is the lift in horizontal flight.

The lift due to the change $\Delta\bar{\eta}$ of elevator angle to trim is

$$L_E = \tfrac{1}{2}\rho V^2 S_T a_2\,\Delta\bar{\eta}\ .$$

Thus Eq. (1.16) becomes, in terms of non-dimensional coefficients,

$$S_T l a_2\,\Delta\bar{\eta} + (h_m - h)\ \bar{\bar{c}}\ S n C_L = 0,$$

i.e. from Eq. (1.12),

$$-\ \bar{V}\ a_2\,\Delta\bar{\eta}/nC_L = h_m - h.$$

From this equation it can be seen that $\Delta\bar{\eta}$ is zero if $h = h_m$, i.e. there is no change in elevator angle to trim (i.e. in stick travel) in the pull-out with normal acceleration $ng$ if $O$ coincides with $D$. The point $D$ is known as the *manoeuvre point stick fixed.*

For any other position of the centre of gravity,

$$-\ \bar{V} a_2\,\Delta\bar{\eta}/nC_L = h_m - h = H_m\ , \tag{1.17}$$

where $H_m$ is the *manoeuvre margin with stick fixed.*

We see that, in general, if the aircraft is trimmed in the glide, the stick will have to be moved to a new position to trim the aircraft in steady circular flight, the stick movement (proportional to $\Delta\bar{\eta}$) depending on both the manoeuvre margin stick fixed and the normal acceleration.

The theory given in this chapter is valid at low speeds (above the stalling speed). However, at high speeds compressibility and aeroelastic effects become of importance, and the aerodynamic force and moment coefficients vary with the speed. Eq. (1.4) is then no longer an adequate criterion for static stability. Both the static and manoeuvre margins become functions of the speed (see also Chapters 3, 6 and 12, and references 1 and 2).

## REFERENCES

1. BABISTER, A.W. *Aircraft Stability and Control.* Pergamon Press (1961).
2. ETKIN, B. *Dynamics of Atmospheric Flight.* Wiley (1972).

## PROBLEMS

1. How many degrees of freedom does an aircraft possess? Name the physical motions corresponding to each degree of freedom.

2. Discuss the lack of symmetry of a helicopter.

3. What conditions must the pitching moment satisfy for (i) equilibrium, (ii) static stability in gliding flight? Show that, by proper choice of c.g. position, any aircraft having a positive value of $C_m$ at zero lift can satisfy the conditions for steady stable flight.

4. Using the results of the previous question, find the direction of the tail load at zero wing lift for (i) a conventional tail, (ii) a tail-first aircraft. (The pitching moment due to the fuselage is to be neglected in this example).

5. Show that the stick movement required to trim in steady circular flight is inversely proportional to the square of the aircraft speed (if compressibility and distortion effects are neglected).

# Chapter 2
# THE EQUATIONS OF MOTION

## INTRODUCTION

In this chapter we shall set out the equations of motion of an aircraft considered as a rigid body (i.e. neglecting any distortion of the structure) referred to moving axes. We shall derive the form in which these equations can be expressed for small disturbances of a symmetric aircraft. We shall determine both the gravitational and the aerodynamic forces and moments acting on the aircraft, and finally express the equations in terms of non-dimensional quantities. This approach was first used in reference 1, but we shall use the notation for the aerodynamic derivatives adopted in reference 2 and in the Engineering Sciences Data Sheets.

## THE GENERAL DYNAMICAL EQUATIONS FOR A RIGID AIRCRAFT REFERRED TO MOVING AXES

We take a set of rectangular axes $Oxyz$, where $O$ is the centre of gravity of the aircraft (Fig. 2.1). The axes (known as 'body axes') are fixed in the aircraft and move with the aircraft. $Ox$ and $Oz$ are in the plane of symmetry of the aircraft, with $Oz$ downwards. $Oy$ is to starboard.

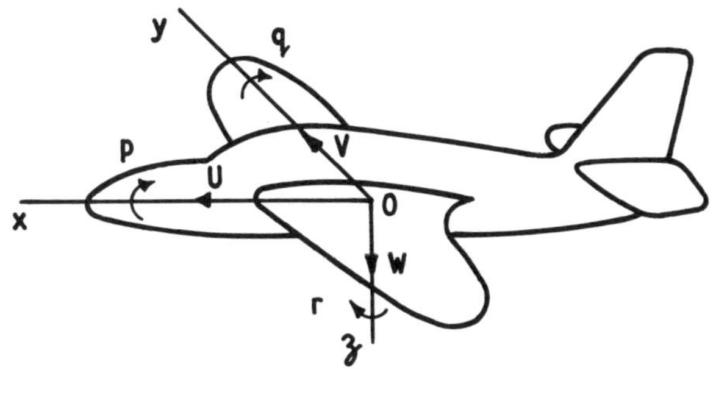


Fig. 2.1 Axes and velocity components

Let $U$, $V$, $W$ be the velocity components of the centre of gravity along $Ox$, $Oy$, $Oz$ respectively; let $p$, $q$, $r$ be the components of angular velocity of the axis frame $Oxyz$ about $Ox$, $Oy$, $Oz$ respectively. The positive senses of these angular velocities are in the clockwise sense about the respective axes.

Let $m$ be the mass of the aircraft and $I_x$, $I_y$, $I_z$ the moments of inertia of the aircraft about $Ox$, $Oy$, $Oz$. Let $I_{yz}$, $I_{zx}$, $I_{xy}$ denote the products of inertia with respect to $Oyz$, $Ozx$, $Oxy$. The main advantage of using body axes is that, provided the mass distribution of the aircraft remains the same, the moments and products of inertia with respect to these axes will be constant.

The aircraft is acted upon by external forces which have components $X$, $Y$, $Z$ along $Ox$, $Oy$, $Oz$ respectively. The moments of the external forces about $Ox$, $Oy$, $Oz$ are $L$, $M$, $N$ respectively.

Considered as a rigid body, as shown in Appendix 1, the motion of the aircraft is completely defined by the following six equations:

*Motion parallel to Ox:* $$m(\dot{U} - rV + qW) = X \;, \tag{2.1}$$

*parallel to Oy:* $$m(\dot{V} - pW + rU) = Y \;, \tag{2.2}$$

*parallel to Oz:* $$m(\dot{W} - qU + pV) = Z \;, \tag{2.3}$$

*Angular motion about Ox:*

$$I_x\dot{p} - (I_y - I_z)qr - I_{yz}(q^2 - r^2) - I_{zx}(\dot{r} + pq) - I_{xy}(\dot{q} - rp) = L \;, \tag{2.4}$$

*about Oy:*

$$I_y\dot{q} - (I_z - I_x)rp - I_{zx}(r^2 - p^2) - I_{xy}(\dot{p} + qr) - I_{yz}(\dot{r} - pq) = M \;, \tag{2.5}$$

*about Oz:*

$$I_z\dot{r} - (I_x - I_y)pq - I_{xy}(p^2 - q^2) - I_{yz}(\dot{q} + rp) - I_{zx}(\dot{p} - qr) = N \;. \tag{2.6}$$

## EQUATIONS OF MOTION FOR SMALL DISTURBANCES OF A SYMMETRIC AIRCRAFT

Equations (2.1) to (2.6) are a set of non-linear differential equations. We shall now show how they can be linearised, provided the disturbances from steady trimmed rectilinear motion are small.

In the steady state, the aircraft is moving with wings level, with no bank, yaw or sideslip, and the axes $Ox$ and $Oz$ lie in the vertical plane. Thus, in the steady flight, the aircraft is moving forward with uniform velocity and with no angular rotation.

Let $U_e$, $W_e$ be the constant velocity components of the centre of gravity along $Ox$, $Oz$ in steady flight, in which there is no sideslip and hence no velocity component along $Oy$. Let $U_e + u$, $v$, $W_e + w$ be the velocity components of the centre of gravity in the disturbed motion, with angular velocities $p$, $q$, $r$ about the axes $Ox$, $Oy$, $Oz$ respectively. We shall take $u$, $v$, $w$, $p$, $q$ and $r$ to be small quantities of the first order compared with $U_e$ and we shall neglect terms of the second degree and higher in these quantities.

The external forces and moments will be of two kinds: aerodynamic (and propulsive) forces and moments (denoted by $X_a$, $Y_a$, $Z_a$, $L_a$, $M_a$, $N_a$) and gravitational forces (denoted by $X_g$, $Y_g$, $Z_g$). $X_a$, $X_g$ are the force components along $Ox$; $Z_a$, $Z_g$ the force components along $Oz$. $L_a$, $M_a$, $N_a$ are the moments about $Ox$, $Oy$, $Oz$ respectively.

There are no moments due to gravity, since we have taken axes through the centre of gravity.

From Eqs. (2.1) to (2.3) we obtain (with $V = 0$ initially), neglecting second order terms:

$$m(\dot{u} + qW_e) \quad = X = X_a + X_g \,, \tag{2.7}$$

$$m(\dot{v} - pW_e + rU_e) = Y = Y_a + Y_g \,, \tag{2.8}$$

$$m(\dot{w} - qU_e) \quad = Z = Z_a + Z_g \,. \tag{2.9}$$

We note that the normal acceleration (along $Oz$) is $\dot{w} - qU_e$.

Now the mass distribution of the aircraft is taken to be symmetrical with respect to the plane $Oxz$.

Thus $$I_{xy} = \Sigma\, xy\, \delta m = 0 \tag{2.10}$$

and $$I_{yz} = \Sigma\, yz\, \delta m = 0. \tag{2.11}$$

We note that $I_{zx}$, the product of inertia about $Ox$ and $Oz$, will not be zero (unless $Ox$ and $Oz$ are principal axes of inertia).

From Eqs. (2.4) to (2.6), neglecting second order terms and using Eqs. (2.10) and (2.11), we obtain

$$I_x \dot{p} - I_{zx}\dot{r} = L_a \,, \tag{2.12}$$

$$I_y \dot{q} = M_a \,, \tag{2.13}$$

$$- I_{zx}\dot{p} + I_z \dot{r} = N_a \,. \tag{2.14}$$

## DEFINITION OF THE ANGLE OF PITCH $\theta$, THE ANGLE OF BANK $\phi$ AND ANGLE OF YAW $\psi$

We shall now consider how the positions of the axes $Ox$, $Oy$, $Oz$ are related to their positions in steady flight.

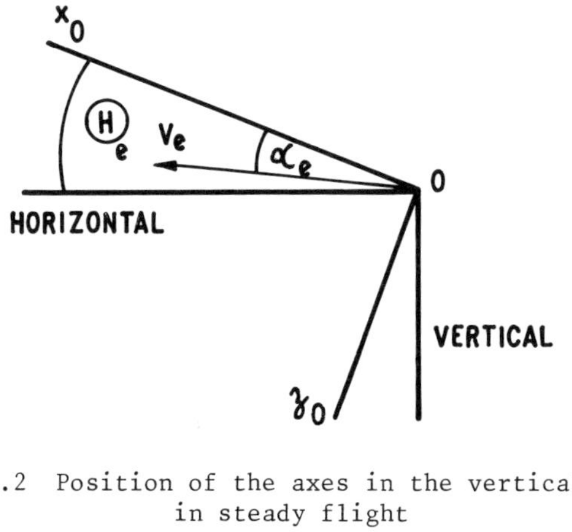


Fig. 2.2 Position of the axes in the vertical plane in steady flight

In the undisturbed state we suppose that the axis $Ox$ is in the vertical plane and makes an angle $\Theta_e$ with the horizontal, and an angle $\alpha_e$ with the resultant direction of motion of the aircraft, speed $V_e$ in steady flight. (Note: we use $V_e$ to denote the resultant speed of the aircraft in steady flight; this must not be confused with the velocity of sideslip, which is zero in the steady state). In the *steady flight* the axis $Oy$ is horizontal (to starboard), and the axis $Oz$ is in the vertical plane (positive downwards) at right angles to $Ox$ and $Oy$. Thus, in the steady state the axes are $Ox_0$, $Oy_0$, $Oz_0$, as shown in Figs. 2.2 and 2.3.

To derive the disturbed position of the axes at time $t$ (Fig. 2.3), we first rotate $Ox_0y_0z_0$ about $Oz_0$ through an angle $\psi$ (*an angle of yaw* $\psi$) in the clockwise direction, to the position $Ox_1y_1z_0$. Thus, $Ox_0$, $Ox_1$, $Oy_0$, $Oy_1$ all lie in the same plane, which is perpendicular to $Oz_0$. The axes $Ox_1y_1z_0$ are then rotated about $Oy_1$ through an angle $\theta$ (*an angle of pitch* $\theta$) in the clockwise direction, to the position $Oxy_1z_2$. Thus, $Ox$, $Ox_1$, $Oz_0$, $Oz_2$ all lie in the same plane, which is perpendicular to $Oy_1$. Finally the axes $Oxy_1z_2$ are rotated about $Ox$ through an angle $\phi$ (*an angle of bank* $\phi$) in the clockwise direction, to the position $Oxyz$. $Oy_1$, $Oy$, $Oz_2$, $Oz$ all lie in the same plane, which is perpendicular to $Ox$. $Oxyz$ is the disturbed position of the axes at time $t$, corresponding to angles of yaw $\psi$, pitch $\theta$ and bank $\phi$ of the aircraft from its steady state position, the axes $Oxyz$ being fixed in the aircraft. In Fig. 2.3 the intersections of the various axes with the sphere of unit radius (with centre $O$) are indicated to clarify the various orientations of the axes.

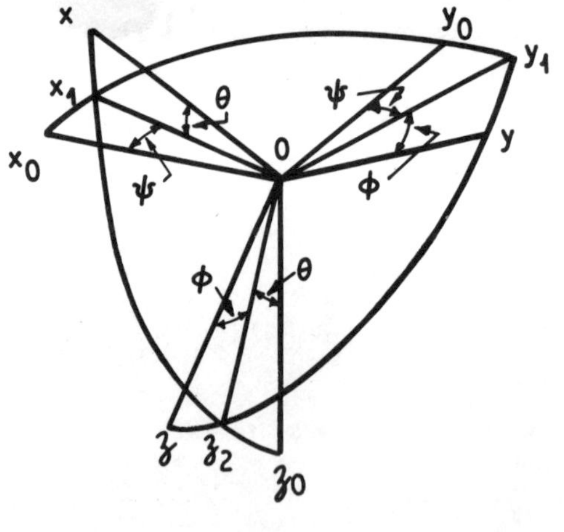


Fig. 2.3 Derivation of the disturbed position of the axes

RELATIONS FOR RATES OF ROLL, PITCH AND YAW

Considering the motion of the aircraft about $O$, we see that the aircraft (and hence the frame $Oxyz$) has the following angular velocities:

$\dot\theta$, rate of change of pitch, about $Oy_1$,
$\dot\phi$, rate of change of bank, about $Ox$,
$\dot\psi$, rate of change of yaw, about $Oz_0$.

We shall now find the components of these angular velocities about $Ox$, $Oy$ and $Oz$.

Considering the rate of change of pitch, we see from Fig. 2.3 (since $Oy_1$, $Oy$, $Oz_2$, $Oz$ all lie in the same plane), that the components of $\dot\theta$ about $Ox$, $Oy$ and $Oz$ are

$$0, \quad \dot\theta\cos\phi, \quad -\dot\theta\sin\phi. \tag{2.15}$$

Considering the rate of change of bank, we see from Fig. 2.3 that the components of $\dot{\phi}$ about $Ox$, $Oy$ and $Oz$ are

$$\dot{\phi}, \quad 0, \quad 0 \tag{2.16}$$

Finally, considering the rate of change of yaw, we see from Fig. 2.3 (since $Ox$, $Ox_1$, $Oz_2$, $Oz_0$ all lie in the same plane) that the components of $\dot{\psi}$ about $Ox$, $Oy_1$, $Oz_2$ are

$$-\dot{\psi}\sin\theta, \quad 0, \quad \dot{\psi}\cos\theta.$$

Hence, since $Oy_1$, $Oy$, $Oz_2$, $Oz$ all lie in the same plane, the components of $\dot{\psi}$ about $Ox$, $Oy$ and $Oz$ are

$$-\dot{\psi}\sin\theta, \quad \dot{\psi}\cos\theta\sin\phi, \quad \dot{\psi}\cos\theta\cos\phi. \tag{2.17}$$

But we have defined the components of angular velocity of the axes $Oxyz$ as $p$, $q$ and $r$ about $Ox$, $Oy$, $Oz$ respectively. Therefore from Eqs. (2.15) to (2.17) we have

$$p = \dot{\phi} - \dot{\psi}\sin\theta, \tag{2.18}$$

$$q = \dot{\theta}\cos\phi + \dot{\psi}\cos\theta\sin\phi, \tag{2.19}$$

$$r = -\dot{\theta}\sin\phi + \dot{\psi}\cos\theta\cos\phi. \tag{2.20}$$

Now for small disturbances, $\theta$, $\phi$ and $\psi$ will all be small quantities of the first order, and, as above, we take $p$, $q$ and $r$ (and $\dot{\theta}$, $\dot{\phi}$ and $\dot{\psi}$) to be small quantities of the first order compared with $U_e$. Then from Eqs. (2.18) to (2.20), neglecting second-order quantities,

$$p = \dot{\phi} \text{ (rate of roll)}, \tag{2.21}$$

$$q = \dot{\theta} \text{ (rate of pitch)}, \tag{2.22}$$

and

$$r = \dot{\psi} \text{ (rate of yaw)}. \tag{2.23}$$

## DETERMINATION OF THE GRAVITATIONAL FORCES

We shall now derive simple expressions for the gravitational forces $X_g$, $Y_g$, $Z_g$ appearing on the right hand sides of Eqs. (2.7) to (2.9). We shall determine the components of the weight $mg$ of the aircraft with respect to $Ox$, $Oy$ and $Oz$.

From Fig. 2.2, we see that the components of the weight along $Ox_0$, $Oy_0$, $Oz_0$ are

$$-\, mg\sin\Theta_e, \quad 0, \quad mg\cos\Theta_e.$$

From Fig. 2.3, since $Ox_0$, $Ox_1$, $Oy_0$, $Oy_1$ all lie in the same plane, the components of the weight along $Ox_1$, $Oy_1$, $Oz_0$ are

$$-\, mg\sin\Theta_e\cos\psi, \quad mg\sin\Theta_e\sin\psi, \quad mg\cos\Theta_e.$$

Similarly, since $Ox$, $Ox_1$, $Oz_2$, $Oz_0$ all lie in the same plane, the components of the weight along $Ox$, $Oy_1$, $Oz_2$ are

$$-\, mg\,(\sin\Theta_e\cos\psi\cos\theta + \cos\Theta_e\sin\theta),$$

$$mg\sin\Theta_e\sin\psi, \quad mg\,(\cos\Theta_e\cos\theta - \sin\Theta_e\cos\psi\sin\theta).$$

Finally, since $Oy_1$, $Oy$, $Oz_2$, $Oz$ all lie in the same plane, the components of the weight along $Ox$, $Oy$, $Oz$ are

$$- mg\,(\sin\Theta_e \cos\psi \cos\theta + \cos\Theta_e \sin\theta),$$
$$mg\,(\sin\Theta_e \sin\psi \cos\phi + \cos\Theta_e \cos\theta \sin\phi \doteq \sin\Theta_e \cos\psi \sin\theta \sin\phi),$$
$$mg\,(\cos\Theta_e \cos\theta \cos\phi - \sin\Theta_e \cos\psi \sin\theta \cos\phi - \sin\Theta_e \sin\psi \sin\phi). \qquad (2.24)$$

Now for small disturbances, $\theta$, $\phi$ and $\psi$ will all be small quantities of the first order. Thus, from Eq. (2.24), neglecting small quantities of the second and higher orders, and denoting the components of the weight $mg$ along $Ox$, $Oy$, $Oz$ by $X_g$, $Y_g$ and $Z_g$, we have

$$X_g = -m(g_2 + g_1\theta)\ , \qquad (2.25)$$
$$Y_g = m(g_2\psi + g_1\phi) \qquad (2.26)$$
$$Z_g = m(g_1 - g_2\theta)\ , \qquad (2.27)$$

where $$g_1 = g\cos\Theta_e \qquad (2.28)$$

and $$g_2 = g\sin\Theta_e. \qquad (2.29)$$

In general $\Theta_e$, the inclination of $Ox$ to the horizontal in steady flight, cannot be taken to be small.

The condition $\phi = 0$ does not necessarily imply that the wings are level. From Eq. (2.26), for the wings to be level we must have $Y_g = 0$,

i.e. $$\psi\sin\Theta_e + \phi\cos\Theta_e = 0.$$

## ANGLES OF YAW AND SIDESLIP

We must note the difference between the angle of yaw and the angle of sideslip. The angle of yaw is related to the change in *orientation* of a line $Ox$, fixed in the aircraft, with respect to a fixed plane, the vertical plane $Ox_0z_0$. Thus the angle of yaw is independent of the direction of motion of $O$, the centre of gravity of the aircraft.

The angle of sideslip $\beta$ is the angle between the resultant direction of motion of the centre of gravity $O$ and the plane of symmetry $Oxz$ of the aircraft in the disturbed motion. $\beta$ is positive when the sideslip is to starboard. Thus the angle of sideslip is, in general, independent of the angle of yaw.

To illustrate the difference between yaw and sideslip, consider an aircraft disturbed from its steady flight position with zero angle of pitch $\theta$ and zero bank $\phi$. Figure 2.4 shows plan views of the aircraft in a plane perpendicular to $Oz$ (which in this particular case coincides with $Oz_0$). Figure 2.4(a) shows the steady flight position with no yaw and no sideslip. Figure 2.4(b) shows the disturbed position, in which there is no relation between the angle of yaw and the angle of sideslip. Figure 2.4(c) shows a particular disturbed position of the aircraft, in which the direction of motion of the centre of gravity $O$ coincides with its direction in steady flight. The aircraft in this position has both yaw and sideslip, and in this particular case the sideslip is related to the angle of yaw. Remembering that sideslip is positive to starboard, we have, from Fig. 2.4(c),

$$\beta = -\psi.$$

Conditions such as those in Fig. 2.4(c) occur when an aircraft model is being tested at an angle of yaw in a wind tunnel, where the direction of motion in the free stream is unaffected by the yaw of the model.

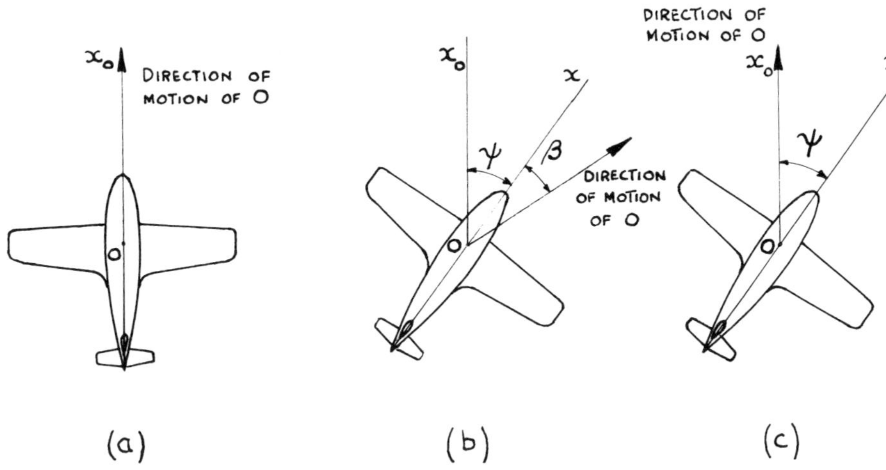


Fig. 2.4 Angles of yaw and sideslip

## DETERMINATION OF THE AERODYNAMIC FORCES

We shall next derive simple expressions for the aerodynamic forces and moments ($X_a$, $Y_a$, $Z_a$, $L_a$, $M_a$, $N_a$) which appear on the right hand sides of Eqs. (2.7) to (2.14).

The aerodynamic forces and moments acting on the aircraft are functions of the incidence and velocity components of the aircraft, i.e. of $u$, $v$, $w$, $p$, $q$ and $r$ (all small quantities of the first order). For small disturbances, neglecting second-order terms, we write

$$X_a = \mathring{X}_{ae} + \mathring{X}_u\, u + \mathring{X}_v\, v + \mathring{X}_w\, w + \mathring{X}_{\dot{w}}\, \dot{w} + \mathring{X}_p\, p + \mathring{X}_q\, q + \mathring{X}_r\, r + \mathring{X}(t) \quad (2.30)$$

$$Y_a = \mathring{Y}_{ae} + \mathring{Y}_u\, u + \mathring{Y}_v\, v + \mathring{Y}_w\, w + \mathring{Y}_{\dot{w}}\, \dot{w} + \mathring{Y}_p\, p + \mathring{Y}_q\, q + \mathring{Y}_r\, r + \mathring{Y}(t) \quad (2.31)$$

$$Z_a = \mathring{Z}_{ae} + \mathring{Z}_u\, u + \mathring{Z}_v\, v + \mathring{Z}_w\, w + \mathring{Z}_{\dot{w}}\, \dot{w} + \mathring{Z}_p\, p + \mathring{Z}_q\, q + \mathring{Z}_r\, r + \mathring{Z}(t) \quad (2.32)$$

$$L_a = \mathring{L}_u\, u + \mathring{L}_v\, v + \mathring{L}_w\, w + \mathring{L}_{\dot{w}}\, \dot{w} + \mathring{L}_p\, p + \mathring{L}_q\, q + \mathring{L}_r\, r + \mathring{L}(t) \quad (2.33)$$

$$M_a = \mathring{M}_u\, u + \mathring{M}_v\, v + \mathring{M}_w\, w + \mathring{M}_{\dot{w}}\, \dot{w} + \mathring{M}_p\, p + \mathring{M}_q\, q + \mathring{M}_r\, r + \mathring{M}(t) \quad (2.34)$$

$$N_a = \mathring{N}_u\, u + \mathring{N}_v\, v + \mathring{N}_w\, w + \mathring{N}_{\dot{w}}\, \dot{w} + \mathring{N}_p\, p + \mathring{N}_q\, q + \mathring{N}_r\, r + \mathring{N}(t) \quad (2.35)$$

The coefficients $\mathring{X}_u$, $\mathring{X}_v$, ..., $\mathring{X}_r$, $\mathring{Y}_u$, $\mathring{Y}_v$, ..., $\mathring{Y}_r$, $\mathring{Z}_u$, $\mathring{Z}_v$, ..., $\mathring{Z}_r$, $\mathring{L}_u$, $\mathring{L}_v$, ..., $\mathring{L}_r$, $\mathring{M}_u$, $\mathring{M}_v$, ..., $\mathring{M}_r$, $\mathring{N}_u$, $\mathring{N}_v$, ..., $\mathring{N}_r$ are constants and are called aerodynamic derivatives. Thus $\mathring{X}_u = \partial X/\partial u$, etc. The 'dressing' ord (°) as in $\mathring{X}_u$ denotes that the quantity is expressed in ordinary units (usually S.I. units). $\mathring{X}_{ae}$, $\mathring{Y}_{ae}$, $\mathring{Z}_{ae}$ are the steady state values of $X_a$, $Y_a$, $Z_a$. The aerodynamic moments are zero in the steady flight, since the aircraft is then in trim. $\mathring{X}(t)$, $\mathring{Y}(t)$, $\mathring{Z}(t)$, $\mathring{L}(t)$, $\mathring{M}(t)$, $\mathring{N}(t)$ are the aerodynamic forces and moments due to movement of the controls from their trimmed positions (and may thus vary with the time).

As can be seen from Eqs. (2.30) to (2.35), in general we assume that the aerodynamic forces and moments depend solely on the instantaneous motion of the aircraft. When an aircraft is in unsteady oscillatory motion, these forces and moments are not in phase with the oscillatory motion; thus they depend also on the rate of change of the aircraft motion. In addition, the flow field at the tail depends on the time history of the wing motion (e.g. on the rate of change of wing incidence, as measured by $\dot{w}$).

To allow for these effects, we should introduce additional terms in Eqs. (2.30) to (2.35) of the form $\mathring{X}_{\dot{u}}\, \dot{u}$, $\mathring{X}_{\dot{v}}\, \dot{v}$, etc. In general, the effects of all such terms are small (with the exception of the $\dot{w}$ effect mentioned above). The latter terms (involving $\mathring{X}_{\dot{w}}$, $\mathring{Y}_{\dot{w}}$, $\mathring{Z}_{\dot{w}}$, $\mathring{L}_{\dot{w}}$, $\mathring{M}_{\dot{w}}$, $\mathring{N}_{\dot{w}}$) are therefore included, as some of them are found to be important in accounting for the longitudinal pitching oscillation which occurs with aircraft.

It is assumed that the aircraft has a longitudinal plane of symmetry, this being the vertical plane through the centre line of the fuselage in steady rectilinear flight with no bank or yaw. For such an aircraft, a symmetric disturbance cannot cause an asymmetric reaction, e.g. a small change in forward speed or angle of pitch cannot produce any sideforce, or rolling or yawing moment. We see therefore, from Eqs. (2.30) to (2.35), that the aerodynamic derivatives $\mathring{Y}_u$, $\mathring{Y}_w$, $\mathring{Y}_{\dot{w}}$, $\mathring{Y}_q$, $\mathring{L}_u$, $\mathring{L}_w$, $\mathring{L}_{\dot{w}}$, $\mathring{L}_q$, $\mathring{N}_u$, $\mathring{N}_w$, $\mathring{N}_{\dot{w}}$ and $\mathring{N}_q$ must all be zero.

Again, consider the effect of an asymmetric disturbance, such as sideslipping, on a symmetric aircraft. From Eq. (2.30), sideslip with velocity $v$ produces a force $\mathring{X}_v\, v$ along $Ox$ in the plane of symmetry. By symmetry, sideslip with velocity $(-v)$ must produce the same force in the plane of symmetry. Therefore $\mathring{X}_v$ must be zero. In a similar way we find that all the symmetric forces and moments arising from asymmetric disturbances such as sideslip, rate of roll and rate of yaw are zero, when second order terms are neglected. Thus $\mathring{X}_v$, $\mathring{X}_p$, $\mathring{X}_r$, $\mathring{Z}_v$, $\mathring{Z}_p$, $\mathring{Z}_r$, $\mathring{M}_v$, $\mathring{M}_p$ and $\mathring{M}_r$ are all zero.

We can now write Eqs.(2.30) to (2.35) in the form

$$\mathring{X}_a = \mathring{X}_{ae} + \mathring{X}_u\, u + \mathring{X}_w\, w + \mathring{X}_{\dot{w}}\, \dot{w} + \mathring{X}_q\, q + \mathring{X}(t), \tag{2.36}$$

$$\mathring{Z}_a = \mathring{Z}_{ae} + \mathring{Z}_u\, u + \mathring{Z}_w\, w + \mathring{X}_{\dot{w}}\, \dot{w} + \mathring{Z}_q\, q + \mathring{Z}(t), \tag{2.37}$$

$$\mathring{M}_a = \mathring{M}_u\, u + \mathring{M}_w\, w + \mathring{M}_{\dot{w}}\, \dot{w} + \mathring{M}_q\, q + \mathring{M}(t), \tag{2.38}$$

$$\mathring{Y}_a = \mathring{Y}_{ae} + \mathring{Y}_v\, v + \mathring{Y}_p\, p + \mathring{Y}_r\, r + \mathring{Y}(t), \tag{2.39}$$

$$\mathring{L}_a = \mathring{L}_v\, v + \mathring{L}_p\, p + \mathring{L}_r\, r + \mathring{L}(t), \tag{2.40}$$

$$\mathring{N}_a = \mathring{N}_v\, v + \mathring{N}_p\, p + \mathring{N}_r\, r + \mathring{N}(t). \tag{2.41}$$

Thus, for a symmetric aircraft, when second order terms are neglected, we can divide the aerodynamic forces and moments into two groups: the symmetric forces and moments given by Eqs.(2.36) to (2.38), which depend only on symmetric disturbances, and the asymmetric forces and moments, given by Eqs.(2.39) to (2.41), which depend only on asymmetric disturbances.

Consider next the values of $\mathring{X}_{ae}$, $\mathring{Y}_{ae}$ and $\mathring{Z}_{ae}$, the aerodynamic (and propulsive) forces in the initial steady rectilinear flight, with wings level.

Since the aircraft is initially in steady flight at constant speed $V_e$, the forces acting will be equilibrium. Thus, from Fig. 2.5,

$$\mathring{X}_{ae} = mg \sin \Theta_e = mg_2 \tag{2.42}$$

$$\mathring{Z}_{ae} = -mg \cos \Theta_e = mg_1 \tag{2.43}$$

and
$$\mathring{Y}_{ae} = 0, \tag{2.44}$$

where $g_1$ and $g_2$ are given by Eqs. (2.28) and (2.29).

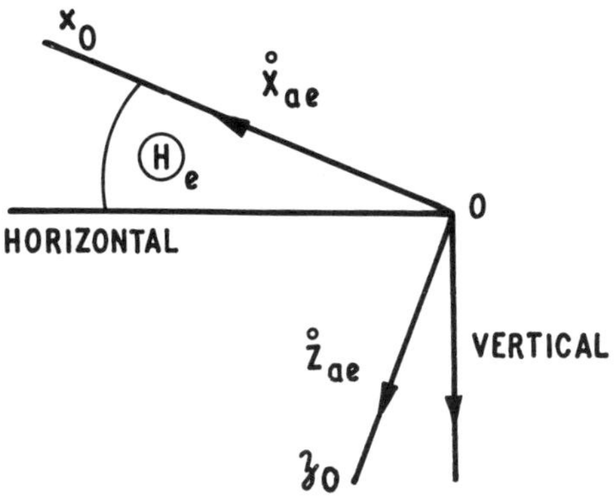


Fig. 2.5 Forces acting in steady flight

## SEPARABILITY OF LONGITUDINAL AND LATERAL MOTION

From Eqs. (2.7) to (2.14), (2.25) to (2.27) and (2.36) to (2.44), we see that the equations of motion for small disturbances can be split up into two groups.

(i) The general equations of longitudinal symmetric motion for small disturbances

$$m\dot{u} - \mathring{X}_u u - \mathring{X}_{\dot{w}} \dot{w} - \mathring{X}_w w + (mW_e - \mathring{X}_q)q + mg_1\theta = \mathring{X}(t) \quad (2.45)$$

$$-\mathring{Z}_u u + (m - \mathring{Z}_{\dot{w}})\dot{w} - \mathring{Z}_w w - (mU_e + \mathring{Z}_q)q + mg_2\theta = \mathring{Z}(t) \quad (2.46)$$

$$-\mathring{M}_u u - \mathring{M}_{\dot{w}}\dot{w} - \mathring{M}_w w + I_y\dot{q} - \mathring{M}_q q = \mathring{M}(t) \quad (2.47)$$

where $q = \dot{\theta}$ . (2.48)

These equations involve only symmetric disturbances ($u$ the increment in the velocity of $O$ along $Ox$, $w$ the increment in the velocity of $O$ along $Oz$, $\theta$ the angle of pitch, and their derivatives with respect to $t$).

(ii) The general equations of lateral asymmetric motion for small disturbances

$$m\dot{v} - \mathring{Y}_v v - (mW_e + \mathring{Y}_p)p + (mU_e - \mathring{Y}_r)r - mg_1\phi - mg_2\psi = \mathring{Y}(t), \quad (2.49)$$

$$-\mathring{L}_v v + I_x\dot{p} - \mathring{L}_p p - I_{zx}\dot{r} - \mathring{L}_r r = \mathring{L}(t), \quad (2.50)$$

$$-\mathring{N}_v v - I_{zx}\dot{p} - \mathring{N}_p p + I_z\dot{r} - \mathring{N}_r r = \mathring{N}(t), \quad (2.51)$$

where $p = \dot{\phi}$ (2.52)

and $r = \dot{\psi}$ . (2.53)

These equations involve only asymmetric disturbances ($v$ the velocity of sideslip, $\phi$ the angle of bank, $\psi$ the angle of yaw, and their derivatives with respect to $t$). The two groups of equations can thus be solved independently, provided disturbances are small.

## AXIS SYSTEMS USED IN STABILITY ANALYSIS

We are still free to fix the direction of $Ox$ in the initial steady flight. Two systems of body axes are in common use, (i) wind axes (sometimes called stability axes or aerodynamic-body axes) and (ii) principal axes.

If, in the initial steady flight, we take $Ox$ to coincide with the undisturbed direction of motion of the aircraft, our axes are called *wind axes* (the axes are, of course, fixed in the aircraft and $Ox$ will not, in general, coincide with the direction of motion of $O$ in the disturbed motion). With wind axes we have, from Fig. 2.2,

$$\alpha_e = 0 \tag{2.54}$$

and thus
$$U_e = V_e \tag{2.55}$$

and
$$W_e = 0, \tag{2.56}$$

where $V_e$ is the aircraft speed in steady flight.

If we take the direction of $Ox$ to coincide with one of the principal axes of inertia of the aircraft, it follows that $Ox$, $Oy$ and $Oz$ will all lie along the directions of the principal axes of inertia of the aircraft. Our axes are then said to be *principal axes*. With principal axes, the products of inertia with respect to the axes vanish. In particular, $I_{zx}$ is then zero.

We see that either of these axis systems leads to some simplification in the equations of motion. In this book (and in most papers on stability) wind axes are used, unless stated otherwise. Stability derivatives obtained from low speed wind tunnel tests are usually measured about wind axes (this is not necessarily the case in supersonic tunnel tests). Principal axes are of advantage where the primary interest lies in inertia effects (as shown in Part IV, Chapter 9). It must be remembered that the values of the aerodynamic derivatives used in the equations must be those appropriate to the axis system selected. Transformation formulae for the aerodynamic derivatives for a change of body axes are given in the Engineering Sciences Data Sheets.

With wind axes, From Fig. 2.2, $\Theta_e$ is the angle of climb in steady flight, in which there is no bank, yaw or sideslip. On resolving the forces perpendicular to the flight path we have

$$mg\cos\Theta_e = \tfrac{1}{2}\rho_e V_e{}^2 S C_L\ , \tag{2.57}$$

where $m$ is the mass of the aircraft, $\rho$ is the air density, $S$ the wing area, and the suffix $e$ refers to the constant datum value (in the initial steady flight).

## NON-DIMENSIONAL AERODYNAMIC DERIVATIVES (LONGITUDINAL)

We see that the aerodynamic derivatives $\mathring{X}_u$, $\mathring{X}_w$, $\mathring{X}_{\dot{w}}$, $\mathring{X}_q$, $\mathring{Z}_u$, $\mathring{Z}_w$, $\mathring{Z}_{\dot{w}}$, $\mathring{Z}_q$, $\mathring{M}_u$, $\mathring{M}_w$, $\mathring{M}_{\dot{w}}$, $\mathring{M}_q$ occur in the equations of longitudinal symmetric motion. The corresponding aero-normalised non-dimensional derivatives are defined as follows (in general agreement with the notation of the Engineering Sciences Data Sheets):

FORCE VELOCITY DERIVATIVES

due to forward velocity,

$$X_u = \mathring{X}_u / \tfrac{1}{2}\rho_e V_e S \ , \tag{2.58}$$

$$Z_u = \mathring{Z}_u / \tfrac{1}{2}\rho_e V_e S \ , \tag{2.59}$$

due to downward velocity,

$$X_w = \mathring{X}_w / \tfrac{1}{2}\rho_e V_e S \ , \tag{2.60}$$

$$Z_w = \mathring{Z}_w / \tfrac{1}{2}\rho_e V_e S \ . \tag{2.61}$$

FORCE ACCELERATION DERIVATIVES

due to rate of change of downward velocity,

$$X_{\dot{w}} = \mathring{X}_{\dot{w}} / \tfrac{1}{2}\rho_e S\bar{\bar{c}} \ , \tag{2.62}$$

$$Z_{\dot{w}} = \mathring{Z}_{\dot{w}} / \tfrac{1}{2}\rho_e S\bar{\bar{c}} \ , \tag{2.63}$$

where $\bar{\bar{c}}$ is the mean aerodynamic chord of the wing (this being the datum reference length in longitudinal stability analysis).

FORCE ROTARY DERIVATIVES

due to rate of pitch,

$$X_q = \mathring{X}_q / \tfrac{1}{2}\rho_e V_e S\bar{\bar{c}} \ , \tag{2.64}$$

$$Z_q = \mathring{Z}_q / \tfrac{1}{2}\rho_e V_e S\bar{\bar{c}} \ . \tag{2.65}$$

PITCHING MOMENT DERIVATIVES

due to forward velocity,

$$M_u = \mathring{M}_u / \tfrac{1}{2}\rho_e V_e S\bar{\bar{c}} \ , \tag{2.66}$$

due to downward velocity,

$$M_w = \mathring{M}_w / \tfrac{1}{2}\rho_e V_e S\bar{\bar{c}} \tag{2.67}$$

due to rate of change of downward velocity,

$$M_{\dot{w}} = \mathring{M}_{\dot{w}} / \tfrac{1}{2}\rho_e S\bar{\bar{c}}^2 , \tag{2.68}$$

due to rate of pitch,

$$M_q = \mathring{M}_q / \tfrac{1}{2}\rho_e V_e S\bar{\bar{c}}^2 \ . \tag{2.69}$$

CONTROL DERIVATIVES

As stated above, the applied forces and moments $\mathring{X}(t)$, $\mathring{Z}(t)$, $\mathring{M}(t)$ are due to the application of controls, i.e. to the application of the elevator in the case of symmetric disturbances. We write

$$\mathring{X}(t) = \mathring{X}_\eta \, \eta' \ , \qquad (2.70)$$

$$\mathring{Z}(t) = \mathring{Z}_\eta \, \eta' \ , \qquad (2.71)$$

$$\mathring{M}(t) = \mathring{M}_\eta \, \eta' \ , \qquad (2.72)$$

where $\eta'$ is the change in elevator angle (in radians) from the trimmed position. $\eta'$ is positive for down elevator.

The corresponding aero-normalised non-dimensional derivatives are defined by

$$X_\eta = \mathring{X}_\eta / \tfrac{1}{2}\rho_e V_e^{\,2} S \ , \qquad (2.73)$$

$$Z_\eta = \mathring{Z}_\eta / \tfrac{1}{2}\rho_e V_e^{\,2} S \ , \qquad (2.74)$$

$$M_\eta = \mathring{M}_\eta / \tfrac{1}{2}\rho_e V_e^{\,2} S\bar{\bar{c}} \ . \qquad (2.75)$$

## NON-DIMENSIONAL AERODYNAMIC DERIVATIVES (LATERAL)

The aerodynamic derivatives $\mathring{Y}_v$, $\mathring{Y}_p$, $\mathring{Y}_r$, $\mathring{L}_v$, $\mathring{L}_p$, $\mathring{L}_r$, $\mathring{N}_v$, $\mathring{N}_p$, $\mathring{N}_r$ occur in the equations of lateral asymmetric motion. The corresponding aero-normalised non-dimensional derivatives are defined as follows (in general agreement with the notation of the Engineering Sciences Data Sheets):

### SIDE FORCE DERIVATIVES

due to sideslip, $$Y_v = \mathring{Y}_v / \tfrac{1}{2}\rho_e V_e S \ , \qquad (2.76)$$

due to rate of roll, $$Y_p = \mathring{Y}_p / \tfrac{1}{2}\rho_e V_e S b \ , \qquad (2.77)$$

due to rate of yaw, $$Y_r = \mathring{Y}_r / \tfrac{1}{2}\rho_e V_e S b \ , \qquad (2.78)$$

where $b$ is the wing span (this being the datum reference length in lateral stability analysis).

### ROLLING MOMENT DERIVATIVES

due to sideslip, $$L_v = \mathring{L}_v / \tfrac{1}{2}\rho_e V_e S b \ , \qquad (2.79)$$

due to rate of roll, $$L_p = \mathring{L}_p / \tfrac{1}{2}\rho_e V_e S b^2 \ , \qquad (2.80)$$

due to rate of yaw, $$L_r = \mathring{L}_r / \tfrac{1}{2}\rho_e V_e S b^2 \ . \qquad (2.81)$$

### YAWING MOMENT DERIVATIVES

due to sideslip, $$N_v = \mathring{N}_v / \tfrac{1}{2}\rho_e V_e S b \ , \qquad (2.82)$$

due to rate of roll, $$N_p = \mathring{N}_p / \tfrac{1}{2}\rho_e V_e S b^2 \ , \qquad (2.83)$$

due to rate of yaw, $$N_r = \mathring{N}_r / \tfrac{1}{2}\rho_e V_e S b^2 \ . \qquad (2.84)$$

### CONTROL DERIVATIVES

As stated above, the applied forces and moments $\mathring{Y}(t)$, $\mathring{L}(t)$, $\mathring{N}(t)$ are due to the application of controls. In asymmetric flight we need only consider the contributions from the ailerons and rudder, these being the only controls which can by themselves give rise to asymmetric disturbances.

We write

$$\mathring{Y}(t) = \mathring{Y}_\xi \, \xi + \mathring{Y}_\zeta \, \zeta \tag{2.85}$$

$$\mathring{L}(t) = \mathring{L}_\xi \, \xi + \mathring{L}_\zeta \, \zeta \tag{2.86}$$

$$\mathring{N}(t) = \mathring{N}_\xi \, \xi + \mathring{N}_\zeta \, \zeta , \tag{2.87}$$

where $\xi$ = aileron angle, positive with right aileron down and left aileron up,
and $\zeta$ = rudder angle, positive to the left.

Thus positive aileron gives an anti-clockwise rolling moment about $Ox$ and positive rudder gives an anti-clockwise yawing moment about $Oz$. $\xi$ and $\zeta$ are in radians and are measured from their positions in steady straight flight.

The corresponding non-dimensional control derivatives are defined as follows:

SIDE FORCE DERIVATIVES

due to ailerons, $$Y_\xi = \mathring{Y}_\xi / \tfrac{1}{2}\rho_e V_e^2 S \, , \tag{2.88}$$

due to rudder, $$Y_\zeta = \mathring{Y}_\zeta / \tfrac{1}{2}\rho_e V_e^2 S \, . \tag{2.89}$$

ROLLING MOMENT DERIVATIVES

due to ailerons, $$L_\xi = \mathring{L}_\xi / \tfrac{1}{2}\rho_e V_e^2 Sb \, , \tag{2.90}$$

due to rudder, $$L_\zeta = \mathring{L}_\zeta / \tfrac{1}{2}\rho_e V_e^2 Sb \, . \tag{2.91}$$

YAWING MOMENT DERIVATIVES

due to ailerons, $$N_\xi = \mathring{N}_\xi / \tfrac{1}{2}\rho_e V_e^2 Sb, \tag{2.92}$$

due to rudder, $$N_\zeta = \mathring{N}_\zeta / \tfrac{1}{2}\rho_e V_e^2 Sb. \tag{2.93}$$

## NON-DIMENSIONAL DISTURBANCES

Before writing the equations of motion in non-dimensional form, it is convenient to define the following non-dimensional quantities:

$$\hat{u} = u/V_e \qquad \text{(sometimes called } u \text{ cap)}, \tag{2.94}$$

$$\hat{v} = v/V_e \, , \tag{2.95}$$

$$\hat{w} = w/V_e \, , \tag{2.96}$$

$$\hat{p} = \tau p \, , \tag{2.97}$$

$$\hat{q} = \tau q \, , \tag{2.98}$$

$$\hat{r} = \tau r \, . \tag{2.99}$$

The non-dimensional time $\hat{t}$ is given by $$\hat{t} = t/\tau \, , \tag{2.100}$$

where $$\tau = m/\tfrac{1}{2}\rho_e V_e S = V_e C_L / g \cos\Theta_e \, . \tag{2.101}$$

From Eqs.(2.95) and (2.96), for small disturbances, $\hat{v}$ is equal to the angle of the sideslip and, when wind axes are used, $\hat{w}$ is equal to the change of incidence in the disturbed flight.

We see also that
$$\hat{p} = d\phi/d\hat{t} \,, \tag{2.102}$$
$$\hat{q} = d\theta/d\hat{t} \,, \tag{2.103}$$
and
$$\hat{r} = d\psi/d\hat{t} \,. \tag{2.104}$$

## NON-DIMENSIONAL MASS AND INERTIA

The aircraft longitudinal relative density parameter $\mu_1$ is given by

$$\mu_1 = m/\tfrac{1}{2}\rho_e S\bar{\bar{c}} = V_e\tau/\bar{\bar{c}} \,, \tag{2.105}$$

where $\bar{\bar{c}}$ is the mean aerodynamic chord of the wing.

The aircraft lateral relative density parameter $\mu_2$ is given by

$$\mu_2 = m/\tfrac{1}{2}\rho_e Sb = V_e\tau/b \,, \tag{2.106}$$

where $b$ is the wing span.

The non-dimensional inertia parameters are:

non-dimensional rolling moment of inertia, $i_x = I_x/mb^2$ , (2.107)

non-dimensional pitching moment of inertia, $i_y = I_y/m\bar{\bar{c}}^2$ , (2.108)

non-dimensional yawing moment of inertia, $i_z = I_z/mb^2$ , (2.109)

non-dimensional product of inertia about $Ox$ and $Oz$, $i_{zx} = I_{zx}/mb^2$. (2.110)

## NON-DIMENSIONAL FORM OF THE EQUATIONS OF MOTION

Using the non-dimensional parameters defined above, we can express the equations of motion in non-dimensional form. The coefficients of the various terms in the resulting equations then become independent of the size of the aircraft; comparison between the stability characteristics of large and small aircraft can then be more easily appreciated. The equations are referred to wind axes. Thus $U_e = V_e$ and $W_e = 0$.

### (i) The equations of longitudinal symmetric motion for small disturbances

The equations of longitudinal symmetric motion can be expressed in non-dimensional form by multiplying Eqs.(2.45) and (2.46) by $1/\tfrac{1}{2}\rho_e V_e^2 S$ and multiplying Eq.(2.47) by $\mu_1/\tfrac{1}{2}\rho_e V_e^2 S\bar{\bar{c}}\, i_y$.

To simplify the resulting equations, we use the following concise derivatives:

$$x_u = -X_u, \quad x_w = -X_w, \quad x_{\dot{w}} = -X_{\dot{w}}/\mu_1, \quad x_q = -X_q/\mu_1,$$
$$z_u = -Z_u, \quad z_w = -Z_w, \quad z_{\dot{w}} = -Z_{\dot{w}}/\mu_1, \quad z_q = -Z_q/\mu_1,$$
$$m_u = -\mu_1 M_u/i_y, \; m_w = -\mu_1 M_w/i_y, \; m_{\dot{w}} = -M_{\dot{w}}/i_y, \; m_q = -M_q/i_y, \tag{2.111}$$

$$x_\eta = -X_\eta, \quad z_\eta = -Z_\eta, \quad m_\eta = -\mu_1 M_\eta / i_y \; . \tag{2.112}$$

Eqs.(2.45) to (2.47) then become (referred to wind axes)

$$(\hat{D} + x_u)\hat{u} + (x_{\dot{w}}\hat{D} + x_w)\hat{w} + x_q\hat{q} + \hat{g}_1\theta + x_\eta\eta' = 0 \; , \tag{2.113}$$

$$z_u\hat{u} + [(1 + z_{\dot{w}})\hat{D} + z_w]\hat{w} + (z_q - 1)\hat{q} + \hat{g}_2\theta + z_\eta\eta' = 0 \; , \tag{2.114}$$

$$m_u\hat{u} + (m_{\dot{w}}\hat{D} + m_w)\hat{w} + (\hat{D} + m_q)\hat{q} + m_\eta\eta' = 0 \; , \tag{2.115}$$

where

$$\hat{q} = \hat{D}\theta \tag{2.116}$$

$$\left.\begin{aligned} \hat{g}_1 &= \hat{g}\cos\Theta_e = C_L \\ \hat{g}_2 &= \hat{g}\sin\Theta_e = C_L\tan\Theta_e \\ \hat{g} &= mg/\tfrac{1}{2}\rho_e V_e{}^2 S = C_L\sec\Theta_e \end{aligned}\right\} \tag{2.117}$$

and the differential operator is

$$\hat{D} = d/d\hat{t}. \tag{2.118}$$

(ii) <u>The equations of lateral asymmetric motion for small disturbances</u>

The equations of lateral asymmetric motion can be expressed in non-dimensional form by multiplying Eq. (2.49) by $1/\frac{1}{2}\rho_e V_e{}^2 S$, Eq. (2.50) by $\mu_2/\frac{1}{2}\rho_e V_e{}^2 S b i_x$ and Eq. (2.51) by $\mu_2/\frac{1}{2}\rho_e V_e{}^2 S b i_z$.

To simplify the resulting equations, we use the following concise derivatives:

$$\left.\begin{aligned} &y_v = -Y_v, \quad y_p = -Y_p/\mu_2, \quad y_r = -Y_r/\mu_2 \; , \\ &l_v = -\mu_2 L_v/i_x, \quad l_p = -L_p/i_x, \quad l_r = -L_r/i_x \; , \\ &n_v = -\mu_2 N_v/i_z, \quad n_p = -N_p/i_z, \quad n_r = -N_r/i_z \; , \end{aligned}\right\} \tag{2.119}$$

$$\left.\begin{aligned} &y_\xi = -Y_\xi, \quad y_\zeta = -Y_\zeta \; , \\ &l_\xi = -\mu_2 L_\xi/i_x, \quad l_\zeta = -\mu_2 L_\zeta/i_x \; , \\ &n_\xi = -\mu_2 N_\xi/i_z, \quad n_\zeta = -\mu_2 N_\zeta/i_z \; . \end{aligned}\right\} \tag{2.120}$$

Eqs.(2.49) to (2.51) then become (referred to wind axes)

$$(\hat{D} + y_v)\hat{v} + y_p\hat{p} + (1 + y_r)\hat{r} - \hat{g}_1\phi - \hat{g}_2\psi + y_\xi\xi + y_\zeta\zeta = 0 \; , \tag{2.121}$$

$$l_v\hat{v} + (\hat{D} + l_p)\hat{p} + (e_x\hat{D} + l_r)\hat{r} + l_\xi\xi + l_\zeta\zeta = 0 \; , \tag{2.122}$$

$$n_v\hat{v} + (e_z\hat{D} + n_p)\hat{p} + (\hat{D} + n_r)\hat{r} + n_\xi\xi + n_\zeta\zeta = 0 \; , \tag{2.123}$$

where

$$\hat{p} = \hat{D}\phi \; , \tag{2.124}$$

$$\hat{r} = \hat{D}\psi \; , \tag{2.125}$$

$$\left.\begin{aligned} e_x &= -i_{zx}/i_x = -I_{zx}/I_x \; , \\ e_z &= -i_{zx}/i_z = -I_{zx}/I_z \; , \end{aligned}\right\} \tag{2.126}$$

and $\hat{g}_1$ and $\hat{g}_2$ are given by Eq.(2.117).

As above, the differential operator is

$$\hat{D} = d/d\hat{t} \ . \tag{2.127}$$

It should be noted that the present notation for both the aerodynamic derivatives and the concise derivatives differs from that used before 1970 (see references 2 and 3). Considerable care must therefore be exercised when using data from older reports. The main advantage of the present notation is that it enables the non-dimensional equations of motion to be written in a very concise form, with very few minus signs occurring in the equations of motion. Most of the concise derivatives are positive (notable exceptions are $x_w$, $l_r$, $n_v$ and $y_\zeta$).

## THE MOTION OF THE CENTRE OF GRAVITY OF THE AIRCRAFT

It is sometimes necessary to determine the deviations $x_G$, $y_G$, $z_G$ of the centre of gravity $O$ of the aircraft from the position it would have occupied in the steady rectilinear flight path at time $t$. These deviations are measured parallel to $Ox_0$, $Oy_0$ and $Oz_0$, the steady state positions of the axes.

From Fig. 2.3, the direction cosines of $Ox_0$ with respect to $Ox_1y_1z_0$ are

$$(\cos\psi, \ -\sin\psi, \ 0)$$

and with respect to $Oxy_1z_2$ are

$$(\cos\psi\cos\theta, -\sin\psi, \ \cos\psi\sin\theta) \ .$$

Thus the direction cosines of $Ox_0$ with respect to $Oxyz$ are

$$(\cos\psi\cos\theta, \cos\psi\sin\theta\sin\phi - \sin\psi\cos\phi \ , \ \cos\psi\sin\theta\cos\theta \ + \sin\psi\sin\phi) \ .$$

Similarly the direction cosines of $Oy_0$ with respect to $Oxyz$ are

$$(\sin\psi\cos\theta, \ \cos\psi\cos\phi \ + \sin\psi\sin\theta\sin\phi, \ \sin\psi\sin\theta\cos\phi \ - \cos\psi\sin\phi)$$

and those of $Oz_0$ are

$$(-\sin\theta, \ \cos\theta\sin\phi, \ \cos\theta\cos\phi) \ .$$

Now $\theta$, $\phi$ and $\psi$ are all small. Thus, to the first order, the direction cosines of $Ox_0$ are $(1, -\psi, \theta)$, those of $Oy_0$ are $(\psi, 1, -\phi)$ and those of $Oz_0$ $(-\theta, \phi, 1)$. Hence the velocity component of $O$ along $Ox_0$ is $(U + W\theta)$, along $Oy_0$ $(U\psi + V - W\phi)$ and along $Oz_0$ $(-U\theta + W)$.

Thus, if $x_G$, $y_G$ and $z_G$ are the *deviations* of the centre of gravity from the position it would have occupied in the steady state at time $t$, we have, neglecting second order terms,

$$\dot{x}_G = u + W_e\theta \ , \tag{2.128}$$

$$\dot{y}_G = v - W_e\phi + U_e\psi \ , \tag{2.129}$$

$$\dot{z}_G = w - U_e\theta \ . \tag{2.130}$$

We see that, in asymmetric flight, when second order terms are neglected, $\dot{x}_G$ and $\dot{z}_G$ are zero.

Using wind axes and writing

$$\hat{x} = x_G/V_e\tau \ , \tag{2.131}$$

$$\hat{y} = y_G/V_e\tau \ , \tag{2.132}$$

and

$$\hat{z} = z_G/V_e\tau \ , \tag{2.133}$$

we have, using Eqs.(2.94) to (2.100),

$$\hat{D}\hat{x} = \hat{u} \ , \tag{2.134}$$

$$\hat{D}\hat{y} = \hat{v} + \psi \ , \tag{2.135}$$

$$\hat{D}\hat{z} = \hat{w} - \theta \ . \tag{2.136}$$

We see that, if the velocity of the centre of gravity in the disturbed flight is parallel to its original direction in steady flight,

$$\hat{v} = -\psi$$

and

$$\hat{w} = \theta.$$

In that case, the change in incidence ($=\hat{w}$) is equal to the angle of pitch of the aircraft, and the angle of sideslip $\beta$ ($=\hat{v}$) is given by

$$\beta = -\psi \ ,$$

as shown in Fig. 2.4(c).

## REFERENCES


1. BRYAN, G.H. *Stability in Aviation.* Macmillan (1911).
2. HOPKIN, H.R. A scheme of notation and nomenclature for aircraft dynamics and associated aerodynamics. R. & M. 3562 (1970).
3. BABISTER, A.W. *Aircraft Stability and Control.* Pergamon Press (1961).


## PROBLEMS

1. Define and distinguish between static and dynamic stability. Show with a sketch the system of axes used in deriving the equations of motion of a symmetric aircraft, indicating all the velocity components.

   Determine the linearised equations of motion for small disturbances of an aircraft in steady forward flight with speed $U_e$ with an initial steady pitching velocity $Q_e$.

2. Define the terms wind axes, body axes and principal axes, and state the merits of the different axis systems.

3. What is the reason for using non-dimensional derivatives? Use the theory of dimensional analysis to verify that these derivatives are, in fact, non-dimensional.

4. A symmetric aircraft in steady level flight at speed $V_e$ is given a small symmetric disturbance. Write down (i) the equations of motion along and perpendicular to the flight path, and (ii) the pitching moment equation. Show

that these equations can be put in the form of two linear second order differential equations involving $\theta$ (angle of pitch) and $\gamma$ (angle between flight path and the horizontal) and their derivatives with respect to $t$. (The drag may be neglected, as well as $X_q$, $X_{\dot{w}}$, $Z_q$, $Z_{\dot{w}}$, $M_u$ and $M_{\dot{w}}$).

Hence show that, in flight at constant incidence, the motion is simple harmonic with period $\pi\sqrt{2}V_e/g$.

5. Show that, for an axially symmetric missile (without wings and tail) there are only ten aerodynamic derivatives which are not identically zero. For such a missile show that

$$\mathring{Y}_v = \mathring{Z}_w, \quad \mathring{Y}_r = -\mathring{Z}_q, \quad \mathring{M}_w = -\mathring{N}_v \text{ and } \mathring{M}_q = \mathring{N}_r.$$

# Chapter 3

# AERODYNAMIC DERIVATIVES (LONGITUDINAL)

## INTRODUCTION

As shown in the previous chapter, there are three basic symmetric motions of an aircraft: forward motion, downward motion and pitch. The aerodynamic forces and moments in longitudinal symmetric motion can be expressed in terms of the non-dimensional derivatives $X_u$, $X_w$, $X_{\dot{w}}$, $X_q$, $Z_u$, $Z_w$, $Z_{\dot{w}}$, $Z_q$, $M_u$, $M_w$, $M_{\dot{w}}$, $M_q$ and the non-dimensional control derivatives $X_\eta$, $Z_\eta$, $M_\eta$, defined by Eqs.(2.58) to (2.69) and (2.73) to (2.75). For a given aircraft disturbed from a given state of steady flight, these derivatives are constant; their values depend on the aerodynamic characteristics of the whole aircraft (and will thus, in general, depend upon the aircraft incidence). We shall now derive simple expressions for these derivatives, the aim being to emphasize the physical nature of the various contributions to them. More elaborate theories are needed to account for the interaction of the various parts of the aircraft structure (e.g. fuselage-tailplane effects).

As pointed out in Chapter 2, the present notation differs from that used before 1970; a table of conversion factors when using the old symbols is given in reference 1. We refer all the derivatives to wind axes.

## FORCE VELOCITY DERIVATIVES $X_u$, $X_w$, $Z_u$, $Z_w$

These derivatives depend upon the lift and drag coefficients for the whole aircraft and upon their rates of change with incidence and speed.

## INCIDENCE CHANGE ASSOCIATED WITH CHANGE IN VELOCITY COMPONENTS

Let $V$ be the resultant velocity of the c.g. of the aircraft in the motion following a symmetric disturbance (note that this should not be confused with $V$, the side-slipping velocity, which is zero in longitudinal symmetric motion).

Let $V_e$ = resultant velocity of the c.g. in the undisturbed motion.
Let $A$ = incidence of $Ox$ in the disturbed motion (see Fig. 3.1).

Then $$V^2 = U^2 + W^2, \tag{3.1}$$

$$U = V \cos A, \tag{3.2}$$
$$W = V \sin A. \tag{3.3}$$

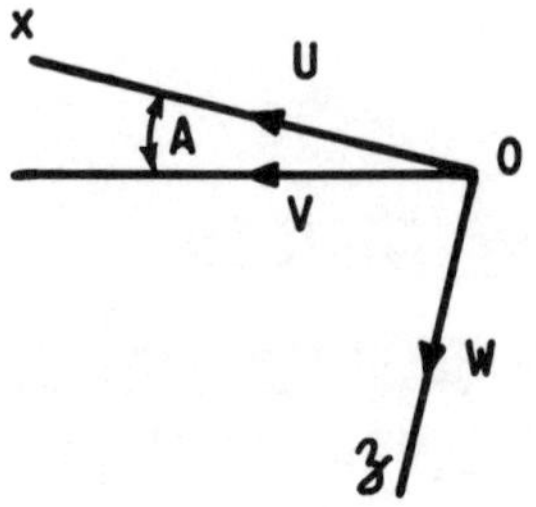


Fig. 3.1 Velocity components and angle of incidence

From Eqs. (3.1) to (3.3), treated $U$ and $V$ as the two independent variables,

$$\frac{\partial V}{\partial U} = \frac{U}{V} = \cos A, \tag{3.4}$$

$$\frac{\partial V}{\partial U} = \frac{W}{V} = \sin A. \tag{3.5}$$

Also, as $\tan A = \dfrac{W}{U}$ ,

$$\sec^2 A \,\mathrm{d} A = \frac{U \,\mathrm{d} W - W \,\mathrm{d} U}{U^2} ,$$

i.e.

$$\mathrm{d} A = \frac{U \,\mathrm{d} W - W \,\mathrm{d} U}{V^2} .$$

Therefore

$$\frac{\partial A}{\partial U} = - \frac{\sin A}{V} , \tag{3.6}$$

$$\frac{\partial A}{\partial W} = - \frac{\cos A}{V} . \tag{3.7}$$

Now with *wind axes* the incidence of $Ox$ in the undisturbed motion is zero. Thus, in the initial condition, with wind axes

$$A = 0, \quad U = V_e \text{ and } W = 0.$$

Now $A$ is always small. Thus, from Eqs. (3.4) to (3.7), when terms of small magnitude are neglected,

$$\left.\begin{aligned} \frac{\partial V}{\partial U} &= 1, \\ \frac{\partial V}{\partial W} &= 0, \\ \frac{\partial A}{\partial U} &= 0, \\ \text{and} \quad \frac{\partial A}{\partial W} &= \frac{1}{V_e}. \end{aligned}\right\} \tag{3.8}$$

Also, as $Ox$ is fixed in the aircraft, the wing incidence $\alpha$ is given by

$$\alpha = A + \text{constant}.$$

Thus $$d\alpha = dA\,. \tag{3.9}$$

Consider now the aerodynamic forces acting on the aircraft (the lift $L$ and drag $D$) together with the thrust $T$ from the engines. The line of action of the thrust is fixed in the aircraft (along $Ox$). Resolving these forces into components $X$ and $Z$ along $Ox$ and $Oz$ respectively, we find (from Fig. 3.2),

$$\left.\begin{aligned} X &= L\sin A - D\cos A + T \\ &= \tfrac{1}{2}\rho V^2 S(C_L \sin A - C_D \cos A) + T \end{aligned}\right\} \tag{3.10}$$

$$\left.\begin{aligned} Z &= -L\cos A - D\sin A \\ &= -\tfrac{1}{2}\rho V^2 S(C_L \cos A + C_D \sin A). \end{aligned}\right\} \tag{3.11}$$

Now $C_L$ and $C_D$ are functions of wing incidence $\alpha$ and velocity $V$ (due to compressibility effects).

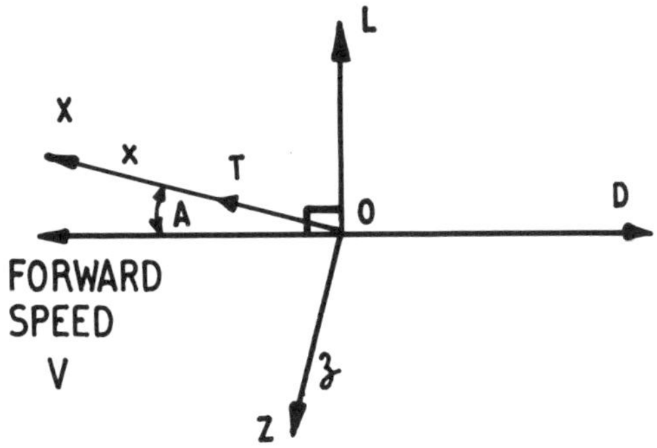


Fig. 3.2 Forces acting on the aircraft

Differentiating Eq. (3.10) with respect to $U$, and then using Eq. (3.8), we find

$$\left.\begin{aligned} \overset{\circ}{X}_u &= \frac{\partial X}{\partial u} = \frac{\partial X}{\partial U} = \frac{\partial X}{\partial V}\frac{\partial V}{\partial U} + \frac{\partial X}{\partial A}\frac{\partial A}{\partial U} = \frac{\partial X}{\partial V} \\ &= \rho_e V_e S(-C_D) + \tfrac{1}{2}\rho_e V_e^2 S(-\partial C_D/\partial V) + dT/dV\,, \end{aligned}\right\} \tag{3.12}$$

where the incidence $A$, the density $\rho$ and the speed $V$ have been given their constant datum values (for the given state of steady flight) after the differentiation. The dressing ord (°) denotes that the aerodynamic derivative is expressed in ordinary units.

Similarly

$$\left.\begin{aligned} \overset{\circ}{X}_w &= \frac{\partial X}{\partial w} = \frac{\partial X}{\partial W} = \frac{\partial X}{\partial V}\frac{\partial V}{\partial W} + \frac{\partial X}{\partial A}\frac{\partial A}{\partial W} = \frac{1}{V_e}\frac{\partial X}{\partial A} \\ &= \tfrac{1}{2}\rho_e V_e S(C_L - \partial C_D/\partial\alpha) \end{aligned}\right\} \tag{3.13}$$

and, from Eq. (3.11),

$$\left.\begin{aligned}\mathring{Z}_u &= \frac{\partial Z}{\partial u} = \frac{\partial Z}{\partial U} = \frac{\partial Z}{\partial V}\frac{\partial V}{\partial U} + \frac{\partial Z}{\partial A}\frac{\partial A}{\partial U} = \frac{\partial Z}{\partial V} \\ &= -\rho_e V_e S C_L - \tfrac{1}{2}\rho_e V_e{}^2 S\ (\partial C_L/\partial V)\end{aligned}\right\} \tag{3.14}$$

and

$$\left.\begin{aligned}\mathring{Z}_w &= \frac{\partial Z}{\partial w} = \frac{\partial Z}{\partial W} = \frac{\partial Z}{\partial V}\frac{\partial V}{\partial W} + \frac{\partial Z}{\partial A}\frac{\partial A}{\partial W} = \frac{1}{V_e}\frac{\partial Z}{\partial A} \\ &= -\tfrac{1}{2}\rho_e V_e S(\partial C_L/\partial\alpha + C_D).\end{aligned}\right\} \tag{3.15}$$

Dividing Eqs. (3.12) to (3.15) by $\frac{1}{2}\rho_e V_e S$, we obtain the *non-dimensional derivatives*

$$X_u = \mathring{X}_u/\tfrac{1}{2}\rho_e V_e S = -2C_D - V_e\frac{\partial C_D}{\partial V} + \frac{1}{\frac{1}{2}\rho_e V_e S}\frac{\mathrm{d}T}{\mathrm{d}V}, \tag{3.16}$$

$$X_w = \mathring{X}_w/\tfrac{1}{2}\rho_e V_e S = C_L - \partial C_D/\partial\alpha , \tag{3.17}$$

$$Z_u = \mathring{Z}_u/\tfrac{1}{2}\rho_e V_e S = -2C_L - V_e\partial C_L/\partial V , \tag{3.18}$$

$$Z_w = \mathring{Z}_w/\tfrac{1}{2}\rho_e V_e S = -(C_D + \partial C_L/\partial\alpha) . \tag{3.19}$$

The values of $C_L$ and $C_D$ will be known for the steady flight conditions. The variation of $C_L$ and $C_D$ with incidence can be estimated from the Engineering Sciences Data Sheets. Their variation with speed is best obtained from wind tunnel results, from which compressibility effects can be observed. The variation of the thrust with speed can be found when the engine conditions are known.

## PITCHING MOMENT DERIVATIVES $M_u$, $M_w$

The pitching moment $M$ of the aircraft about its c.g. is given by

$$M = \tfrac{1}{2}\rho V^2 S\ \bar{\bar{c}}\ C_m , \tag{3.20}$$

where $\bar{\bar{c}}$ is the mean aerodynamic chord of the wing. As in the derivation of $X_u$ and $X_w$ we have, with wind axes,

$$\mathring{M}_u = \frac{\partial M}{\partial u} = \frac{\partial M}{\partial V} = \rho_e V_e S\ \bar{\bar{c}}\ (C_m + \tfrac{1}{2}V_e\ \partial C_m/\partial V) ,$$

$$\mathring{M}_w = \frac{\partial M}{\partial w} = \frac{1}{V_e}\frac{\partial M}{\partial A} = \tfrac{1}{2}\rho_e V_e S\ \bar{\bar{c}}\ \partial C_m/\partial\alpha .$$

Now in the steady state the aircraft is in trim, i.e. $C_m = 0$ initially. Therefore the non-dimensional derivatives are given by

$$M_u = \mathring{M}_u/\tfrac{1}{2}\rho_e V_e S\ \bar{\bar{c}} = V_e\ \partial C_m/\partial V , \tag{3.21}$$

$$M_w = \mathring{M}_w/\tfrac{1}{2}\rho_e V_e S\ \bar{\bar{c}} = \partial C_m/\partial\alpha . \tag{3.22}$$

We note that $M_u = 0$ if $C_m$ is independent of speed at a given incidence, e.g. when compressibility and slipstream effects can be neglected.

From Eq. (3.22) we see that, when compressibility effects are neglected,

$$M_w = \frac{dC_m}{dC_L} \bullet \frac{dC_L}{d\alpha} = -\frac{dC_L}{d\alpha} K_n , \tag{3.23}$$

where $K_n$ is the static margin stick fixed (defined in Chapter 1). When compressibility effects are taken into account, this simple relation between $M_w$ and $K_n$ is replaced by one involving $M_u$, $M_w$, $Z_u$ and $Z_w$. Thus

$$\begin{aligned} K_n &= -\frac{dC_m}{dC_L} = -\left(\frac{\partial C_m}{\partial \alpha} + \frac{\partial C_m}{\partial V}\frac{dV}{d\alpha}\right)\bigg/\left(\frac{\partial C_L}{\partial \alpha} + \frac{\partial C_L}{\partial V}\frac{dV}{d\alpha}\right) \\ &= -\left(M_w + \frac{M_u}{V_e}\frac{dV}{d\alpha}\right)\bigg/\left(\frac{\partial C_L}{\partial \alpha} + \frac{\partial C_L}{\partial V}\frac{dV}{d\alpha}\right) \end{aligned} \tag{3.24}$$

Now, in horizontal flight,

$$C_L\ V^2 = \frac{mg}{\frac{1}{2}\rho S} = \text{constant.}$$

Differentiating with respect to $\alpha$, we obtain

$$\left(\frac{\partial C_L}{\partial \alpha} + \frac{\partial C_L}{\partial V}\frac{dV}{d\alpha}\right) V^2 + 2C_L V\frac{dV}{d\alpha} = 0. \tag{3.25}$$

Therefore

$$\begin{aligned} \frac{dV}{d\alpha} &= -\frac{V}{2C_L}\frac{\partial C_L}{\partial \alpha}\bigg/\left(1 + \frac{V}{2C_L}\frac{\partial C_L}{\partial V}\right) \\ &\triangleq -V_e Z_w / Z_u\ . \end{aligned} \tag{3.26}$$

From Eqs. (3.24) to (3.26), we see that, when compressibility effects are allowed for, the static margin stick fixed $K_n$ is given by

$$K_n = \frac{1}{2C_L(\partial C_L/\partial \alpha)}(M_w Z_u - M_u Z_w)\ . \tag{3.27}$$

## DERIVATIVES DUE TO RATE OF PITCH $X_q$, $Z_q$, $M_q$

The derivatives dealt with so far have only involved the static characteristics of the aircraft. We now consider the derivatives due to rate of pitch. The most important contribution to these derivatives arises from the change of incidence at the tailplane due to the angular velocity in pitch, $q$, of the aircraft. The tailplane then has a downward velocity $ql_T$, where $l_T$ is the distance of the aerodynamic centre of the tailplane aft of the centre of gravity of the aircraft. Combining this with the forward velocity $V_e$ of the aircraft, we see that the change in incidence at the tailplane is $ql_T/V_e$.

Differentiating Eq. (3.10) with respect to $q$, and then using Eq. (3.8), we have, with wind axes,

$$\mathring{X}_q = \frac{\partial X}{\partial q} = -\tfrac{1}{2}\rho_e V_e{}^2 S\ \frac{\partial C_D}{\partial (ql_T/V)}\ \frac{l_T}{V_e}\ .$$

Similarly, from Eq. (3.11),

$$\mathring{Z}_q = \frac{\partial Z}{\partial q} = -\tfrac{1}{2}\rho_e V_e{}^2 S \frac{\partial C_L}{\partial(q l_T/V)} \frac{l_T}{V_e}$$

and from Eq. (3.20),

$$\mathring{M}_q = \frac{\partial M}{\partial q} = \tfrac{1}{2}\rho_e V_e{}^2 S\,\bar{\bar{c}} \frac{\partial C_m}{\partial(q l_T/V)} \frac{l_T}{V_e}$$

The corresponding non-dimensional derivatives are given by

$$X_q = \frac{\mathring{X}_q}{\tfrac{1}{2}\rho_e V_e S\,\bar{\bar{c}}} = -\frac{\partial C_D}{\partial(q\bar{\bar{c}}/V)} \tag{3.28}$$

$$Z_q = \frac{\mathring{Z}_q}{\tfrac{1}{2}\rho_e V_e S\,\bar{\bar{c}}} = -\frac{\partial C_L}{\partial(q\bar{\bar{c}}/V)} \tag{3.29}$$

and

$$M_q = \frac{\mathring{M}_q}{\tfrac{1}{2}\rho_e V_e S\,\bar{\bar{c}}^2} = \frac{\partial C_m}{\partial(q\bar{\bar{c}}/V)} \tag{3.30}$$

In practice $X_q$ is negligible. The contributions to $Z_q$ and $M_q$ from the tailplane can be expressed more simply as follows. If $\alpha_T$ is the tailplane incidence, the increment in downward force on the tailplane due to the rate of pitch $q$ is

$$q\mathring{Z}_q(\text{tail}) = -\tfrac{1}{2}\rho_e V_e{}^2 S_T \frac{\partial C_{LT}}{\partial \alpha_T} \frac{q l_T}{V_e}$$

where the suffix $T$ refers to the tailplane.

Therefore

$$\mathring{Z}_q(\text{tail}) = -\tfrac{1}{2}\rho_e V_e S_T l_T\, \partial C_{LT}/\partial\alpha_T$$

and

$$Z_q(\text{tail}) = -\,a_1\,\bar{V}_T \tag{3.31}$$

where $a_1$ is the tailplane lift curve slope and

$$\bar{V}_T = S_T l_T / S\bar{\bar{c}} \tag{3.32}$$

is the tail-volume ratio.

Similarly, considering the increment in pitching moment from the tailplane due to the rate of pitch $q$, we find

$$q\mathring{M}_q(\text{tail}) = -\tfrac{1}{2}\rho_e V_e{}^2 S_T l_T \frac{\partial C_{LT}}{\partial \alpha_T} \frac{q l_T}{V_e}$$

Therefore $$\mathring{M}_q(\text{tail}) = -\tfrac{1}{2}\rho_e V_e S_T l_T{}^2\, \partial C_{LT}/\partial\alpha_T$$

and

$$M_q(\text{tail}) = -\,a_1\,\bar{V}_T\, l_T/\bar{\bar{c}} \tag{3.33}$$

We see that $M_q(\text{tail}) = (l_T/\bar{\bar{c}})\, Z_q(\text{tail})$. (3.34)

As stated above, the tailplane provides the main contribution to $M_q$, and hence to the damping in pitch; however, for aircraft with delta or sweptback wings, the contribution from the wing may be important. References 2 and 3 give some information on the contribution to $M_q$ from the various parts of the aircraft.

## DERIVATIVES DUE TO RATE OF CHANGE OF DOWNWARD VELOCITY $X_{\dot{w}}$, $Z_{\dot{w}}$, $M_{\dot{w}}$

As stated in Chapter 2, the terms involving $\dot{w}$ are included in the equations of motion as some of them are found to be important in accounting for the longitudinal pitching oscillation. This effect was first noticed in 1921 (reference 4) in an attempt to explain some discrepancies between measured and estimated values of $M_q$.

These terms arise because of the unsteady oscillatory motion of the wing following a disturbance. The changing incidence of the wing affects the flow field (and, in particular, the downwash) at the tail, and the main contribution to $X_{\dot{w}}$, $Z_{\dot{w}}$ and $M_{\dot{w}}$. is due to the downwash lag at the tailplane. There is also a small contribution from the wing, which can be of special importance for tailless aircraft.

In estimating the downwash at the tail, we can assume (without loss of accuracy) that the lift forces generated by the wing and tail at any time are those due to the instantaneous incidences of these surfaces. Now the downwash $\varepsilon$ at the tail, at time $t$, is that generated by the wing when it passed the present position of the tail, i.e. at time $t - l_T/V$, when (by Taylor series expansion) the wing incidence was

$$\alpha + \frac{d\alpha}{dt}(-l_T/V);$$

for small incidence we can write

$$\varepsilon = \frac{d\varepsilon}{d\alpha}\left(\alpha - \frac{d\alpha}{dt}\, l_T/V\right).$$

Now, from Eqs. (3.2), (3.3) and (3.9),

$$\frac{d\alpha}{dt} = \frac{dA}{dt} = \frac{d}{dt}\frac{W}{U} = \frac{\dot{W}}{U} - \frac{W\dot{U}}{U^2} = \frac{\dot{w}}{V}$$

to the first order of small quantities, with wind axes.

Therefore $$\varepsilon = \frac{d\varepsilon}{d\alpha}\left(\alpha - \frac{\dot{w}}{V}\frac{l_T}{V}\right).$$

Thus the increment in downwash due to lag is

$$\Delta\varepsilon = -\frac{d\varepsilon}{d\alpha}\frac{\dot{w}\, l_T}{V^2},$$

and the corresponding increase in incidence at the tailplane is

$$\Delta\alpha_T = \frac{d\varepsilon}{d\alpha}\frac{\dot{w}\, l_T}{V^2}. \qquad (3.35)$$

By analogy with the analysis given above for the effect of rate of pitch, we find

$$\overset{\circ}{X}_{\dot{w}} = \frac{\partial X}{\partial \dot{w}} = -\tfrac{1}{2}\rho_e V_e{}^2 S \frac{\partial C_D}{\partial(\dot{w} l_T/V^2)}\frac{l_T}{V_e{}^2},$$

$$\overset{\circ}{Z}_{\dot{w}} = \frac{\partial Z}{\partial \dot{w}} = -\tfrac{1}{2}\rho_e V_e^{\,2} S \, \frac{\partial C_L}{\partial(\dot{w} l_T/V^2)} \, \frac{l_T}{V_e^{\,2}}$$

and
$$\overset{\circ}{M}_{\dot{w}} = \frac{\partial M}{\partial \dot{w}} = \tfrac{1}{2}\rho_e V_e^{\,2} S \, \bar{\bar{c}} \, \frac{\partial C_m}{\partial(\dot{w} l_T/V^2)} \, \frac{l_T}{V_e^{\,2}} .$$

The corresponding non-dimensional derivatives are given by

$$X_{\dot{w}} = \frac{\overset{\circ}{X}_{\dot{w}}}{\tfrac{1}{2}\rho_e S \, \bar{\bar{c}}} = -\frac{\partial C_D}{\partial(\dot{w}\,\bar{\bar{c}}/V^2)} \tag{3.36}$$

$$Z_{\dot{w}} = \frac{\overset{\circ}{Z}_{\dot{w}}}{\tfrac{1}{2}\rho_e S \, \bar{\bar{c}}} = -\frac{\partial C_L}{\partial(\dot{w}\,\bar{\bar{c}}/V^2)} \tag{3.37}$$

$$M_{\dot{w}} = \frac{\overset{\circ}{M}_{\dot{w}}}{\tfrac{1}{2}\rho_e S \, \bar{\bar{c}}^2} = \frac{\partial C_m}{\partial(\dot{w}\,\bar{\bar{c}}/V^2)} \tag{3.38}$$

In practice $X_{\dot{w}}$ is negligible. The contributions to $Z_{\dot{w}}$ and $M_{\dot{w}}$ from the tailplane can be simple related to those of $Z_q$ and $M_q$. The increment in downward force on the tailplane due to the rate of change of downward velocity is

$$\dot{w}\, Z_{\dot{w}}(\text{tail}) = -\tfrac{1}{2}\rho_e V_e^{\,2} S_T \, (\partial C_{LT}/\partial \alpha_T) \, \Delta\alpha_T$$

where $\Delta\alpha_T$ is given by Eq. (3.35).

Therefore $\quad \overset{\circ}{Z}_{\dot{w}}(\text{tail}) = -\tfrac{1}{2}\rho_e S_T l_T \, (\partial C_{LT}/\partial \alpha_T)(d\varepsilon/d\alpha)$

and
$$Z_{\dot{w}}(\text{tail}) = -a_1 \bar{V}_T \, d\varepsilon/d\alpha = Z_q(\text{tail}) \, d\varepsilon/d\alpha. \tag{3.39}$$

Similarly, considering the increment in pitching moment about the c.g., we find

$$\overset{\circ}{M}_{\dot{w}}(\text{tail}) = -\tfrac{1}{2}\rho_e S_T l_T^{\,2} \, (\partial C_{LT}/\partial \alpha_T)(d\varepsilon/d\alpha)$$

and
$$M_{\dot{w}}(\text{tail}) = -a_1 \bar{V}_T (l_T/\bar{\bar{c}}) \, d\varepsilon/d\alpha = M_q(\text{tail}) \, d\varepsilon/d\alpha. \tag{3.40}$$

## CONTROL DERIVATIVES

The non-dimensional control derivatives $X_\eta$, $Z_\eta$ and $M_\eta$ due to application of the elevator were defined in Chapter 2. They can be simply related to the tailplane-elevator characteristics. Thus the increase in forward force due to the increment in elevator angle $\eta'$ is

$$\overset{\circ}{X}_\eta \, \eta' = -\tfrac{1}{2}\rho_e V_e^{\,2} S_T \, (\partial C_{DT} \; \partial \eta) \, \eta'$$

where the suffix $T$ refers to the tailplane.

Therefore
$$X_\eta = \frac{\overset{\circ}{X}_\eta}{\tfrac{1}{2}\rho_e V_e^{\,2} S} = -\frac{S_T}{S}\frac{\partial C_{DT}}{\partial \eta} \tag{3.41}$$

Similarly $\mathring{Z}_\eta \eta' = -\frac{1}{2}\rho_e V_e{}^2 S_T \; (\partial C_{LT}/\partial\eta) \; \eta'$

and $$Z_\eta = \frac{\mathring{Z}_\eta}{\frac{1}{2}\rho_e V_e{}^2 S} = -\frac{S_T}{S} a_2 \; , \tag{3.42}$$

where $a_2 = \partial C_{LT}/\partial\eta$, the tailplane lift curve slope due to the elevator.

Considering the pitching moment about the c.g., we find

$$\mathring{M}_\eta \eta' = -\frac{1}{2}\rho_e V^2 S_T \; (\partial C_{LT}/\partial\eta) \; \eta' l_T$$

and $$M_\eta = \frac{\mathring{M}_\eta}{\frac{1}{2}\rho_e V_e{}^2 S \; \bar{\bar{c}}} = -\, a_2 \bar{V}_T \; . \tag{3.43}$$

The value of $a_2$ can be estimated using the Engineering Sciences Data Sheets.

## NON-DIMENSIONAL FORMS OF THE AERODYNAMIC DERIVATIVES USED IN AMERICA

There are some important differences between the British and American notation for these derivatives. The American non-dimensional force derivatives

$$C_{X_u}, \; C_{X_\alpha}, \; C_{X_q}, \; C_{Z_u}, \; C_{Z_\alpha}, \; C_{Z_q}$$

are derived by direct differentiation of the non-dimensional coefficients $C_X$ (= $X/\frac{1}{2}\rho V^2 S$) and $C_Z$ (= $Z/\frac{1}{2}\rho V^2 S$) with respect to the appropriate variable ($u/V_e$, $w/V_e$ or $q\bar{\bar{c}}/2V_e$). We here derive formulae relating the American derivatives to the corresponding non-dimensional British derivatives.

## AMERICAN NON-DIMENSIONAL FORCE-VELOCITY DERIVATIVES $C_{X_u}$, $C_{X_\alpha}$, $C_{Z_u}$, $C_{Z_\alpha}$

If $X$ and $Z$ are the components of the aerodynamic forces (and of the thrust) along $Ox$ and $Oz$, wind axes through the c.g. of the aircraft, we write

$$X = \frac{1}{2}\rho V^2 S \; C_X \tag{3.44}$$

and $$Z = \frac{1}{2}\rho V^2 S \; C_Z \; . \tag{3.45}$$

Differentiating Eq. (3.44) with respect to $U$, and using Eq. (3.8), we have

$$\mathring{X}_u = \frac{\partial X}{\partial u} = \frac{\partial X}{\partial U} = \rho_e V_e S C_X + \frac{1}{2}\rho_e V_e S \frac{\partial C_X}{\partial(u/V_e)} \; , \tag{3.46}$$

where the incidence, the density and the speed have all been given their constant datum values after the differentiation. Similarly

$$\mathring{X}_w = \frac{\partial X}{\partial w} = \frac{\partial X}{\partial W} = \frac{1}{V_e}\frac{\partial X}{\partial A} = \frac{1}{2}\rho_e V_e S \frac{\partial C_X}{\partial\alpha} \tag{3.47}$$

and, from Eq. (3.45),

$$\mathring{Z}_u = \frac{\partial Z}{\partial u} = \frac{\partial Z}{\partial U} = \rho_e V_e S C_Z + \tfrac{1}{2}\rho_e V_e S \frac{C_Z}{\partial(u/V_e)} \tag{3.48}$$

and

$$\mathring{Z}_w = \frac{\partial Z}{\partial w} = \frac{\partial Z}{\partial W} = \frac{1}{V_e}\frac{\partial Z}{\partial A} = \tfrac{1}{2}\rho_e V_e S \frac{\partial C_Z}{\partial \alpha} \, . \tag{3.49}$$

Now, in steady flight, from Eq. (3.10), with wind axes, we obtain, on dividing throughout by $\frac{1}{2}\rho V^2 S$, and putting $A = 0$ and $V = V_e$,

$$C_X = \frac{T}{\frac{1}{2}\rho_e V_e{}^2 S} - C_D \, . \tag{3.50}$$

Similarly, from Eq. (3.11),

$$C_Z = - C_L \tag{3.51}$$

in the initial steady flight.

Dividing Eqs. (3.46) to (3.49) by $\frac{1}{2}\rho_e V_e S$, we obtain the American non-dimensional derivatives

$$C_{X_u} = \frac{\partial C_X}{\partial(u/V_e)} = X_u - 2C_X \tag{3.52}$$

$$C_{X_\alpha} = \frac{\partial C_X}{\partial \alpha} = X_w \tag{3.53}$$

$$C_{Z_u} = \frac{\partial C_Z}{\partial(u/V_e)} = Z_u - 2C_Z \tag{3.54}$$

$$C_{Z_\alpha} = \frac{\partial C_Z}{\partial \alpha} = Z_w . \tag{3.55}$$

## AMERICAN NON-DIMENSIONAL PITCHING MOMENT DERIVATIVES $C_{m_u}$, $C_{m_\alpha}$

$$C_{m_u} = \frac{\partial C_m}{\partial(u/V_e)} = \frac{\partial(M/\frac{1}{2}\rho V^2 S\bar{\bar{c}})}{\partial(u/V_e)} = \frac{\mathring{M}_u}{\frac{1}{2}\rho_e V_e S\bar{\bar{c}}} = M_u \, . \tag{3.56}$$

$$C_{m_\alpha} = \frac{\partial C_m}{\partial \alpha} = \frac{\partial(M/\frac{1}{2}\rho V^2 S\bar{\bar{c}})}{\partial(w/V_e)} = \frac{\mathring{M}_w}{\frac{1}{2}\rho_e V_e S\bar{\bar{c}}} = M_w \, . \tag{3.57}$$

## AMERICAN NON-DIMENSIONAL DERIVATIVES DUE TO RATE OF PITCH $C_{X_q}$, $C_{Z_q}$, $C_{m_q}$

$$C_{X_q} = \frac{\partial C_X}{\partial(q\bar{\bar{c}}/2V_e)} = \frac{\partial(X/\frac{1}{2}\rho V^2 S)}{\partial(q\bar{\bar{c}}/2V_e)} = \frac{4\mathring{X}_q}{\rho_e V_e S\bar{\bar{c}}} = 2X_q \, . \tag{3.58}$$

$$C_{Z_q} = \frac{\partial C_Z}{\partial(q\bar{\bar{c}}/2V_e)} = \frac{\partial(Z/\frac{1}{2}\rho V^2 S)}{\partial(q\bar{\bar{c}}/2V_e)} = \frac{4\mathring{Z}_q}{\rho_e V_e S\bar{\bar{c}}} = 2Z_q \, . \tag{3.59}$$

$$C_{m_q} = \frac{\partial C_m}{\partial(q\bar{\bar{c}}/2V_e)} = \frac{\partial(M/\frac{1}{2}\rho V^2 S\bar{\bar{c}})}{\partial(q\bar{\bar{c}}/2V_e)} = \frac{4\mathring{M}_q}{\rho_e V_e S\bar{\bar{c}}^2} = 2M_q$$

AMERICAN NON-DIMENSIONAL DERIVATIVES DUE TO RATE OF CHANGE OF DOWNWARD VELOCITY $C_{X_{D\alpha}}$, $C_{Z_{D\alpha}}$, $C_{m_{D\alpha}}$

$$C_{X_{D\alpha}} = \frac{\partial C_X}{\partial(\dot{\alpha}\bar{\bar{c}}/2V_e)} = \frac{\partial(X/\frac{1}{2}\rho V^2 S)}{\partial(\dot{w}\bar{\bar{c}}/2V_e{}^2)} = \frac{4\mathring{X}_{\dot{w}}}{\rho_e S\bar{\bar{c}}} = 2X_{\dot{w}} \; . \tag{3.61}$$

$$C_{Z_{D\alpha}} = \frac{\partial C_Z}{\partial(\dot{\alpha}\bar{\bar{c}}/2V_e)} = \frac{\partial(Z/\frac{1}{2}\rho V^2 S)}{\partial(\dot{w}\bar{\bar{c}}/2V_e{}^2)} = \frac{4\mathring{Z}_{\dot{w}}}{\rho_e S\bar{\bar{c}}} = 2Z_{\dot{w}} \; . \tag{3.62}$$

$$C_{m_{D\alpha}} = \frac{\partial C_m}{\partial(\dot{\alpha}\bar{\bar{c}}/2V_e)} = \frac{\partial(M/\frac{1}{2}\rho V^2 S\bar{\bar{c}})}{\partial(\dot{w}\bar{\bar{c}}/2V_e{}^2)} = \frac{4\mathring{M}_{\dot{w}}}{\rho_e S\bar{\bar{c}}^2} = 2M_{\dot{w}} \; . \tag{3.63}$$

AMERICAN NON-DIMENSIONAL CONTROL DERIVATIVES $C_{X_{\delta_e}}$, $C_{Z_{\delta_e}}$, $C_{m_{\delta_e}}$ DUE TO ELEVATOR

In American notation, the elevator angle is denoted by $\delta_e$.

$$C_{X_{\delta_e}} = \frac{\partial C_X}{\partial \delta_e} = \frac{\partial(X/\frac{1}{2}\rho V^2 S)}{\partial \eta} = \frac{\mathring{X}_\eta}{\frac{1}{2}\rho_e V_e{}^2 S} = X_\eta \; . \tag{3.64}$$

$$C_{Z_{\delta_e}} = \frac{\partial C_Z}{\partial \delta_e} = \frac{\partial(Z/\frac{1}{2}\rho V^2 S)}{\partial \eta} = \frac{\mathring{Z}_\eta}{\frac{1}{2}\rho_e V_e{}^2 S} = Z_\eta \; .$$

$$C_{m_{\delta_e}} = \frac{\partial C_m}{\partial \delta_e} = \frac{\partial(M/\frac{1}{2}\rho V^2 S\bar{\bar{c}})}{\partial \eta} = \frac{\mathring{M}_\eta}{\frac{1}{2}\rho_e V_e{}^2 S\bar{\bar{c}}} = M_\eta \; . \tag{3.66}$$

REFERENCES

1. HOPKIN, H.R. A scheme of notation and nomenclature for aircraft dynamics and associated aerodynamics. R. & M. 3562 (1970).

2. THOMAS, H.H.B.M. Estimation of stability derivatives (State of the art). A.R.C. Tech. Report C.P. No. 664 (1963); also AGARD Report 339 (1961).

3. WOLOWICZ, C.H. and YANCEY, R.B. Longitudinal aerodynamic characteristics of light twin-engine propeller-driven airplanes. NASA TN D-6800 (1972).

4. COWLEY, W.L. and GLAUERT, H. The effect of the lag of the downwash on the longitudinal stability of an aeroplane and on the rotary derivative $M_q$. R. & M. 718 (1921).

PROBLEMS

1. With a certain aircraft in level flight, the thrust $T$ and forward speed $V$ satisfy the relation $TV^n$ = constant, where $n$ is some constant. Show that then $X_u = -(n+2)\,C_D$.

2. The pitching moment coefficient for a wing is given by $C_m = [k/\sqrt{(1-V^2/a^2)}]\sin\alpha$ where $k$ and $a$ are constants. Obtain expressions for $M_u$ and $M_w$.

3. Verify that, when compressibility effects are neglected, the American non-dimensional derivatives $C_{X_u}$ and $C_{Z_u}$ are zero in gliding flight. Find expressions for these derivatives in steady climbing flight.

4. Using potential flow theory, it can be shown that the velocity at the point $(x,0)$ on a flat plate (chord $2a$) lying along $Ox$ and rotating with angular velocity $q$ about its mid-point $O$ is

$$U - V\frac{1+\cos\eta}{\sin\eta} + aq\sin\eta\ ,$$

where $x = a\cos\eta$ and $U$, $V$ are the components of the two-dimensional external stream in the negative directions of $Ox$, $Oy$.

Use this result to find the normal force and pitching moment about the origin per unit span for a flat plate in translation and rotation about its mid-point. Deduce the results for rotation about a general point in the plate. Hence find $Z_w$, $Z_q$, $M_w$ and $M_q$ for a flat plate.

5. The downwash increases as the distance of the tailplane from the wing decreases. Discuss the effect of this on the tailplane effectiveness and hence on the static stability and the pitching moment derivatives.

# Chapter 4

# AERODYNAMIC DERIVATIVES (LATERAL)

## INTRODUCTION

As shown in Chapter 2, there are three basic asymmetric motions of an aircraft: sideslip, roll and yaw. The corresponding velocities are the sideslip velocity $v$ of the centre of gravity $O$, the rate of roll $p$ about the axis $Ox$, and the rate of yaw $r$ about the axis $Oz$ (see Fig. 2.1). The aerodynamic forces and moments due to these velocities can be expressed in terms of the following non-dimensional derivatives, defined by Eqs. (2.76) to (2.84):

| | Rolling moment derivative | Yawing moment derivative | Side force derivative |
|---|---|---|---|
| Due to sideslip velocity $v$ | $L_v$ | $N_v$ | $Y_v$ |
| Due to rate of roll $p$ | $L_p$ | $N_p$ | $Y_p$ |
| Due to rate of yaw $r$ | $L_r$ | $N_r$ | $Y_r$ |

The derivatives $L_v$, $N_v$ and $Y_v$ are sometimes called the static lateral stability derivatives; they arise from the changes in incidence (and hence in forces and moments) on the surfaces of the aircraft due to sideslip. The other derivatives are rotary derivatives. In addition there are the non-dimensional control derivatives $L_\xi$, $N_\xi$, $Y_\xi$ due to ailerons and $L_\zeta$, $N_\zeta$, $Y_\zeta$ due to rudder, defined by Eqs. (2.88) to (2.93).

The values of these derivatives will be determined by the aerodynamic characteristics of the aircraft wing, fuselage, fin, rudder and ailerons, and by flaps and nacelles. As stated in Chapter 2, for a given aircraft disturbed from a given state of steady flight, these derivatives are constant; however, they will, in general, vary with variation in the initial steady flight conditions. We assume, as in Chapter 2, that the disturbances in yaw, bank and sideslip and their velocities are all small quantities compared with the forward speed of the aircraft.

## ESTIMATION OF LATERAL STABILITY DERIVATIVES

The numerical values of the derivatives can, in general, be found from the Engineering Sciences Data Sheets. In addition, references 1-4 give a comprehensive bibliography of references for estimating all these derivatives. The present notation differs from that used before 1970; a table of conversion factors when using the old symbols is given in reference 5.

In this chapter we shall show how approximate values of the derivatives can be determined by a simplified analysis using strip theory, the contributions to each derivative which are due to the various parts of the aircraft being obtained separately. More accurate values of the wing contribution to the derivatives can be obtained by using lifting surface theory. We shall confine our attention to low speeds and to incidences at which the flow has not separated from any part of the aircraft; for sweptback wings at moderate and high incidence, flow separation can greatly affect the value of some of the derivatives.

## DERIVATIVES DUE TO SIDESLIP

### Rolling Moment Derivative due to Sideslip $L_v = \mathring{L}_v/\frac{1}{2}\rho_e V_e S b$

This is one of the most important lateral stability derivatives and is treated in some detail. The chief contribution to $L_v$ is from the wing and the wing-fuselage interference effects. As is shown below, $L_v$ is influenced by wing dihedral, sweepback, wing-body arrangement and fin and rudder design.

#### *Effect of wing dihedral on $L_v$*

Consider first a straight untwisted wing *ABCD* without sweepback (Fig. 4.1), at an angle of incidence $\alpha$ in the straight flight without sideslip. $\alpha$ is the incidence of the zero lift line of the wing. We take the origin $O_1$ on the root chord *EF* (the centre section of the wing), and two sets of perpendicular axes $O_1xyz$ and $O_1x_1yz_1$.

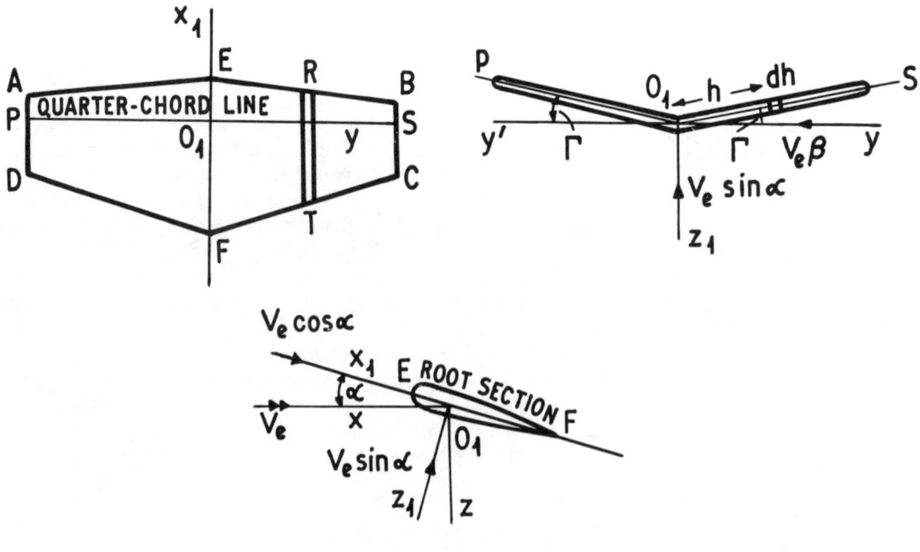


Fig. 4.1 Unswept wing in sideslipping flow

$O_1$ is the quarter chord point of the root chord, i.e. $EO_1 = \frac{1}{4}EF$. We suppose that the quarter chord line of the wing is unswept, i.e. that $PO_1S$ is perpendicular to $EF$. $O_1x$ is taken parallel to the flight path in the steady flight with no sideslip. $O_1x_1$ is in the wing plane of symmetry, parallel to the zero lift line of the wing. Thus $\alpha$ (assumed small) is the angle between $O_1x$ and $O_1x_1$. $O_1z$ and $O_1z_1$ are in the plane of symmetry, perpendicular to $O_1x$ and $O_1x_1$ respectively, and $O_1y$ is to starboard. We suppose that the wing has a dihedral angle $\Gamma$, where $\Gamma$ is small. Thus, if we consider the projection of the wing in the plane $O_1yz_1$ and take $PO_1S$ to represent the mean of the projection of the upper and lower surfaces of the wing in that plane, then $\Gamma$ is the angle between $O_1S$ (the starboard projection) and $O_1y$; similarly the angle between $O_1P$ (the port projection) and $O_1y'$ (the negative $y$ axis) is also $\Gamma$. We assume here, for simplicity, that each half of the wing has a constant dihedral angle along the span. The analysis can, of course, be easily extended to the general case in which the dihedral varies along the span.

Consider the velocity components of the free stream relative to the wing, when the wing is moving forward with velocity $V_e$ and sideslipping with velocity $v$, which is small compared with $V_e$.

The free stream thus has a relative velocity $-V_e$ parallel to $O_1x$ and a velocity $-v$ ($=-V_e\beta$) parallel to $O_1y$, where $\beta$ is the angle of sideslip (considered to be small). Thus the components of velocity referred to $O_1x_1$, $O_1y$, $O_1z_1$, are

$$-V_e \cos\alpha, \quad -V_e\beta, \quad -V_e \sin\alpha.$$

We shall now determine the incidence of a chordwise strip $RT$ of the starboard wing, distance $h$ from the root chord, and of width $dh$.

We see that the velocity components along $O_1y$ and $O_1z_1$ can be resolved into a component parallel to $O_1S$, i.e. parallel to the plane of the wing, which produced no lift, and a component $V_N$ perpendicular to $O_1S$, i.e. perpendicular to the chordwise strip, given by

$$\begin{aligned} V_N &= V_e(\sin\alpha\cos\Gamma + \beta\sin\Gamma) \\ &= V_e(\alpha + \beta\Gamma), \text{ neglecting higher order terms.} \end{aligned} \tag{4.1}$$

The chordwise component of velocity $V_C$ at the strip is given by

$$V_C = V_e\cos\alpha \simeq V_e \; . \tag{4.2}$$

Thus the incidence of the chordwise strip is

$$\alpha_h = V_N/V_C = \alpha + \beta\Gamma, \tag{4.3}$$

as shown in Fig. 4.2. We see that sideslip $\beta$ with dihedral $\Gamma$ increases the local wing incidence on the starboard wing from $\alpha$ to $\alpha + \beta\Gamma$.

If the wing is of large aspect ratio, we can use strip theory to estimate the lift $dL$ on the strip $RT$ (i.e. we neglect the induced effect of the rest of the wing, and consider the strip as being in two-dimensional flow). The lift $dL$ is given by

$$dL = \tfrac{1}{2}\rho_e(V_C^2 + V_N^2)\, c\,dh\, \frac{dC_L}{d\alpha_h}\alpha_h \; ,$$

i.e. from Eqs. (4.1) to (4.3), neglecting small quantities of the third order,

$$dL = \tfrac{1}{2}\rho_e V_e{}^2 (\alpha + \beta\Gamma) \frac{dC_L}{d\alpha_h} c\,dh, \tag{4.4}$$

where $c$ is the local chord length $RT$,
and $dC_L/d\alpha_h$ is the local value of the lift curve slope.

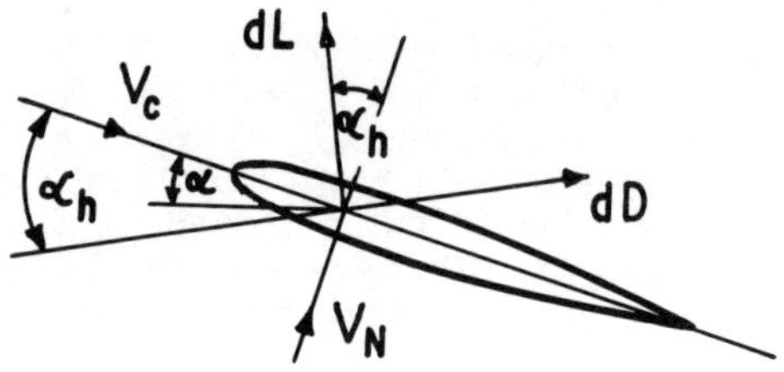


Fig. 4.2 Velocity components and forces on a chordwise strip

As shown in Fig. 4.2, $dL$ will have components $dL \sin(\alpha_h - \alpha)$ parallel to $O_1x$ and $-dL\cos(\alpha_h - \alpha)$ parallel to $O_1z$. Thus, neglecting small quantities of the third order and the component of the drag, and taking moments about the axis $O_1x$, we see that the rolling moment due to the starboard wing is

$$-\tfrac{1}{2}\rho_e V_e{}^2 \int_0^s (\alpha + \beta\Gamma)\left(\frac{dC_L}{d\alpha_h}\right) ch\,dh,$$

where $s$ is the semi-span $(= \tfrac{1}{2}b)$.

The rolling moment due to the port wing is found by changing the sign of $\Gamma$ and of the rolling moment and is

$$\tfrac{1}{2}\rho_e V_e{}^2 \int_0^s (\alpha - \beta\Gamma)\left(\frac{dC_L}{d\alpha_h}\right) ch\,dh.$$

Thus the total rolling moment due to sideslip with velocity $v$ is given by

$$v\mathring{L}_v = -\rho_e V_e{}^2 \beta \int_0^s \Gamma \left(\frac{dC_L}{d\alpha_h}\right) ch\,dh.$$

Now $v = V_e\beta$ and, taking $\Gamma$ constant across each half of the wing, we find

$$L_v = \frac{\mathring{L}_v}{\tfrac{1}{2}\rho_e V_e S b} = -\frac{\Gamma}{Ss}\int_0^s \left(\frac{dC_L}{d\alpha_h}\right) ch\,dh. \tag{4.5}$$

Thus, using simple strip theory, we see that the contribution to $L_v$ due to an unswept wing (of high aspect ratio) is proportional to the dihedral angle and to the lift curve slope, and is independent of $C_L$.

*Effect of sweepback on $L_v$*

By a similar analysis applied to a sweptback wing (sweepback angle $\Lambda$) with sideslip (taking the chordwise strip $RT$ perpendicular to the sweptback quarter-chord line), we find that, on the starboard wing, the velocity components relative to the wing can be resolved into a component $V_N$ normal to the wing, given by Eq. (4.1), a chordwise component $V_C$ parallel to $RT$ given by

$$V_C = V_e \cos\alpha \cos\Lambda - V_e(\sin\alpha \sin\Gamma - \beta\cos\Gamma)\sin\Lambda$$
$$= V_e(\cos\Lambda + \beta\sin\Lambda),$$

neglecting higher order terms. There is also a velocity component parallel to the quarter-chord line, which produces no lift on the element $RT$.

Thus the incidence of the chordwise strip $RT$ of a sweptback wing is

$$\alpha_h = \frac{V_N}{V_C} = \frac{\alpha + \beta\Gamma}{\cos\Lambda + \beta\sin\Lambda} \simeq \sec\Lambda\,(\alpha + \beta\Gamma)(1 - \beta\tan\Lambda), \tag{4.6}$$

and the resultant velocity at $RT$ perpendicular to the quarter-chord line is

$$\sqrt{(V_C{}^2 + V_N{}^2)} \simeq V_e \cos\Lambda(1 + \beta\tan\Lambda). \tag{4.7}$$

We note that, for a sweptback wing in sideslip, there will be an effective change of incidence even if the dihedral angle is zero.

Using strip theory, and taking $\Gamma$ and $\Lambda$ constant across each half of the wing, we find

$$L_v = \frac{\overset{\circ}{L}_v}{\frac{1}{2}\rho_e V_e S b} = -(\Gamma\cos\Lambda + \alpha\sin\Lambda)\,\frac{\cos\Lambda}{Ss}\int_0^{s\sec\Lambda} \frac{dC_L}{d\alpha_h}\, c_n h\,dh, \tag{4.8}$$

where $s$ is the wing semi-span (measured perpendicular to $O_1x_1$).

Now the lift on the chordwise strip $RT$ (length $c_n$) is

$$\tfrac{1}{2}\rho_e(V_C{}^2 + V_N{}^2)\,c_n\,dh\,\frac{dC_L}{d\alpha_h}\,\alpha_h\,,$$

and thus, from Eqs. (4.6) and (4.7), the total lift in steady flight without sideslip is

$$2\,.\,\tfrac{1}{2}\rho_e V_e{}^2\,\alpha\cos\Lambda \int_0^{s\sec\Lambda} \frac{dC_L}{d\alpha_h}\,c_n\,dh.$$

But this must be equal to $\frac{1}{2}\rho_e V_e{}^2 S C_L$.

Thus $$C_L = \frac{2}{S}\,\alpha\cos\Lambda \int_0^{s\sec\Lambda} \frac{dC_L}{d\alpha_h}\,c_n\,dh.$$

For simplicity we take $dC_L/d\alpha_h$ constant across the span.

Then $$C_L = \frac{dC_L}{d\alpha_h}\,\alpha\cos\Lambda,$$

and, from Eq. (4.8),

$$L_v = -\left(\Gamma\,\frac{dC_L}{d\alpha_h}\cos\Lambda + C_L\tan\Lambda\right)\frac{\cos\Lambda}{Ss}\int_0^{s\sec\Lambda} c_n h\,dh. \tag{4.9}$$

Thus, using a simple strip theory, we see that, for a swept wing of large aspect ratio, the contribution to $L_v$ is composed of two parts, the first proportional to dihedral angle $\Gamma$ and independent of $C_L$, the second proportional to $C_L$ and independent of dihedral angle.

*Contribution of the fuselage to $L_v$*

When an aircraft is sideslipping to starboard, the velocity of the free stream relative to the aircraft has a component $(-V_e\beta)$ along $Oy$ (Fig. 4.3). Considering

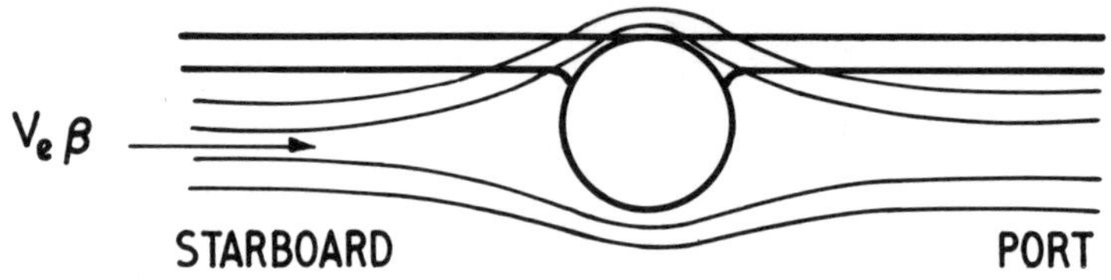


Fig. 4.3 Flow round the fuselage (for a high-wing aircraft)

the fuselage as an infinite cylinder, we see that this sideslipping flow will produce components of velocity in the vertical direction in the neighbourhood of the fuselage. These in turn will alter the local wing incidence. Thus, for a high wing aircraft (Fig. 4.3), if the aircraft is sideslipping to starboard (i.e. the relative wind is coming from starboard), the effect of the fuselage will be to increase the incidence of the starboard wing and decrease that of the port wing, giving a rolling moment from starboard to port, i.e. a negative rolling moment about $Ox$. Thus, for a high wing the effect of the fuselage is to increase $(-L_v)$, i.e. to increase the effective dihedral. For a low wing aircraft (Fig. 4.4), the

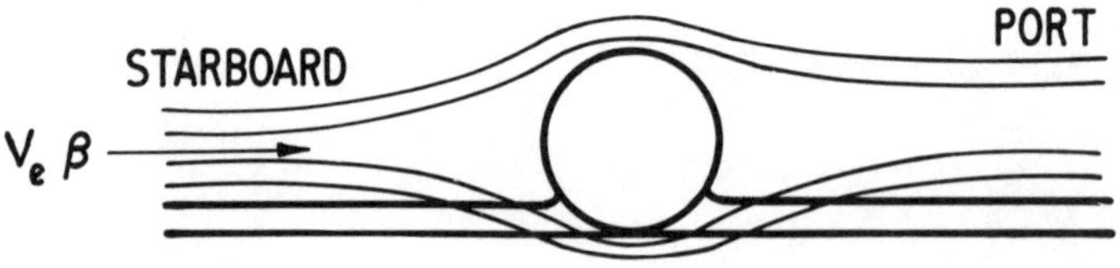


Fig. 4.4 Flow round the fuselage (for a low-wing aircraft)

reverse is true; the effect of the fuselage is to increase $L_v$, i.e. to decrease the effective dihedral. Thus, to maintain the same rolling moment due to sideslip, it is necessary to give a low wing a considerably greater geometric dihedral than that for a high wing.

*Contribution of the fin to $L_v$*

When the aircraft is sideslipping to starboard at an angle $\beta$ ($\beta$ is small), the effective incidence of the fin is $\beta$, see Fig. 4.5 (if sidewash effects are neglected), and the fin contributes a side force $Y_F$ to starboard given by

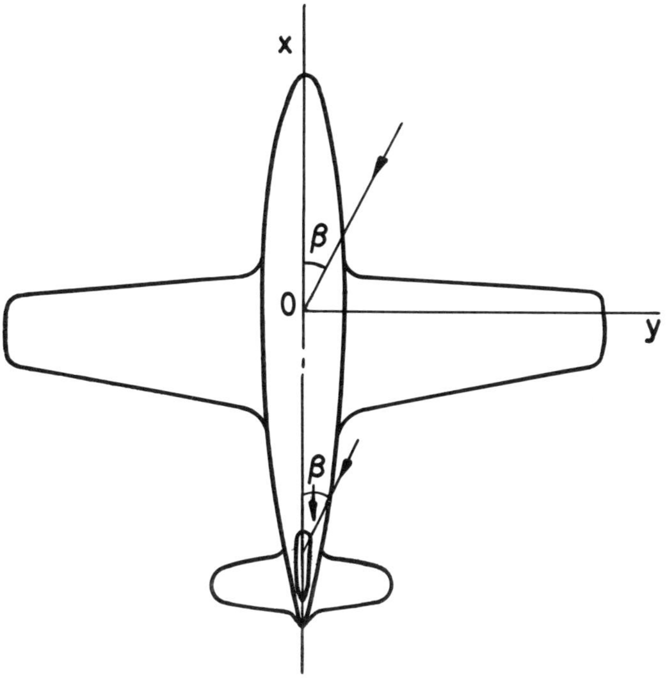


Fig. 4.5 Aircraft in sideslipping flow

$$Y_F = -\tfrac{1}{2}\rho_e V_e{}^2 S_F\, a_1 \beta, \tag{4.10}$$

where $S_F$ = fin area
and $a_1$ = fin lift curve slope.

We note that in a sideslip to starboard, the side force due to the fin alone will be to port.

Therefore the fin contribution to the rolling moment due to sideslip velocity $v$ is given by

$$v\mathring{L}_v(\text{fin}) = Y_F \bullet h_F \tag{4.11}$$

where $h_F$ is the height of the aerodynamic centre of the fin above $Ox$ (with wind axes, $h_F$ will vary with the aircraft incidence).

Now $v = V_e\beta$. Thus, from Eqs. (4.10) and (4.11),

$$L_v(\text{fin}) = \frac{\mathring{L}_v(\text{fin})}{\tfrac{1}{2}\rho_e V_e S b} = -\, a_1\, \frac{S_F}{S} \bullet \frac{h_F}{b}\,. \tag{4.12}$$

We define the fin-volume ratio $\bar{V}_F$ by the equation

$$\bar{V}_F = S_F l_F / Sb, \tag{4.13}$$

where $l_F$ is the distance of the aerodynamic centre of the fin aft of the centre of gravity of the aircraft.

From Eqs. (4.12) and (4.13),

$$L_v(\text{fin}) = -a_1\bar{V}_F\frac{h_F}{l_F}. \tag{4.14}$$

In deriving Eq. (4.14), no allowance has been made for the sidewash due to fuselage. The cross flow round the fuselage (illustrated in Figs. 4.3 and 4.4) will alter the incidence at the fin, the effect varying with the wing incidence. In addition a body vortex system may be generated by the fuselage, which in turn will induce lateral velocity components at the fin. The effect of sidewash is analogous to that of downwash in the longitudinal flow (but it is generally much less important).

Yawing moment derivative due to sideslip $N_v = \mathring{N}_v/\tfrac{1}{2}\rho_e V_e Sb$

This is one of the most important of the yawing moment derivatives. As shown in Chapter 9, the directional (or weathercock) stability of an aircraft is determined by the sign of $N_v$. For aircraft with unswept wings, the main contributions arise from the fuselage and the fin.

*Contribution of the fuselage to $N_v$*

When an aircraft is sideslipping, the forces on the fuselage produce a yawing moment $N_B$ about the c.g. which can be expressed in the form

$$N_B = \tfrac{1}{2}\rho_e V_e^2 S_B l_B \beta\, n_B, \tag{4.15}$$

where $\beta$ = the angle of sideslip = $v/V_e$,
$V_e$ = forward velocity of the aircraft,
$S_B$ = area of side elevation of the fuselage,
$l_B$ = overall length of the fuselage,
and $n_B$ = non-dimensional coefficient.

Thus the contribution to $N_v$ due to the fuselage is

$$N_v(\text{fuselage}) = \frac{1}{\tfrac{1}{2}\rho_e V_e Sb}\frac{\partial N_B}{\partial v} = \frac{S_B l_B}{Sb}n_B. \tag{4.16}$$

The fuselage gives a negative (i.e. destabilising) contribution to $N_v$, the numerical value being greatest for an aft position of the centre of gravity. The destabilising effect of the fuselage increases at high incidence and the flow separates, forming vortices which stream past the fin, reducing its effectiveness as a stabiliser.

*Contribution of the fin to $N_v$*

As shown in Fig. 4.5, for a sideslipping aircraft, if sidewash is neglected, the effective incidence of the fin is $\beta$, and the fin contributes a side force $Y_F$ to starboard given by Eq. (4.10). The fin contribution to the yawing moment due to sideslip velocity $v$ is given by

$$v\mathring{N}_v(\text{fin}) = -Y_F l_F \tag{4.17}$$

where $l_F$ is the distance between the aerodynamic centre of the fin and the aircraft yawing axis $Oz$ through the c.g.

Thus, remembering that $v = V_e\beta$, we have, from Eqs. (4.10) and (4.17),

$$N_v(\text{fin}) = \frac{\overset{\circ}{N}_v(\text{fin})}{\frac{1}{2}\rho_e V_e S b} = a_1 \frac{S_F}{S} \cdot \frac{l_F}{b}, \tag{4.18}$$

i.e. from Eq. (4.13),

$$N_v(\text{fin}) = a_1 \bar{V}_F \tag{4.19}$$

where $\bar{V}_F$ is the fin volume ratio.

In deriving Eq. (4.19), no allowance has been made for interference effects due to the tailplane, or for the induced sidewash due to asymmetric flow over the wing and fuselage.

From Eq. (4.18) we see that the value of $N_v$ (and hence the directional stability) is increased by increasing the fin area or by increasing the fin effectiveness (e.g. by increasing the aspect ratio of the fin).

From the above discussion it is seen that there are contributions to $N_v$ from various parts of the aircraft, the contributions often being of opposite sign. For this reason it is preferable to measure $N_v$ experimentally early on in the design stage of an aircraft.

## Side force derivative due to sideslip $Y_v = \overset{\circ}{Y}_v/\frac{1}{2}\rho_e V_e S$

This is the only side force derivative of importance for a conventional aircraft. The main contribution to $Y_v$ usually arises from the vertical surfaces of the aircraft, especially from the fuselage and fin.

### *Contribution of the fuselage to $Y_v$*

When an aircraft is sideslipping with sideslip velocity $v$, the forces on the fuselage produce a side force $Y_B$ to starboard which can be expressed in the form

$$Y_B = \tfrac{1}{2}\rho_e V_e^2 S_B \beta y_B, \tag{4.20}$$

where $\beta$ = angle of sideslip = $v/V_e$,
$V_e$ = forward velocity of the aircraft,
$S_B$ = area of side elevation of the fuselage,
and $y_B$ = non-dimensional coefficient.

Thus the contribution to $Y_v$ from the fuselage is

$$Y_v(\text{fuselage}) = \frac{1}{\frac{1}{2}\rho_e V_e S} \cdot \frac{\partial Y_B}{\partial v} = \frac{S_B}{S} y_B, \tag{4.21}$$

and is negative.

### *Contribution of the fin to $Y_v$*

As shown above, when the aircraft has an angle of sideslip $\beta$, the fin contributes a side force $Y_F$ to starboard given by

$$Y_F = -\tfrac{1}{2}\rho_e V_e^2 S_F a_1 \beta, \tag{4.22}$$

where $S_F$ = fin area
and $a_1$ = fin lift curve slope.

We note that, in a sideslip to starboard, the side force due to the fin will be to port.

Now $\beta = v/V_e$; thus the contribution of the fin to $Y_v$ is given by

$$Y_v(\text{fin}) = \frac{1}{\frac{1}{2}\rho_e V_e S}\frac{\partial Y_F}{\partial v} = -\frac{S_F}{S}a_1. \tag{4.23}$$

## DERIVATIVES DUE TO RATE OF ROLL

Rolling moment derivative due to rate of roll $L_p = \mathring{L}_p/\frac{1}{2}\rho_e V_e S b^2$

This derivative is almost completely determined by the wing, which provides most of the damping in roll.

### *Contribution of the wing to $L_p$*

Consider a straight tapered untwisted wing *ABCD* without sweepback and without dihedral (Fig. 4.6), at an incidence $\alpha$ in steady straight flight with no rate of roll. $\alpha$ is the incidence of the mean zero lift line of the wing, and is taken to be small. We take the origin $O_1$ in the root chord *EF* (the centre section of the wing), and perpendicular axes $O_1xyz$, $O_1x$ being along the direction of motion in steady flight. We take $O_1$ to be the quarter chord point of the root chord (i.e. $EO_1 = \frac{1}{4}EF$) and we suppose that the lift of any chordwise strip of the wing acts as the quarter chord point of the local chord. We assume that the locus of these quarter chord points (the quarter chord line) has no sweep.

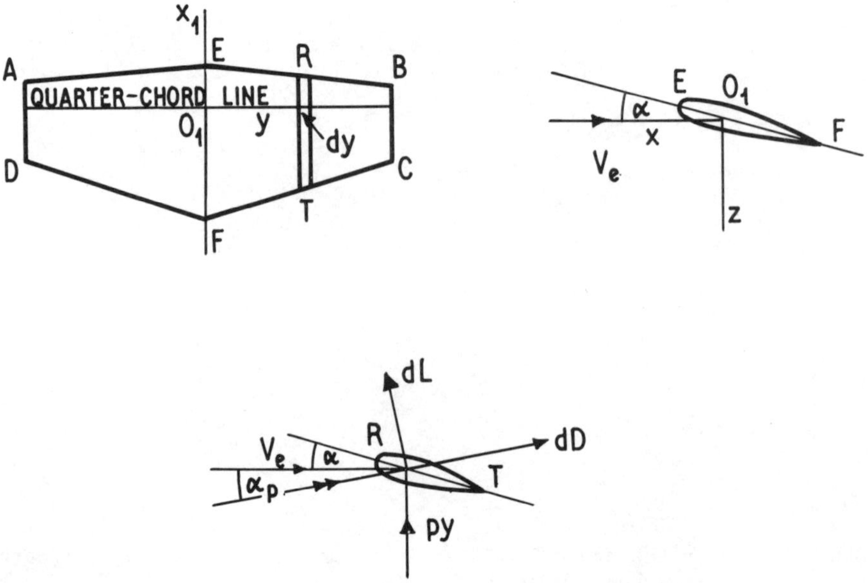


Fig. 4.6 Unswept wing in roll

Consider the forces acting on a chordwise strip $RT$ of the starboard wing, distance $y$ from the root section and width $dy$, when the wing is moving forward with a velocity $V_e$ parallel to $O_1x$ and rolling about $O_1x$ with an angular velocity $p$ ($p$ is small compared with $V_e$). $p$ is taken to be positive when the rolling is in the clockwise sense about $O_1x$, i.e. when the starboard wing is moving down. Due to the angular velocity $p$, the velocity of the free stream *relative* to the element $RT$ will have an additional upward component $py$ (Fig. 4.6). Thus, for the element $RT$ of the starboard wing, there is an increase in incidence $\alpha_p$ given by

$$\tan \alpha_p = \frac{py}{V_e} .$$

Now, since $p$ is small compared with $V_e$, $\alpha_p$ will be small and thus

$$\alpha_p = \frac{py}{V_e} . \tag{4.24}$$

The resultant velocity at the section $RT$ is $\sqrt{(V_e^2 + p^2y^2)} = V_e$, to the first order.

As above, we assume the aspect ratio of the wing is large, and use strip theory, i.e. we neglect any induced effects at the strip $RT$. The lift $dL$ and the drag $dD$ arising from this strip will be perpendicular to and along the direction of the resultant velocity at the strip (see Fig. 4.6). Resolving forces parallel to $O_1z$, we have

$$dZ = -dL \cos \alpha_p - dD \sin \alpha_p . \tag{4.25}$$

Now
$$\left.\begin{aligned} dL &= \tfrac{1}{2}\rho_e V_e^2 (C_L)_l c\,dy \\ &= \tfrac{1}{2}\rho_e V_e^2 \left(\frac{dC_L}{d\alpha}\right)_l (\alpha + \alpha_p) c\,dy \end{aligned}\right\} \tag{4.26}$$

and
$$dD = \tfrac{1}{2}\rho_e V_e^2 (C_D)_l c\,dy , \tag{4.27}$$

where the suffix $l$ denotes the local value of the parameter. From Eqs. (4.24) to (4.27), to the first order of small quantities,

$$dZ = -\tfrac{1}{2}\rho_e V_e^2 \left[\left(\frac{dC_L}{d\alpha}\right)_l \alpha + \left(C_D + \frac{dC_L}{d\alpha}\right)_l \frac{py}{V_e}\right] c\,dy . \tag{4.28}$$

Thus the total rolling moment about $O_1x$ for the wing is

$$\begin{aligned} p\mathring{L}_p &= -\tfrac{1}{2}\rho_e V_e^1 \int_{-s}^{s} \left[\left(\frac{dC_L}{d\alpha}\right)_l \alpha + \left(C_D + \frac{dC_L}{d\alpha}\right)_l \frac{py}{V_e}\right] cy\,dy \\ &= -\rho_e V_e p \int_0^s \left(C_D + \frac{dC_L}{d\alpha}\right)_l cy^2 dy , \end{aligned}$$

where $s$ is the wing semi-span.

Therefore
$$L_p = \frac{\mathring{L}_p}{\tfrac{1}{2}\rho_e V_e S b^2} = -\frac{1}{2S\ s^2} \int_0^s \left(C_D + \frac{dC_L}{d\alpha}\right)_l cy^2 dy . \tag{4.29}$$

From Eq. (4.29) we see that, for a wing of large aspect ratio, the wing contribution to $L_p$ is independent of $C_L$ and depends on the wing plan form and on $dC_L/d\alpha$. For a wing of low aspect ratio, the value of $L_p$ is considerably lower than that given by Eq. (4.29), due to induced effects.

Yawing moment derivative due to rate of roll $N_p = \mathring{N}_p/\frac{1}{2}\rho_e V_e S b^2$

This derivative is almost entirely determined by the contribution from the wing. A large fin may also provide a significant contribution to $N_p$.

*Contribution of the wing to $N_p$*

This can be found in a similar manner to that given above for $L_p$. The lift d$L$ on a chordwise strip is given by Eq. (4.26), and the drag by Eq. (4.27). Now we write

$$(C_D)_l = (C_{D_0})_l + \left(\frac{dC_D}{d\alpha}\right)_l \alpha_p ,$$

where $(C_{D_0})_l$ is the local value of the drag coefficient in the steady flight without rolling.

The yawing moment arises from the moment due to the forces acting in the forward direction on the chordwise strips of the wing. By a similar analysis to that for $L_p$, it can be shown that the contribution of the wing to $N_p$ is given by

$$N_p = \frac{\mathring{N}_p}{\frac{1}{2}\rho_e V_e S b^2} = -\frac{1}{2Ss^2}\int_0^s \left(C_L - \frac{dC_D}{d\alpha}\right)_l cy^2 dy . \tag{4.30}$$

For a wing of small aspect ratio, induced effects will reduce the value of $N_p$.

From Eq. (4.30), we see that, as $C_L$ is generally greater than d$C_D$/d$\alpha$, $N_p$ will be negative for an unswept wing, i.e. positive rolling will produce a negative yawing moment. However, the term in d$C_D$/d$\alpha$ is often very large for highly swept or delta wings at high incidence, and $N_p$ may then become positive.

Side force derivative due to rate of roll $Y_p = \mathring{Y}_p/\frac{1}{2}\rho_e V_e S b$

This derivative is negligible for a conventional aircraft. It might be worth taking into account for an aircraft with highly swept wings or with a large fin.

## DERIVATIVES DUE TO RATE OF YAW

Rolling moment derivative due to rate of yaw $L_r = \mathring{L}_r/\frac{1}{2}\rho_e V_e S b^2$

The main contributions to this derivative arise from the wing and the fin. That due to the wing is usually the more important, unless $C_L$ is very small.

*Contribution of the wing to $L_r$*

Consider the forces on a chordwise strip $RT$ of a straight tapered untwisted wing $ABCD$ without sweepback and without dihedral (Fig. 4.7), at an incidence $\alpha$. The strip $RT$ is at distance $y$ from the root section and width d$y$. The wing is moving forward with velocity $V_e$ parallel to $O_1x$ and yawing about $O_1z$ with an angular velocity $r$ ($r$ is small compared with $V_e$). $r$ is taken to be positive when the yawing

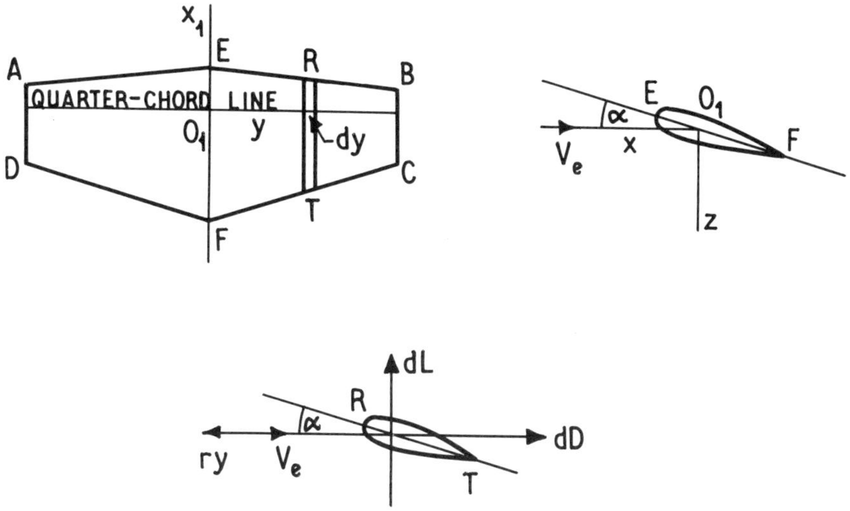


Fig. 4.7 Unswept wing with rate of yaw

is in the clockwise sense about $O_1z$, i.e. when the starboard wing is moving to the rear relative to the point $O_1$. $Y$ is the quarter chord point of $RT$ and thus lies on the quarter chord line of the wing. Due to the angular velocity $r$, the velocity of the free stream *relative* to the element $RT$ will have an additional forward component $ry$ (Fig. 4.7). (This component will vary from $R$ to $T$; we take its value at the point $Y$.) Thus, for the element $RT$ of the starboard wing, there is no change in incidence due to yawing, but the resultant velocity at the element is $V_e - ry$.

As above, we assume that the aspect ratio of the wing is large, and use a simple strip theory, i.e. we neglect any induced effects at the strip $RT$. The lift $\mathrm{d}L$ and the drag $\mathrm{d}D$ arising from this strip will be parallel to $O_1z$ and $O_1x$ respectively. We have

$$\left.\begin{aligned} \mathrm{d}L &= \tfrac{1}{2}\rho_e (V_e - ry)^2 (C_L)_l c\,\mathrm{d}y \\ &= \tfrac{1}{2}\rho_e (V_e{}^2 - 2V_e ry)(C_L)_l c\,\mathrm{d}y, \end{aligned}\right\} \tag{4.31}$$

neglecting second-order terms, where the suffix $l$ denotes the local value of the parameter.

Then the total rolling moment for the wing (positive in the clockwise sense about $O_1x$) is

$$\begin{aligned} r\mathring{L}_r &= -\tfrac{1}{2}\rho_e \int_{-s}^{s} (V_e{}^2 - 2V_e ry)(C_L)_l cy\,\mathrm{d}y \\ &= 2\rho_e V_e r \int_0^s (C_L)_l cy^2\,\mathrm{d}y, \end{aligned}$$

where $s$ is the wing semi-span.

Thus $$L_r = \frac{\mathring{L}_r}{\tfrac{1}{2}\rho_e V_e S b^2} = \frac{1}{Ss^2}\int_0^s (C_L)_l cy^2\,\mathrm{d}y. \tag{4.32}$$

*Contribution of the fin to $L_r$*

If sidewash is neglected, the effect of a rate of yaw $r$ is to increase the fin incidence by $rl_F/V_e$, where $l_F$ is the distance of the aerodynamic centre of the fin from the c.g. of the aircraft. (Figure 4.8 shows the components of velocity relative to the fin.)

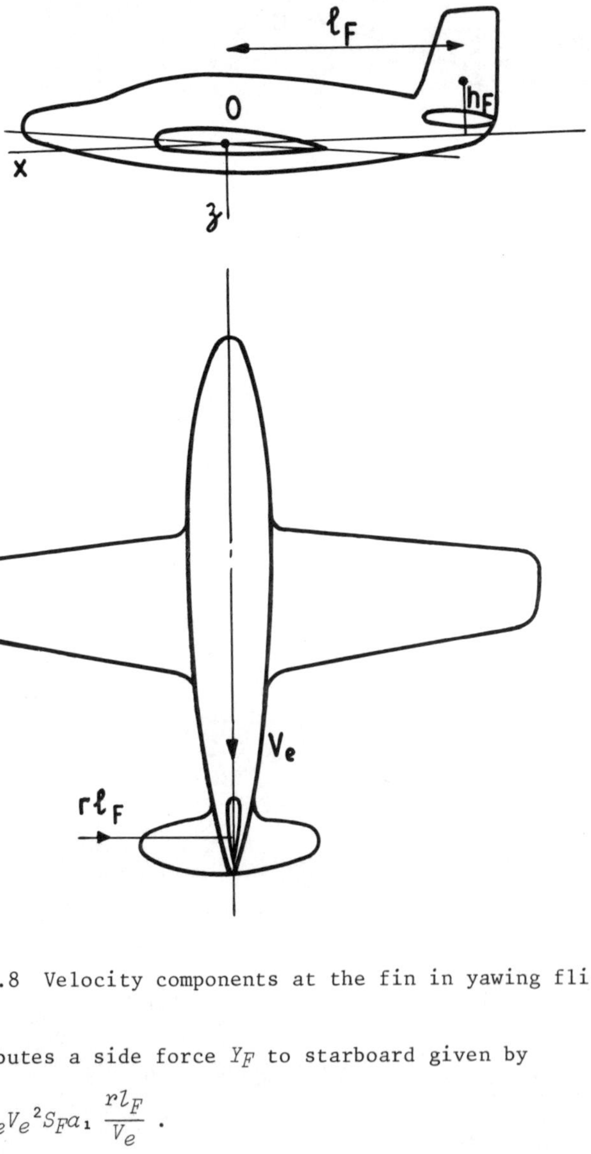


Fig. 4.8 Velocity components at the fin in yawing flight

Thus the fin contributes a side force $Y_F$ to starboard given by

$$Y_F = \tfrac{1}{2}\rho_e V_e{}^2 S_F a_1 \frac{rl_F}{V_e} . \tag{4.33}$$

The increment in rolling moment about $Ox$ (positive in the clockwise direction) due to the rate of yaw $r$ is

$$r\,\mathring{L}_r(\text{fin}) = Y_F h_F ,$$

where $h_F$ is the distance of the aerodynamic centre of the fin above the axis $Ox$ (Fig. 4.8).

Thus $$L_r(\text{fin}) = \frac{\mathring{L}_r(\text{fin})}{\frac{1}{2}\rho_e V_e S b^2} = a_1 \frac{S_F l_F}{Sb} \cdot \frac{h_F}{b} ,$$

i.e. from Eq. (4.13),

$$L_r(\text{fin}) = a_1 \bar{V}_F \frac{h_F}{b} , \tag{4.34}$$

where $\bar{V}_F$ is the fin volume ratio.

<u>Yawing moment derivative due to rate of yaw</u> $N_r = \mathring{N}_r / \frac{1}{2}\rho_e V_e S b^2$

The main contributions to this derivative arise from the wing and the fin.

*Contribution of the wing to* $N_r$

As for $L_r$, we consider a straight tapered untwisted wing without sweepback and without dihedral, moving forward with incidence $\alpha$ and velocity $V_e$. Consider the forces on a chordwise strip $RT$ (Fig. 4.7) of length $c$ and width $\mathrm{d}y$ when the wing has also a rate of yaw $r$ about $O_1 z$ ($r$ is measured positive in the clockwise sense about $O_1 z$). $r$ is small compared with $V_e$. As shown in Fig. 4.7, for the element $RT$ of the starboard wing there is no change in incidence due to yawing, but the resultant velocity at the element is $V_e - ry$.

The drag $\mathrm{d}D$ arising from this strip is parallel to $O_1 x$ and is given by

$$\left.\begin{aligned} \mathrm{d}D &= \tfrac{1}{2}\rho_e (V_e - ry)^2 (C_D)_l c\,\mathrm{d}y \\ &= \tfrac{1}{2}\rho_e (V_e{}^2 - 2V_e ry)(C_D)_l c\,\mathrm{d}y , \end{aligned}\right\} \tag{4.35}$$

neglecting second-order terms, where the suffix $l$ denotes the local value of the parameter.

Therefore the total yawing moment for the wing (positive in the clockwise direction about $O_1 z$) is

$$\begin{aligned} r\mathring{N}_r &= \tfrac{1}{2}\rho_e \int_{-s}^{s} (V_e{}^2 - 2V_e ry)(C_D)_l cy\,\mathrm{d}y \\ &= -2\rho_e V_e r \int_0^s (C_D)_l cy^2\,\mathrm{d}y , \end{aligned}$$

where $s$ is the wing semi-span.

Therefore $$N_r(\text{wing}) = \frac{\mathring{N}_r(\text{wing})}{\frac{1}{2}\rho_e V_e S b^2} = -\frac{1}{Ss^2}\int_0^s (C_D)_l cy^2\,\mathrm{d}y . \tag{4.36}$$

For a wing of low aspect ratio, the induced drag has also to be taken into account. However, the damping moment due to the wing in yawing motion is, in general, much less than that due to the fin.

*Contribution of the fin to $N_r$*

As shown in the derivation of the fin contribution to $L_r$, the fin contributes a side force $Y_F$ to starboard, given by Eq. (4.33). The fin contribution to the yawing moment due to rate of yaw is

$$r\overset{\circ}{N}_r(\text{fin}) = -Y_F l_F \ , \tag{4.37}$$

where $l_F$ is the distance between the aerodynamic centre of the fin and the yawing axis $Oz$ through the aircraft c.g.

Therefore, from Eqs. (4.33) and (4.37),

$$N_r(\text{fin}) = \frac{\overset{\circ}{N}_r(\text{fin})}{\frac{1}{2}\rho_e V_e S b^2} = -a_1 \frac{S_F l_F{}^2}{S b^2} \ ,$$

i.e. from Eq. (4.13),

$$N_r(\text{fin}) = -a_1 \bar{V}_F l_F / b \ , \tag{4.38}$$

where $\bar{V}_F$ is the fin volume ratio.

From Eqs. (4.19) and (4.38),

$$N_r(\text{fin}) = -\frac{l_F}{b} N_v(\text{fin}). \tag{4.39}$$

We note that $N_r(\text{fin})$ is negative.

<u>Side force derivative due to rate of yaw</u> $Y_r = \overset{\circ}{Y}_r / \frac{1}{2}\rho_e V_e S b$

This derivative is negligible for a conventional aircraft. It might be worth taking into account for an aircraft with highly swept wings or with a large fin.

## CONTROL DERIVATIVES

As shown in Chapter 2, when asymmetric controls such as ailerons or rudder are applied, the applied forces and moments on the aircraft can be expressed in terms of the following non-dimensional control derivatives.

| | Rolling moment derivative | Yawing moment derivative | Side force derivative |
|---|---|---|---|
| Due to ailerons | $L_\xi$ | $N_\xi$ | $Y_\xi$ |
| Due to rudder | $L_\zeta$ | $N_\zeta$ | $Y_\zeta$ |

To determine the lateral response characteristics of an aircraft it is necessary to know the values both of the non-dimensional control derivatives and of the non-dimensional stability derivatives. We shall now derive simple expressions for the non-dimensional control derivatives.

DERIVATIVES DUE TO AILERONS

Rolling moment derivative due to ailerons $L_\xi = \mathring{L}_\xi / \frac{1}{2}\rho_e V_e{}^2 Sb$

Consider the rolling moment due to full span ailerons on an unswept wing (Fig. 4.9).

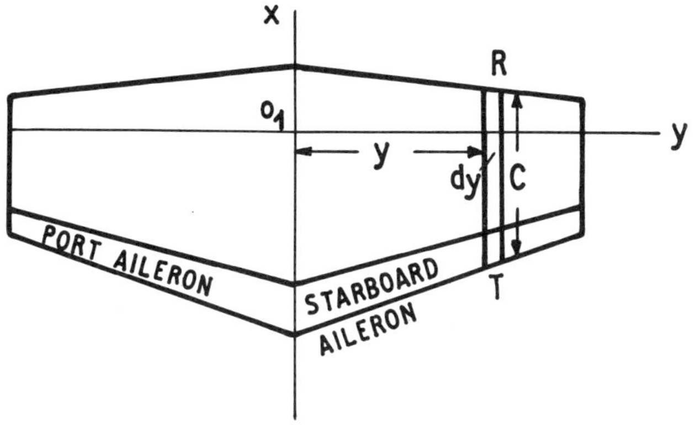


Fig. 4.9 Unswept wing with full-span ailerons

For simplicity we use strip theory. $O_1$ is the quarter chord point of the root chord of the wing. $O_1x$ is in the forward direction of motion, $O_1y$ perpendicular to starboard. The additional lift $dL$ on the strip $RT$, chord $c$, width $dy$, due to the starboard aileron deflection $\xi$ (downwards) is

$$dL = \tfrac{1}{2}\rho_e V_e{}^2 c \, dy \, a_2 \xi,$$

where $a_2$ is the lift curve slope for the control. Therefore the rolling moment due to the starboard aileron (measured positive in the clockwise sense about $O_1x$) is

$$- \tfrac{1}{2}\rho_e V_e{}^2 \xi \int_0^s a_2 c y \, dy \ ,$$

where $s$ is the wing semi-span.

The rolling moment due to port (up) and starboard (down) ailerons is given by

$$\mathring{L}_\xi \xi = - \rho_e V_e{}^2 \xi \int_0^s a_2 \, c y \, dy.$$

Therefore $$L_\xi = \frac{\mathring{L}_\xi}{\frac{1}{2}\rho_e V_e{}^2 Sb} = - \frac{1}{Ss} \int_0^s a_2 c y \, dy \qquad (4.40)$$

We note that $L_\xi$ is negative.

Yawing moment derivative due to ailerons $N_\xi = \mathring{N}_\xi / \frac{1}{2}\rho_e V_e{}^2 Sb$

When a control is deflected, there will be increments in both lift (or side force) and drag. The increment in drag is often neglected except in the case of the ailerons, where this increment can give rise to an appreciable yawing moment (depending partly on the type of ailerons used). We assume, for simplicity, that there is no differential between the two ailerons. Consider an aircraft going into a banked turn to port. When the starboard aileron is deflected downwards and the port aileron is deflected upwards (to give an anti-clockwise rolling moment) the drag due to the ailerons gives a clockwise (positive) yawing moment. Now the port wing will be down and the aircraft will be yawing to port. Hence the yawing moment from the ailerons will oppose this yawing motion, and the ailerons are said to produce an adverse yawing moment.

From Fig. 4.9 we see that, for an unswept wing, the addition drag $dD$ of the strip $RT$ due to the starboard aileron deflection $\xi$ (downwards) is

$$\mathrm{d}D = \tfrac{1}{2}\rho_e V_e{}^2 c \, \mathrm{d}y \left(\frac{\partial C_D}{\partial \xi}\right)_l \xi \,,$$

where the suffix $l$ denotes the local value.

Therefore the yawing moment due to the starboard aileron (positive in the clockwise sense about $O_1z$) is

$$\tfrac{1}{2}\rho_e V_e{}^2 \xi \int_0^s \left(\frac{\partial C_D}{\partial \xi}\right)_l cy \, \mathrm{d}y \,,$$

where $s$ is the wing semi-span.

The total yawing moment due to port and starboard ailerons is given by

$$\mathring{N}_\xi \xi = \rho_e V_e{}^2 \xi \int_0^s (\partial C_D/\partial \xi)_l \, cy \, \mathrm{d}y$$

and

$$N_\xi = \frac{\mathring{N}_\xi}{\tfrac{1}{2}\rho_e V_e{}^2 S b} = \frac{1}{Ss}\int_0^s (\partial C_D/\partial \xi)_l \, cy \, \mathrm{d}y \,. \tag{4.41}$$

<u>Side force derivative due to ailerons</u> $Y_\xi = \mathring{Y}_\xi / \tfrac{1}{2}\rho_e V_e{}^2 S$

This derivative is negligible except for very highly swept wings with ailerons having a large drag.

## DERIVATIVES DUE TO RUDDER

<u>Rolling moment derivative due to rudder</u> $L_\zeta = \mathring{L}_\zeta / \tfrac{1}{2}\rho_e V_e{}^2 S b$

When the rudder is deflected (to the left) through an angle $\zeta$ (assumed small), there is a side force $Y_R$ to starboard given by

$$Y_R = \tfrac{1}{2}\rho_e V_e{}^2 S_F a_2 \zeta \,, \tag{4.42}$$

where $S_F$ = area of the fin
and $a_2$ = lift curve slope for the rudder.

Therefore the rudder contribution to the rolling moment is given be

$$\zeta \mathring{L}_\zeta = Y_R h_R \,, \tag{4.43}$$

where $h_R$ is the distance of the point of application of the rudder side force above the axis $Ox$. Thus, from Eqs. (4.42) and (4.43),

$$L_\zeta = \frac{\mathring{L}_\zeta}{\frac{1}{2}\rho_e V_e{}^2 Sb} = a_2 \frac{S_F}{S} \cdot \frac{h_R}{b}\,, \tag{4.44}$$

i.e. from Eq. (4.13),

$$L_\zeta = a_2 \bar{V}_F \frac{h_R}{l_F}\,, \tag{4.45}$$

where $l_F$ is the distance of the aerodynamic centre of the fin aft of the centre of gravity of the aircraft. This derivative is usually small; it may be important if the rudder is large.

Yawing moment derivative due to rudder $N_\zeta = \mathring{N}_\zeta / \frac{1}{2}\rho_e V_e{}^2 Sb$

The side force due to rudder is given by Eq. (4.42). Taking moments about $Oz$, the yawing axis through the centre of gravity $O$ of the aircraft, we find the rudder contribution to the yawing moment is given by

$$\zeta \mathring{N}_\zeta = -\, Y_R l_R\,, \tag{4.46}$$

where $l_R$ is the distance between the point of application of the rudder side force and the axis $Oz$.

Thus, from Eqs. (4.42) and (4.46),

$$N_\zeta = \frac{\mathring{N}_\zeta}{\frac{1}{2}\rho_e V_e{}^2 Sb} = -\, a_2 \frac{S_F l_R}{Sb}$$

or, since $l_R \simeq l_F$,

$$N_\zeta = -\, a_2\, \bar{V}_F\,. \tag{4.47}$$

From Eqs. (4.19) and (4.47), we see that

$$N_\zeta = -\,\frac{a_2}{a_1} N_v(\text{fin})\,. \tag{4.48}$$

The value of $a_2$ can be estimated using the Engineering Sciences Data Sheets.

Side force derivative due to rudder $Y_\zeta = \mathring{Y}_\zeta / \frac{1}{2}\rho_e V_e{}^2 S$

The side force $Y_R$ due to rudder deflection $\zeta$ (assumed small) is given by

$$\mathring{Y}_\zeta \zeta = Y_R\,. \tag{4.49}$$

Therefore, from Eqs. (4.42) and (4.49),

$$Y_\zeta = \frac{\mathring{Y}_\zeta}{\frac{1}{2}\rho_e V_e{}^2 S} = a_2 \frac{S_F}{S}\,. \tag{4.50}$$

## NON-DIMENSIONAL FORMS OF THE AERODYNAMIC DERIVATIVES USED IN AMERICA

There are some important differences between the British and American notations for these derivatives. The American non-dimensional lateral stability derivatives are derived by direct differentiation of the non-dimensional coefficients $C_l(=L/\tfrac{1}{2}\rho_e V_e{}^2 Sb)$, $C_n(=N/\tfrac{1}{2}\rho_e V_e{}^2 Sb)$ and $C_Y(=Y/\tfrac{1}{2}\rho_e V_e{}^2 S)$ with respect to the appropriate variable ($\beta$, $pb/2V_e$ or $rb/2V_e$), where $b$ is the wing span and the suffix $e$ refers to the constant datum value in the initial steady flight. We give here a list of the American derivatives, together with formulae relating them to the corresponding British derivatives.

$$C_{l_\beta} = \frac{\partial C_l}{\partial \beta} = \frac{\partial(L/\tfrac{1}{2}\rho_e V_e{}^2 Sb)}{\partial(v/V_e)} = \frac{\mathring{L}_v}{\tfrac{1}{2}\rho_e V_e Sb} = L_v. \tag{4.51}$$

$$C_{l_p} = \frac{\partial C_l}{\partial(pb/2V_e)} = \frac{\partial(L/\tfrac{1}{2}\rho_e V_e{}^2 Sb)}{\partial(pb/2V_e)} = \frac{4\mathring{L}_p}{\rho_e V_e Sb^2} = 2L_p. \tag{4.52}$$

$$C_{l_r} = \frac{\partial C_l}{\partial(rb/2V_e)} = \frac{\partial(L/\tfrac{1}{2}\rho_e V_e{}^2 Sb)}{\partial(rb/2V_e)} = \frac{4\mathring{L}_r}{\rho_e V_e Sb^2} = 2L_r. \tag{4.53}$$

$$C_{n_\beta} = \frac{\partial C_n}{\partial \beta} = \frac{\partial(N/\tfrac{1}{2}\rho_e V_e{}^2 Sb)}{\partial(v/V_e)} = \frac{\mathring{N}_v}{\tfrac{1}{2}\rho_e V_e Sb} = N_v. \tag{4.54}$$

$$C_{n_p} = \frac{\partial C_n}{\partial(pb/2V_e)} = \frac{\partial(N/\tfrac{1}{2}\rho_e V_e{}^2 Sb)}{\partial(pb/2V_e)} = \frac{4\mathring{N}_p}{\rho_e V_e Sb^2} = 2N_p. \tag{4.55}$$

$$C_{n_r} = \frac{\partial C_n}{\partial(rb/2V_e)} = \frac{\partial(N/\tfrac{1}{2}\rho_e V_e{}^2 Sb)}{\partial(rb/2V_e)} = \frac{4\mathring{N}_r}{\rho_e V_e Sb^2} = 2N_r. \tag{4.56}$$

$$C_{Y_\beta} = \frac{\partial C_Y}{\partial \beta} = \frac{\partial(Y/\tfrac{1}{2}\rho_e V_e{}^2 S)}{\partial(v/V_e)} = \frac{\mathring{Y}_v}{\tfrac{1}{2}\rho_e V_e S} = Y_v. \tag{4.57}$$

$$C_{Y_p} = \frac{\partial C_Y}{\partial(pb/2V_e)} = \frac{\partial(Y/\tfrac{1}{2}\rho_e V_e{}^2 S)}{\partial(pb/2V_e)} = \frac{4\mathring{Y}_p}{\rho_e V_e Sb} = 2Y_p. \tag{4.58}$$

$$C_{Y_r} = \frac{\partial C_Y}{\partial(rb/2V_e)} = \frac{\partial(Y/\tfrac{1}{2}\rho_e V_e{}^2 S)}{\partial(rb/2V_e)} = \frac{4\mathring{Y}_r}{\rho_e V_e Sb} = 2Y_r. \tag{4.59}$$

## NON-DIMENSIONAL FORMS OF THE CONTROL DERIVATIVES USED IN AMERICA

In American notation, the aileron and rudder angles are denoted by $\delta_a$ and $\delta_r$ respectively. In a precisely similar way to that given above, we find

$$C_{l_{\delta_a}} = \frac{\partial C_l}{\partial \delta_a} = L_\xi\ , \tag{4.60}$$

$$C_{l_{\delta_r}} = \frac{\partial C_l}{\partial \delta_r} = L_\zeta , \tag{4.61}$$

$$C_{n_{\delta_a}} = \frac{\partial C_n}{\partial \delta_a} = N_\xi , \tag{4.62}$$

$$C_{n_{\delta_r}} = \frac{\partial C_n}{\partial \delta_r} = N_\zeta , \tag{4.63}$$

$$C_{Y_{\delta_a}} = \frac{\partial C_Y}{\partial \delta_a} = Y_\xi , \tag{4.64}$$

$$C_{Y_{\delta_r}} = \frac{\partial C_Y}{\partial \delta_r} = Y_\zeta . \tag{4.65}$$

## REFERENCES

1. CAMPBELL, J.P. and McKINNEY, M.O. Summary of methods for calculating dynamic lateral stability and response and for estimating lateral stability derivatives. NACA Report 1098 (1952).

2. BABISTER, A.W. *Aircraft Stability and Control.* Pergamon Press (1961).

3. THOMAS, H.H.B.M. Estimation of stability derivatives (State of the art). A.R.C. Tech. Report C.P. No. 664 (1963); also AGARD Report 339 (1961).

4. WOLOWICZ, C.H. and YANCEY, R.B. Lateral-directional aerodynamic characteristics of light twin-engine propeller-driven airplanes. NASA TN D 6946 (1972).

5. HOPKIN, H.R. A scheme of notation and nomenclature for aircraft dynamics and associated aerodynamics. R. & M. 3562 (1970).

## PROBLEMS

1. What do you understand by downwash and sidewash? Discuss the origins and significance of these two effects.

2. An untapered untwisted wing (sweepback $\Lambda$) without dihedral is at a small incidence in a sideslipping flow (angle of sideslip $\beta$). Find the angle of incidence and the resultant velocity (perpendicular to the leading edge) for a chordwise strip of the wing (perpendicular to the leading edge). How is the incidence of such a strip related to that of a strip in the line of flight? When second orders terms in $\beta$ are included, show that the pitching moment about an axis through the quarter-chord point of the root chord is of the form $C_0 + C_1\beta^2$, where $C_0$ and $C_1$ are constants. (Induced effects can be neglected and the spanwise distance of the centre of pressure from the root chord of either *half* of the wing is to be taken as $K_0 + K_1\theta$, where $K_0$ and $K_1$ are constants and $\theta$ is the *effective* sweepback of that half of the wing). The extent of the tip stall on the given wing is increased when the effective sweep is

increased. How would sideslip affect the curve of $C_{m_v} \cdot \alpha$ at high incidence?

3. What assumptions are involved in the use of strip theory? When would the errors of such a method be least? Compare the values of $L_p$ obtained by strip theory with those given in the Engineering Sciences Data Sheets for rectangular wings of aspect ratio 2, 4 and 8. How does $L_p$ vary as incidence increases?

4. An aileron deflection may be regarded as being equivalent to an anti-symmetric change in incidence over that part of the wing containing the aileron. Hence show that, for full chord ailerons, on an unswept wing, $L_\xi = L_v/\Gamma$. How would this formula be modified for ailerons of smaller chord?

5. How does the action of a spoiler differ from that of an aileron? Discuss the signs of the rolling and yawing moments due to spoilers.

# Part II

# LONGITUDINAL DYNAMIC STABILITY AND RESPONSE

# Chapter 5
# BASIC LONGITUDINAL MOTIONS

## INTRODUCTION

In Part I we saw that, when a symmetric aircraft flying on a straight path (with no bank or sideslip) is subject only to symmetric disturbances, the motion consists only of horizontal and vertical motion of the centre of gravity and pitching about the centre of gravity. The equations of longitudinal symmetric motion (for small disturbances) were derived in Chapter 2. These equations are, in general, rather complicated. There are, however, two simple approximate longitudinal motions, one of short period and one of long period, which we shall now consider.

## THE SHORT PERIOD OSCILLATION

Suppose an aircraft, initially in equilibrium, is given a symmetric disturbance, e.g. due to a sudden up-gust. The incidence of the aircraft will change and the aircraft will start to pitch. If the aircraft is stable, the angle of incidence will soon return to its original value; this movement is sometimes called the rapid incidence adjustment of the aircraft. There will also be a change in the aircraft forward speed, but this change will be small compared with the changes in the angles of incidence and pitch. In this approximate theory we shall assume that the aircraft speed $V_e$ remains constant. For simplicity, we shall neglect the velocity (and acceleration) of the aircraft normal to the steady flight path; thus the aircraft is assumed to oscillate in pitch about its centre of gravity as a pivoted body. In this case, the change in incidence is equal to the angle of pitch.

Let $\theta$ be the change in the angle of pitch of the aircraft from its initial steady state. As shown in Chapters 1 and 3, the change in angle of pitch $\theta$ (assumed to be small) will give rise to a moment $M$ about the centre of gravity of the aircraft where

$$\begin{aligned} M &= \tfrac{1}{2}\rho_e V_e{}^2 S \bar{\bar{c}}\, C_m \\ &= \tfrac{1}{2}\rho_e V_e{}^2 S \bar{\bar{c}} \frac{\partial C_m}{\partial \alpha} \cdot \theta \end{aligned} \qquad (5.1)$$

(as the aircraft is in trim initially, and the incidence is increased by an angle $\theta$).

There will also be a moment about the centre of gravity due to the angular velocity in pitch $q = \mathrm{d}\theta/\mathrm{d}t$, which affects the incidence at the tailplane. This is equivalent to a tail damping moment.

Let $l_T$ be the distance from the centre of gravity of the aircraft to the aerodynamic centre of the tailplane. Due to the rate of pitch, the tailplane has a downward velocity $ql_T$. Combining this with the forward velocity $V_e$ of the aircraft, we see that the change in tailplane incidence due to the angular velocity in pitch is $ql_T/V_e$. This produces an increase in tail lift $\Delta L_T$ given by

$$\Delta L_T = \tfrac{1}{2}\rho_e V_e{}^2 S_T \frac{dC_{LT}}{d\alpha_T} \cdot \frac{ql_T}{V_e}$$

$$= \tfrac{1}{2}\rho_e V_e S_T a_1 l_T \frac{d\theta}{dt},$$

where $S_T$ is the tailplane area. Hence the moment $\Delta M$ about the centre of gravity due to this force is

$$\Delta M = -\tfrac{1}{2}\rho_e V_e S_T a_1 l_T{}^2 \frac{d\theta}{dt}. \tag{5.2}$$

Finally, considering the inertia of the aircraft, we let $I_y$ be the moment of inertia of the aircraft about a pitching axis through the centre of gravity.

Then, from Eqs. (5.1) and (5.2), the equation of motion is

$$I_y \frac{d^2\theta}{dt^2} = -\tfrac{1}{2}\rho_e V_e S_T a_1 l_T{}^2 \frac{d\theta}{dt} + \tfrac{1}{2}\rho_e V_e{}^2 S\bar{\bar{c}} \frac{\partial C_m}{\partial\alpha} \cdot \theta,$$

i.e.

$$I_y \frac{d^2\theta}{dt^2} + \tfrac{1}{2}\rho_e V_e S_T a_1 l_T{}^2 \frac{d\theta}{dt} + \tfrac{1}{2}\rho_e V_e{}^2 S\bar{\bar{c}} \left(-\frac{\partial C_m}{\partial\alpha}\right)\theta = 0. \tag{5.3}$$

As shown in Chapter 1, when compressibility effects are neglected, $\partial C_m/\partial\alpha < 0$ for an aircraft with positive static stability. Putting $\theta = \sigma e^{\mu t}$, where $\sigma$ and $\mu$ are constants, we have, from Eq. (5.3),

$$\mu^2 + b\mu + c = 0, \tag{5.4}$$

where

$$b = \frac{\rho_e V_e S_T a_1 l_T{}^2}{2I_y} \tag{5.5}$$

and

$$c = \frac{\rho_e V_e{}^2 S\bar{\bar{c}}}{2I_y}\left(-\frac{\partial C_m}{\partial\alpha}\right). \tag{5.6}$$

It is found that, for a conventional aircraft with positive static stability, the roots of Eq. (5.4) are complex and are given by

$$\mu = -\frac{b}{2} \pm i\sqrt{\left(c - \frac{b^2}{4}\right)}$$

and, in terms of real quantities,

$$\theta = \sigma_1 e^{-bt/2} \sin\sqrt{\left[\left(c - \frac{b^2}{4}\right)\right]}\, t + \sigma_2 e^{-bt/2} \cos\sqrt{\left[\left(c - \frac{b^2}{4}\right)\right]}\, t, \tag{5.7}$$

where $\sigma_1$ and $\sigma_2$ are constants determined by the initial conditions, and $b$ and $c$ are constants given by Eqs. (5.5) and (5.6).

Now, from Eq. (5.5), $b$ is positive; we see too that, if the aircraft has a large positive value of $(-\partial C_m/\partial\alpha)$, i.e. a large positive static margin, then

$$c > \frac{b^2}{4}$$

and, from Eq. (5.7), the motion is a damped oscillation. The time $t_{\frac{1}{2}}$ to half-amplitude is given by

$$\tfrac{1}{2} = e^{-(b/2)t_{\frac{1}{2}}}$$

i.e. using Eq. (5.5),

$$t_{\frac{1}{2}} = \frac{2 \log_e 2}{b} = 4(\log_e 2) \frac{I_y}{\rho_e V_e S_T a_1 l_T{}^2}. \tag{5.8}$$

From Eq. (5.7), the period $T$ in seconds is

$$T = \frac{2\pi}{\sqrt{(c - b^2/4)}} = 2\pi \left[ \frac{\rho_e V_e{}^2 S\bar{\bar{c}}}{2I_y} \left( -\frac{\partial C_m}{\partial \alpha} \right) - \frac{1}{16} \frac{\rho_e{}^2 V_e{}^2 S_T{}^2 a_1{}^2 l_T{}^4}{I_y{}^2} \right]^{-\frac{1}{2}} \tag{5.9}$$

We see that both the period and the time to half amplitude are *inversely* proportional to the forward speed of the aircraft. For conventional aircraft at low speed, $t_{\frac{1}{2}}$ is of the order of ½ to 1 sec and the period is 4 to 10 sec, these times decreasing as the aircraft speed increases. From Eq. (5.8) we see that $t_{\frac{1}{2}}$ is inversely proportional to $\rho_e$, resulting in poorer damping at high altitudes. It must be emphasized that this is only a very rough approximation to the short period motion; in particular, we have neglected the normal acceleration of the aircraft and the effect of the lag in the downwash at the tailplane. This is considered in detail in Chapter 6.

## THE PHUGOID (LONG PERIOD) OSCILLATION

When an aircraft receives a symmetric disturbance the resulting motion is composed of two modes. One of these is the short period oscillation treated in the previous section. For a conventional low speed aircraft this motion in pitch is very quickly damped, but the remaining motion may still be unstable. This motion consists principally of slow sinusoidal motion, in which the height and the forward speed of the aircraft vary while the angle of incidence remains practically unchanged; this is known as the phugoid oscillation.

In the phugoid motion we assume that the static stability of the aircraft is large and that the rapid incidence adjustment has restored the incidence to its equilibrium value, in which the aircraft is in trim, i.e. the aerodynamic pitching moment is zero. With fixed elevator, constant incidence implies constant lift coefficient (neglecting compressibility effects). We also neglect the drag. The aircraft is considered to be slightly disturbed from steady horizontal flight at speed $V_e$.

Thus we can consider the aircraft as a body moving with velocity $V$ in a flight path inclined at angle $\phi$ to the horizontal and acted upon by two forces, (i) its weight $W$ acting vertically downwards and (ii) the lift $L$ acting perpendicular to the flight path (see Fig. 5.1).

Now we have neglected the drag, and no work is done by the lift force, since it acts at right angles to the flight path. Thus the total energy of the aircraft is constant (by the conservation of energy). In the phugoid oscillation the angular pitching motion of the aircraft is small and we can neglect the rotary kinetic energy. Hence the energy equation becomes

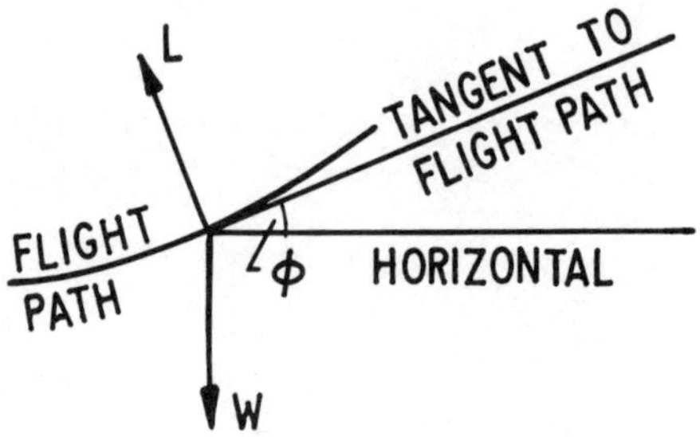


Fig. 5.1 Forces acting in the phugoid motion

$$\tfrac{1}{2}\frac{W}{g}V^2 + Wh = \tfrac{1}{2}\frac{W}{g}V_e^{\,2},$$

where $h$ is the increase in height of flight above its steady-state value,

i.e. $$V^2 + 2gh = V_e^{\,2}. \tag{5.10}$$

The equation of vertical motion is

$$\frac{W}{g}\frac{\mathrm{d}^2h}{\mathrm{d}t^2} = L\cos\phi - W, \tag{5.11}$$

where $\phi$ is the inclination of the disturbed flight path to the horizontal; $\phi$ and $h$ are small quantities of the first order, the flight path being only slightly disturbed from the horizontal. Thus, to the first, order, $\cos\phi = 1$.

In the phugoid oscillation, the incidence being constant (i.e. $C_L$ constant), the lift varies only from its steady flight value $L_e$ due to change in speed (we neglect the effect of change of air density with height). We note that $L_e = W$.

Therefore, from Eq. (5.10),

$$L = L_e\left(\frac{V}{V_e}\right)^2 = W\left(1 - \frac{2gh}{V_e^{\,2}}\right). \tag{5.12}$$

Substituting in Eq. (5.11) and neglecting small quantities of the second order and above, we obtain

$$\frac{\mathrm{d}^2h}{\mathrm{d}t^2} = -\frac{2g^2h}{V_e^{\,2}} \tag{5.13}$$

Putting $$h = k\mathrm{e}^{\mu t},$$

where $k$ and $\mu$ are constants, we have, from Eq. (5.13),

$$\mu^2 = -\frac{2g^2}{V_e^{\,2}}.$$

Thus $$h = k_1\sin\left(\sqrt{2}\,\frac{gt}{V_e}\right) + k_2\cos\left(\sqrt{2}\,\frac{gt}{V_e}\right), \tag{5.14}$$

where $k_1$ and $k_2$ are constants determined by the initial conditions.

From Eq. (5.14) we see that the phugoid oscillation is a simple harmonic motion, the period $T$ in seconds being given by

$$T = \pi\sqrt{2}\,\frac{V_e}{g} = 4.44\,\frac{V_e}{g}\,. \tag{5.15}$$

We see that the period is directly proportional to the forward speed. Thus, for a forward speed of 200 km/hr ($V_e$ = 55.6 m/s) the period is 25 sec, whereas for a forward speed of 800 km/hr the period is 100 sec. Thus the period of the phugoid oscillation is very long compared with that of the short period oscillation. Eq. (5.14) shows that, with the given assumptions, the motion is undamped.

Here again it must be emphasized that the theory of the phugoid oscillation, as given here, is only a rough approximation. In practice there is, in general, damping due to the drag; the static stability of the aircraft also affects the phugoid motion. This is considered in detail in the following chapter.

## PROBLEMS

1. An aircraft model is pivoted in a wind tunnel and is able to oscillate with one degree of freedom in pitch. Describe the characteristics of the resulting motion. How does the tail size affect the damping and frequency of the motion?

2. Discuss the change in the short period mode when the aircraft is statically unstable.

3. An aircraft is describing a vertical circle with constant incidence. Show that, when drag and pitching motions are neglected, the radius $R$ of the circle is given by $R = 3V_e^2/2g$, where $V_e$ is the speed for steady level flight.

4. By considering a wing in gliding flight, obtain a relation for the glide speed $V$ and glide angle, and show that the speed increases as the wing weight increases. If such a wing is launched at a speed slightly different from $V$, show that it will follow a wave-like trajectory, and find the period of oscillation for this motion. (In this part of the question, the drag and the inertia in pitch may be neglected, and the wing incidence may be taken to be constant). What effect will the drag have on (i) the oscillation, and (ii) the trajectory?

5. Show how the analysis of the simple phugoid oscillation is altered if the variation of air density with height is allowed for.

# Chapter 6
# LONGITUDINAL DYNAMIC STABILITY

## INTRODUCTION

In Chapter 2 the equations of longitudinal symmetric motion were derived. We saw that, provided the disturbances (in speed or in incidence) were small, the equations could be reduced to a set of linear differential equations with constant coefficients in terms of $u$ (the increment in forward velocity along $Ox$), $w$ (the increment in downward velocity along $Oz$) and $\theta$ (the angle of pitch about $Oy$), and their derivatives with respect to $\hat{t}$ (the non-dimensional aerodynamic time).

There are two main uses of these equations: (i) to determine whether the aircraft is stable for small disturbances, and (ii) to determine the motion (or response) of the aircraft following some small disturbance. In this chapter we shall deal with the first of these problems, i.e. the determination of the longitudinal dynamic stability of the aircraft.

More generally, we shall determine the types of motion occurring in a dynamical system following some small disturbance, investigating the stability, damping and frequency of the various modes of motion. We shall derive the necessary and sufficient conditions for a dynamical system to be stable and we shall discuss certain critical stability criteria, showing the close connection between static and dynamic stability. Finally, we shall see how these criteria can be presented in a simple manner in the form of stability diagrams enabling the physical nature of the criteria to be made manifest.

## STICK FIXED DYNAMIC STABILITY

The equations of motion (2.113) to (2.116) are linear differential equations in the variables $\hat{u}$, $\hat{w}$ and $\theta$. To determine the stick fixed dynamic stability of the aircraft we put $\eta_1 = 0$, i.e. the elevator is kept fixed in its original trimmed position.

In the usual way of solving such a system of linear differential equations with constant coefficients, we assume that there is a solution of the form

$$\hat{u} = u/V_e = \rho_1 e^{\lambda \hat{t}}, \quad \hat{w} = w/V_e = \rho_2 e^{\lambda \hat{t}} \text{ and } \theta = \rho_3 e^{\lambda \hat{t}}, \qquad (6.1)$$

where $\rho_1$, $\rho_2$, $\rho_3$ and $\lambda$ are constants, and $\hat{t} = t/\tau$.

Substituting in Eqs. (2.113) to (2.116), and cancelling throughout by $e^{\lambda\hat{t}}$, we obtain the three equations

$$(\lambda + x_u)\rho_1 + (x_{\dot{w}}\lambda + x_w)\rho_2 + (x_q\lambda + \hat{g}_1)\rho_3 = 0,$$

$$z_u\rho_1 + [(1 + z_{\dot{w}})\lambda + z_w]\rho_2 + [(z_q - 1)\lambda + \hat{g}_2]\rho_3 = 0,$$

$$m_u\rho_1 + (m_{\dot{w}}\lambda + m_w)\rho_2 + (\lambda^2 + m_q\lambda)\rho_3 = 0.$$

These equations have the trivial solution $\rho_1 = \rho_2 = \rho_3 = 0$; this solution, which corresponds to zero deviations, is not of interest. For certain values of $\lambda$, these equations will be satisfied by non-zero values of $\rho_1$, $\rho_2$ and $\rho_3$. To find these values of $\lambda$, we eliminate $\rho_1$, $\rho_2$ and $\rho_3$ from these equations, and derive the determinantal, or characteristic, equation for $\lambda$, given by

$$\begin{vmatrix} \lambda + x_u & x_{\dot{w}}\lambda + x_w & x_q\lambda + \hat{g}_1 \\ z_u & (1+z_{\dot{w}})\lambda + z_w & (z_q - 1)\lambda + \hat{g}_2 \\ m_u & m_{\dot{w}}\lambda + m_w & \lambda^2 + m_q\lambda \end{vmatrix} = 0. \tag{6.2}$$

This is a quartic equation in $\lambda$ and is written

$$A_1\lambda^4 + B_1\lambda^3 + C_1\lambda^2 + D_1\lambda + E_1 = 0, \tag{6.3}$$

where $A_1$, $B_1$, $C_1$, $D_1$, $E_1$ are constants given by

$$A_1 = 1 + z_{\dot{w}}, \tag{6.4}$$

$$B_1 = x_u(1 + z_{\dot{w}}) + z_w - x_{\dot{w}}z_u + (1 + z_{\dot{w}})m_q + (1 - z_q)m_{\dot{w}}, \tag{6.5}$$

$$\left.\begin{aligned} C_1 = {} & x_u z_w - x_w z_u + [x_u(1 + z_{\dot{w}}) + z_w - x_{\dot{w}}z_u]m_q + \\ & + [x_u(1 - z_q) + x_q z_u - \hat{g}_2]m_{\dot{w}} + (1 - z_q)m_w - \\ & - [x_{\dot{w}}(1 - z_q) + x_q(1 + z_{\dot{w}})]m_u, \end{aligned}\right\} \tag{6.6}$$

$$\left.\begin{aligned} D_1 = {} & (x_u z_w - x_w z_u)m_q + (\hat{g}_1 z_u - \hat{g}_2 x_u)m_{\dot{w}} + \\ & + [x_u(1 - z_q) + x_q z_u - \hat{g}_2]m_w - \\ & - [x_w(1 - z_q) + x_q z_w + \hat{g}_1(1 + z_{\dot{w}}) - \hat{g}_2 x_{\dot{w}}]m_u, \end{aligned}\right\} \tag{6.7}$$

$$E_1 = (\hat{g}_1 z_u - \hat{g}_2 x_u)m_w - (\hat{g}_1 z_w - \hat{g}_2 x_w)m_u. \tag{6.8}$$

We note that $z_{\dot{w}}(= -Z_{\dot{w}}/\mu_1)$ is small compared with unity. Thus, from Eq. (6.4), $A_1 > 0$.

## THE GENERAL SOLUTION OF THE EQUATIONS OF MOTION

Equation (6.3) will have four roots $\lambda_1$, $\lambda_2$, $\lambda_3$ and $\lambda_4$ which may be real or complex. The general solution of the equations of motion is then given by

$$\hat{u} = k_{11}e^{\lambda_1\hat{t}} + k_{12}e^{\lambda_2\hat{t}} + k_{13}e^{\lambda_3\hat{t}} + k_{14}e^{\lambda_4\hat{t}} \tag{6.9}$$

$$\hat{w} = k_{21}e^{\lambda_1\hat{t}} + k_{22}e^{\lambda_2\hat{t}} + k_{23}e^{\lambda_3\hat{t}} + k_{24}e^{\lambda_4\hat{t}} \tag{6.10}$$

and

$$\theta = k_{31}e^{\lambda_1\hat{t}} + k_{32}e^{\lambda_2\hat{t}} + k_{33}e^{\lambda_3\hat{t}} + k_{34}e^{\lambda_4\hat{t}} \tag{6.11}$$

The ratios $k_{1s} : k_{2s} : k_{3s}$ ($s$ = 1, 2, 3, 4) can be determined from the equations of motion (2.113) to (2.116), and their absolute values can be determined from the initial conditions. Methods of obtaining the general solution of the equations of motion are discussed in Chapter 7, where we consider the response of an aircraft following some small disturbance. Here we are only considering the stability of the motion, and for this we do not need to know the values of the $k$'s.

When the characteristic equation (6.3) has a pair of complex roots $-r \pm is$, we write Eq. (6.9) in the form

$$\hat{u} = p_{11}e^{-r\hat{t}}\cos s\hat{t} + p_{12}e^{-r\hat{t}}\sin s\hat{t} + k_{13}e^{\lambda_3\hat{t}} + k_{14}e^{\lambda_4\hat{t}}$$

and similarly for Eqs. (6.10) and (6.11).

## TYPES OF MOTION CORRESPONDING TO THE ROOTS OF THE CHARACTERISTIC EQUATION

From Eqs. (6.9) to (6.11) we see that the motion will be composed of four different modes corresponding to the four roots of the characteristic equation. Each of these roots can give rise to one of four types of motion, depending on whether the particular root is real or complex (see Fig. 6.1).

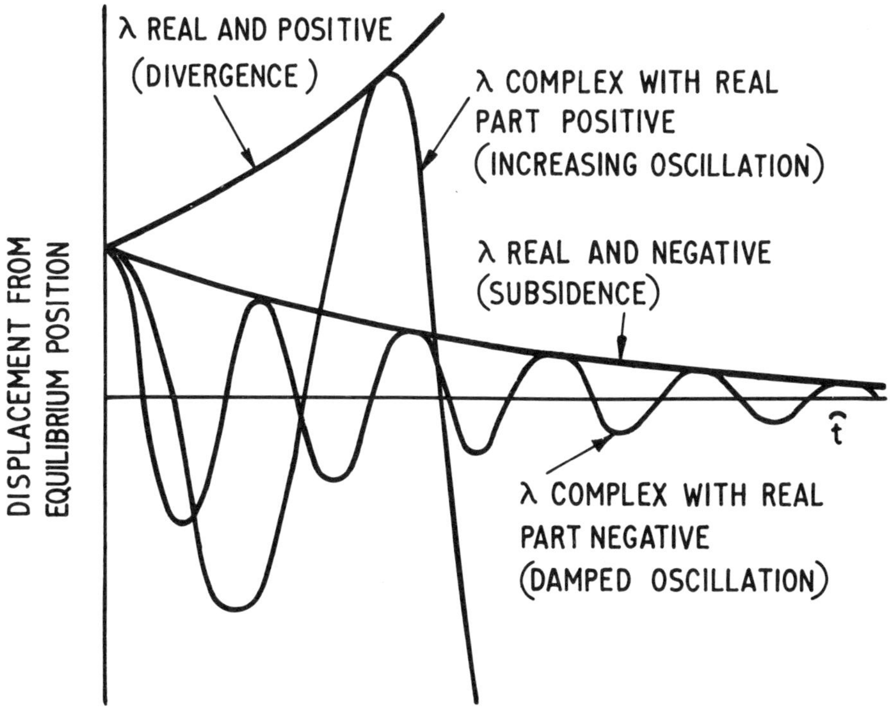


Fig. 6.1 Types of motion corresponding to the roots of the characteristic equation

When $\lambda$ is real and positive, the constituent ($\hat{u}$, $\hat{w}$, $\theta$ or their derivatives with respect to $\hat{t}$) of the disturbed motion increases steadily with time and tends to infinity, as shown by Eq. (6.1); this is called a *divergence*. When $\lambda$ is real and negative, the constituent decreases with time, tending asymptotically to zero; this is called a *subsidence*. When $\lambda$ is complex, we write

$$\lambda = -r + \mathrm{i}s, \tag{6.12}$$

where $r$ and $s$ are real. Now the coefficients occurring in the characteristic equation are real constants, and thus the equation will have another root

$$\lambda = -r - \mathrm{i}s.$$

The two modes corresponding to the roots $-r \pm \mathrm{i}s$ can be combined to give

$$\hat{u} = \sigma_1 e^{-r\hat{t}} \cos s\hat{t} + \sigma_2 e^{-r\hat{t}} \sin s\hat{t}, \tag{6.13}$$

where $\sigma_1$ and $\sigma_2$ are real constants, and similarly for $\hat{w}$ and $\theta$.

Thus, when $r$ is positive (i.e. $\lambda$ complex with real part negative), the constituent of the disturbed motion is a *damped oscillation*, tending to zero. When $r$ is negative (i.e. $\lambda$ complex with real part positive), the constituent of the disturbed motion is an *increasing oscillation* tending to $\pm\infty$ as $\hat{t} \to \infty$.

When $\lambda$ is zero, the original displacement persists undamped; when $\lambda$ is complex with zero real part, there is simple harmonic motion.

When the roots of the characteristic equation are known, the damping and period can be obtained immediately. If the root $\lambda$ is real and positive, the time $t_d$ (in seconds) to double amplitude is, from Eq. (6.1),

$$t_d = \frac{\log_e 2}{\lambda}\,\tau, \tag{6.14}$$

where, from (2.101),

$$\tau = m/\tfrac{1}{2}\rho_e V_e S = V_e C_L/g \cos\Theta_e . \tag{6.15}$$

If the root $\lambda$ is real and negative, the time $t_{\frac{1}{2}}$ (in seconds) to half-amplitude is given by

$$t_{\frac{1}{2}} = \frac{\log_e 2}{(-\lambda)}\,\tau . \tag{6.16}$$

If $\lambda$ is complex and of the form (6.12), the period $T$ (in seconds) is, from Eq. (6.13),

$$T = \frac{2\pi}{s}\,\tau \tag{6.17}$$

and the time $t_{\frac{1}{2}}$ (in seconds) to half amplitude is

$$t_{\frac{1}{2}} = \frac{\log_e 2}{r}\,\tau . \tag{6.18}$$

When $r$ is negative (as in an undamped oscillation), the time $t_d$ (in seconds) to double amplitude is

$$t_d = \frac{\log_e 2}{(-r)}\,\tau . \tag{6.19}$$

## ANALYSIS OF THE ROOTS OF THE CHARACTERISTIC EQUATION

The complete solution of the equations of motion is needed when we are considering the response of an aircraft to arbitrary applied forces such as gusts, or to movement of the elevator. For the determination of stability, we need only consider the nature of the roots of the characteristic equation (6.3). A dynamical system is said to be stable when the constituents of the disturbed motion ultimately become vanishingly small. For the constituents given by Eqs. (6.9) to (6.11), we see that the conditions for stability are that *all* the real roots of the characteristic equation and the real parts of *all* the complex roots must be negative. The disturbed motion is said to be dynamically stable if it is compounded of subsidences or damped oscillations, and dynamically unstable if it contains a divergence or an increasing oscillation.

We have therefore either (i) to determine the roots of the characteristic equation by an exact or approximate method, or (ii) to show that there are no positive real roots and no complex roots with positive real parts. Various methods for determining the roots of the characteristic equation are given in Appendix 2. The coefficients $A_1$, $B_1$, $C_1$, $D_1$ and $E_1$ depend on the non-dimensional parameters which, in turn, depend on the steady flight conditions (e.g. speed and height), and thus we should investigate the stability of the aircraft under all conditions of flight.

For conventional aircraft the coefficients $D_1$ and $E_1$ in the characteristic equation are usually small compared respectively with $C_1$ and $C_1^2$ and, as shown in Appendix 2, we can approximately factorize Eq. (6.3) in the form

$$(A_1\lambda^2 + B_1\lambda + C_1)\left(\lambda^2 + \frac{C_1D_1 - B_1E_1}{C_1^2}\lambda + \frac{E_1}{C_1}\right) = 0 \qquad (6.20)$$

### The short period oscillation

In general, the equation

$$A_1\lambda^2 + B_1\lambda + C_1 = 0 \qquad (6.21)$$

will have a pair of complex roots, corresponding to the damped short period oscillation. As shown in Chapter 5, this motion involves mainly pitching motion with no change in forward speed. This will now be shown in an alternative manner.

Let us consider the equations of longitudinal symmetric motion when the effect of the change in forward speed is neglected. In addition, we assume that $z_q$ and $z_{\dot{w}}$ are zero, and that the term $\hat{g}_2\theta$ in Eq. (2.114) (arising from the gravity component) can be neglected in comparison with the other terms.

From Eqs. (2.114) and (2.115), omitting the terms in $\hat{u}$, we have

$$(\hat{D} + z_w)\hat{w} - \hat{q} + z_\eta\eta' = 0, \qquad (6.22)$$

$$(m_{\dot{w}}\hat{D} + m_w)\hat{w} + (\hat{D} + m_q)\hat{q} + m_\eta\eta' = 0, \qquad (6.23)$$

where $\hat{D} = d/d\hat{t}$.

As above, for stick fixed motion, $\eta' = 0$. To solve these equations we write

$$\hat{w} = \rho_2 e^{\lambda\hat{t}}, \qquad \hat{q} = \rho_4 e^{\lambda\hat{t}},$$

where $\rho_2$, $\rho_4$ and $\lambda$ are constants. Eliminating $\rho_2$ and $\rho_4$, we see that the characteristic equation for $\lambda$ is given by

$$\begin{vmatrix} \lambda + z_w & -1 \\ m_{\dot{w}}\lambda + m_w & \lambda + m_q \end{vmatrix} = 0.$$

Thus the characteristic equation has been reduced to the quadratic

$$\lambda^2 + B_1'\lambda + C_1' = 0, \tag{6.24}$$

where $B_1' = z_w + m_q + m_{\dot{w}}$

and $C_1' = z_w m_q + m_w$.

Comparing these expressions with those for $B_1$ and $C_1$ in Eqs. (6.5) and (6.6), we find in practice that $B_1' \simeq B_1$ and $C_1' \simeq C_1$, the other terms in these equations being small.

From Eqs. (6.4) to (6.6), if we consider only terms arising from the pitching moments alone, and neglect downwash lag,

$$A_1 \simeq 1,$$

$$B_1 \simeq m_q = -M_q/i_y,$$

and $$C_1 \simeq m_w = -\mu_1 M_w/i_y,$$

i.e. using the results of Chapter 3,

$$B_1 = a_1 \bar{V}_T l_T/\bar{\bar{c}} i_y = a_1 \frac{S_T}{S} \frac{m l_T^2}{I_y} \tag{6.25}$$

and $$C = -\frac{2m^2\bar{\bar{c}}}{\rho_e S I_y} \frac{\partial C_m}{\partial \alpha}. \tag{6.26}$$

From Eq. (6.21), with $A_1 = 1$,

$$\lambda = -\frac{B_1}{2} \pm i\sqrt{\left(C_1 - \frac{B_1^2}{4}\right)}.$$

Thus, if $\lambda = -r \pm is$,

$$r = \frac{B_1}{2}$$

and $$s = \sqrt{\left(C_1 - \frac{B_1^2}{4}\right)}.$$

The time $t_{\frac{1}{2}}$ to half-amplitude is, from Eq. (6.18),

$$\left.\begin{aligned} t_{\frac{1}{2}} &= \frac{\log_e 2}{r}\tau = \frac{\log_e 2}{r} \frac{m}{\frac{1}{2}\rho_e V_e S} \\ &= \frac{4 \log_e 2}{B_1} \frac{m}{\frac{1}{2}\rho_e V_e S} = 4(\log_e 2) \frac{I_y}{\rho_e V_e S_T a_1 l_T^2} \end{aligned}\right\} \tag{6.27}$$

in agreement with Eq. (5.8).

The period $T$ in seconds is, from Eq. (6.17),

$$\left.\begin{aligned} T &= \frac{2\pi}{s}\,\tau = \frac{2\pi}{s}\,\frac{m}{\frac{1}{2}\rho_e V_e S} \\ &= 2\pi\left[\frac{\rho_e V_e^2 S\bar{\bar{c}}}{2I_y}\left(-\frac{\partial C_m}{\partial \alpha}\right) - \frac{\rho_e{}^2 V_e{}^2 S_T{}^2 a_1{}^2 l_T{}^4}{16\ I_y{}^2}\right]^{-\frac{1}{2}} \end{aligned}\right\} \tag{6.28}$$

in agreement with Eq. (5.9).

The phugoid (long period) oscillation

Consider now the second factor in Eq. (6.20). The equation

$$\lambda^2 + \frac{C_1 D_1 - B_1 E_1}{C_1^2}\,\lambda + \frac{E_1}{C_1} = 0 \tag{6.29}$$

will, in general, have a pair of complex roots corresponding to the lightly damped long period oscillation (the phugoid oscillation).

We see, from Eqs. (6.6) to (6.8) that, if the static margin is very large (i.e. $m_w$ large) and if we ignore the drag (i.e. take $x_u = 0$), and take $\Theta_e$ to be zero,

$$C_1 \simeq m_w = -\mu_1 M_w / i_y \ ,$$

$$E_1 \simeq \hat{g}_1 z_u m_w = C_L Z_u \bullet \mu_1 M_w / i_y \ ,$$

and the coefficient of $\lambda$ in Eq. (6.29) will be very small.

Thus $\qquad E_1/C_1 = -C_L Z_u = 2C_L{}^2 \ ,$

where compressibility effects have been ignored.

Equation (6.29) then becomes

$$\lambda^2 + 2C_L{}^2 = 0,$$

i.e. $$\lambda = \pm\, i\,\sqrt{2}C_L \ . \tag{6.30}$$

The phugoid period $T$ in seconds is, from Eq. (6.17),

$$T = \pi\,\sqrt{2}\,\frac{V_e}{g}\ , \tag{6.31}$$

in agreement with Eq. (5.15).

The phugoid motion is analysed in greater detail in reference 1, where it is shown that, when the effect of drag is included, the damping of the oscillation increases as the drag coefficient increases.

The nature of the roots corresponding to the phugoid and to the short period oscillation is further illustrated later in this chapter, in connection with stability diagrams.

## DYNAMIC STABILITY CRITERIA

In general, it is not necessary to find the exact values of the roots in order to determine whether an aircraft is stable or not, but merely to show that the roots satisfy certain stability criteria.

Criteria for stability have been expressed in a convenient determinantal form by Hurwitz and by Routh (ref. 2). It is shown that, for the quartic equation

$$A_1\lambda^4 + B_1\lambda^3 + C_1\lambda^2 + D_1\lambda + E_1 = 0, \tag{6.32}$$

where $A_1 > 0$, the complete set of conditions for stability is that all the test functions $T_1$, $T_2$, $T_3$, $T_4$ must be positive, where

$$T_1 = B_1 , \tag{6.33}$$

$$T_2 = \begin{vmatrix} B_1 & A_1 \\ D_1 & C_1 \end{vmatrix} = B_1C_1 - A_1D_1 , \tag{6.34}$$

$$T_3 = \begin{vmatrix} B_1 & A_1 & 0 \\ D_1 & C_1 & B_1 \\ 0 & E_1 & D_1 \end{vmatrix} = B_1C_1D_1 - B_1^2E_1 - A_1D_1^2 , \tag{6.35}$$

$$T_4 = \begin{vmatrix} B_1 & A_1 & 0 & 0 \\ D_1 & C_1 & B_1 & A_1 \\ 0 & E_1 & D_1 & C_1 \\ 0 & 0 & 0 & E_1 \end{vmatrix} = E_1T_3. \tag{6.36}$$

Now $$T_3 = D_1T_2 - B_1^2E_1 , \tag{6.37}$$

and thus $T_2$ must be positive if $T_3$, $D_1$ and $E_1$ are positive. Also, in the characteristic equation (6.3), $A_1 > 0$.

Thus the simplest set of stability criteria for the characteristic equation (6.3) is

$$B_1 > 0 \tag{6.38}$$

$$D_1 > 0 \tag{6.39}$$

$$E_1 > 0 \tag{6.40}$$

and $$R = T_3 = B_1C_1D_1 - B_1^2E_1 - A_1D_1^2 > 0. \tag{6.41}$$

These criteria for stability are also derived in Appendix 2. For a conventional aircraft, $B_1$ and $D_1$ are always positive, and the critical criteria are $E_1 > 0$ and $R > 0$. We note that, when Eqs. (6.38) to (6.40) are satisfied, Eq. (6.41) implies that $C_1 > 0$; however, the converse is not true.

## ROUTH'S DISCRIMINANT

The function $R$, defined in Eq. (6.41), is called Routh's discriminant; we shall consider some of its properties. Suppose that the characteristic equation has a pair of equal and opposite roots of the form $\lambda = \pm\beta$, where $\beta$ may be complex. Substituting in Eq. (6.3), we have

$$A_1\beta^4 + B_1\beta^3 + C_1\beta^2 + D_1\beta + E_1 = 0$$

and $$A_1\beta^4 - B_1\beta^3 + C_1\beta^2 - D_1\beta + E_1 = 0,$$

i.e. $$A_1\beta^4 + C_1\beta^2 + E_1 = 0 \qquad (6.42)$$

and $$B_1\beta^3 + D_1\beta = 0,$$

i.e. $$B_1\beta^2 + D_1 = 0, \quad \text{as } \beta \neq 0 \text{ in general.} \qquad (6.43)$$

Substituting in Eq. (6.42),

$$B_1C_1D_1 - B_1^2E_1 - A_1D_1^2 = R = 0.$$

Thus, when the characteristic equation has a pair of equal and opposite roots, $R = 0$. We note that this can occur (i) with equal and opposite real roots and (ii) with two roots of the form $\pm is$, where $s$ is real. From Eq. (6.43) we see that, if $B_1$ and $D_1$ are of the same sign, $\beta^2$ is negative, and hence $\beta = \pm is$. Thus, if $B_1$ and $D_1$ are of the same sign and $R = 0$, the characteristic equation will have a conjugate pair of imaginary roots $\lambda = \pm is$; if $B_1$ and $D_1$ are of opposite sign and $R = 0$, the characteristic equation will have equal and opposite real roots.

## THE COEFFICIENT $E_1$

We have seen above that, for a stable aircraft, $E_1$ is positive. When $E_1 < 0$, it is easily seen that the characteristic equation has at least one positive real root, representing a divergence. When $E_1 = 0$, the characteristic equation has a zero root, representing a state of neutral stability. We note that the condition $E_1 > 0$ in isolation gives no information about the stability, except that it is not neutral.

When $A_1$, $B_1$, $C_1$, $D_1$ and $E_1$ are all positive, the characteristic equation (6.3) can have no positive real roots. Then all the roots correspond either to subsidences or to oscillations. Thus from Fig. 6.1, when $A_1$, $B_1$, $C_1$, $D_1$ and $E_1$ are all positive, the constituent of the disturbed motion tends *initially* to decrease (when the system is freed without initial velocity); thus the system is statically stable. $E_1 > 0$ is said to be the critical criterion for static stability.

In horizontal flight, $\hat{g}_1 = C_L$ and $\hat{g}_2 = 0$, and, from Eq. (6.8),

$$E_1 = \hat{g}_1(z_u m_w - z_w m_u) = (\mu_1/i_y)C_L\ (Z_u M_w - Z_w M_u). \qquad (6.44)$$

Now, from Eq. (3.27), the static margin stick fixed $K_n$ is given by

$$K_n = \frac{1}{2C_L(\partial C_L/\partial\alpha)}\ (Z_u M_w - Z_w M_u). \qquad (6.45)$$

Thus $$E_1 = 2(\mu_1/i_y)C_L^2(\partial C_L/\partial\alpha)\ K_n. \qquad (6.46)$$

We see that the coefficient $E_1$ is proportional to (and has the same sign as) the static margin stick fixed.

## STABILITY DIAGRAMS

It is often useful to investigate the dependence of the stability of an aircraft upon some parameter such as $C_L$, $\mu_1$ (the aircraft longitudinal relative density parameter), the static margin or the rotary damping coefficient $M_q$. This is most easily illustrated by means of a stability diagram, in which we vary one or more parameters, keeping the rest fixed.

Figures 6.2 and 6.3 (from ref. 3) show two stability diagrams in which the real and imaginary parts of the roots of the characteristic equation are plotted against $m_w$, where

$$m_w = -\mu_1 M_w / i_y \ .$$

Compressibility effects have been neglected, and thus, from Eq. (3.23),

$$m_w = \frac{\mu_1}{i_y} \frac{dC_L}{d\alpha} K_n . \tag{6.47}$$

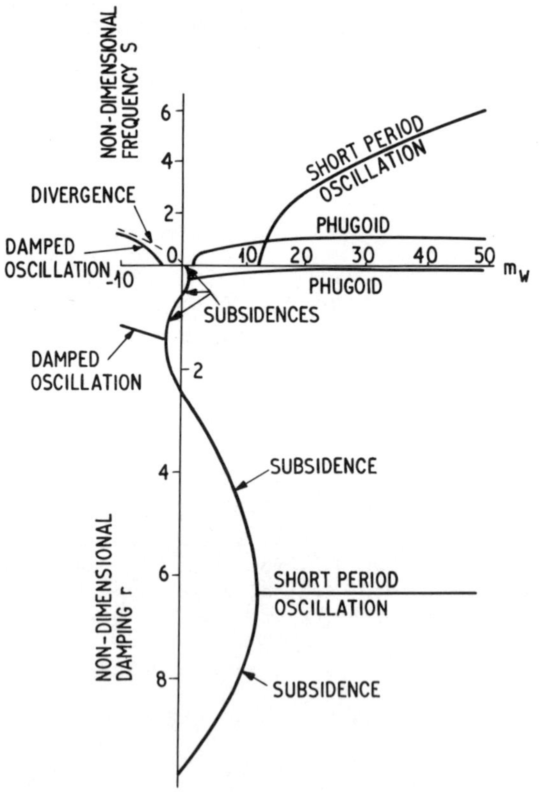


Fig. 6.2 Stability diagram, $C_L = 1$. (Based on data in R. & M. 2078).

Figure 6.2 is drawn for $C_L = 1$, and Fig. 6.3 for $C_L = 0.25$. For simplicity we consider horizontal flight (i.e. $\Theta_e = 0$).

The characteristic equation (6.3) is of the fourth degree, and thus for any value of $m_w$ there will be four roots; we see that these may be (i) four real roots, (ii) two real roots and a pair of conjugate complex roots, or (iii) two pairs of conjugate complex roots. As $m_w$ varies, the coefficients $C_1$, $D_1$ and $E_1$ will vary continuously, and the real and imaginary parts of the roots of the characteristic equation will also vary continuously.

If the roots of the characteristic equation are of the form $\lambda = -r \pm is$, then, as shown in Eq. (6.17), the period $T$ (in seconds) is given by

$$T = \frac{2\pi}{s}\,\tau = \frac{2\pi}{s}\,\frac{V_e C_L}{g}\,, \qquad \text{(since } \Theta_e = 0)$$

and the time $t_{\frac{1}{2}}$ (in seconds) to half-amplitude is

$$t_{\frac{1}{2}} = \frac{\log_e 2}{r}\,\tau = \frac{\log_e 2}{r}\,\frac{V_e C_L}{g}\,.$$

Thus $r$ is the non-dimensional damping and $s$ is the non-dimensional frequency. We see that points in the upper part of Figs. 6.2 and 6.3 (corresponding to values of $s$) will occur only when there are complex roots. The 'branch points' in these

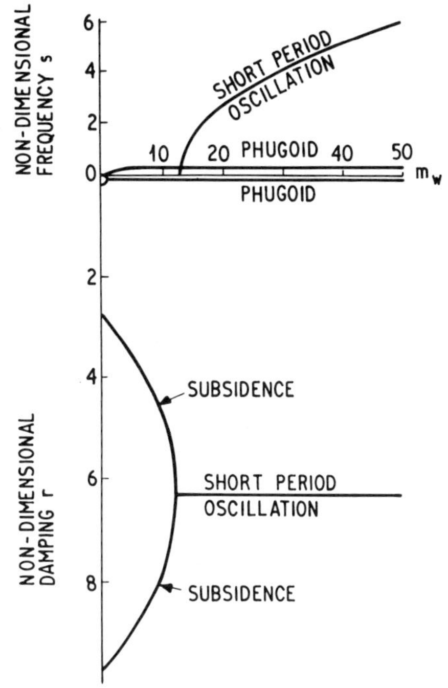


Fig. 6.3 Stability diagram, $C_L = 0.25$. (Based on data in R. & M. 2078)

diagrams correspond to the cases of equal roots (with $s = 0$ for the corresponding pair of roots).

As shown above, for large positive values of the static margin (i.e. for large positive values of $m_w$, the characteristic equation has two pairs of complex roots, one pair corresponding to the damped short period oscillation, and the other pair to the lightly damped long period phugoid motion. For large positive values of the static margin, the roots of the characteristic equation corresponding to the short period oscillation are independent of the speed (and hence of $C_L$), while the roots corresponding to the phugoid motion tend to the limit $\pm i\sqrt{2C_L}$, as shown in Eq. (6.30). We note the low value of the damping factor for the phugoid motion. The damping could be improved by using an auto-pilot.

We see that, as $m_w$ decreases, the short period oscillation breaks up into two subsidences, the damping of one of which increases as $m_w$ decreases, while the damping of the other decreases. From Eq. (6.5), $B_1$ (which equals the sum of the damping factors $r$) is independent of $m_w$. For even smaller positive values of $m_w$ the phugoid oscillation also breaks up into two subsidences. We note that, for the values of the parameters chosen (based on a conventional aircraft), the aircraft is stable for all positive values of the static margin. When $m_w = 0$, i.e. when the static margin is zero, the characteristic equation has one zero root and three real negative roots. For the given system, when $m_w = 0$, $B_1$, $C_1$ and $D_1$ are all positive, and $E_1$ is zero.

For small negative values of $m_w$ (when the aircraft is statically unstable, i.e. when the static margin is negative), there is a divergence and three subsidences, while for more negative values of $m_w$ two of these subsidences coalesce, to give a damped oscillation.

## ROOT-LOCUS PLOT

An alternative method of showing the variation of the roots of the characteristic equation, as one parameter varies, is to use a root-locus plot (ref. 4) in which the real and imaginary parts of the four roots $(-r \pm is)$ are plotted on the one diagram. In such a diagram, all the real roots will, of course, lie on the $r$ axis. Instability (i.e. either a divergence or an increasing oscillation) is indicated by points for which $(-r) > 0$.

The results of Fig. 6.2 have been replotted in Fig. 6.4 in the form of a root-locus plot, showing the variation of the four roots as $m_w$ varies from large positive to small negative values. The lines $AB$ and $CB$ show how the frequency of the short period oscillation decreases as $m_w$ decreases, the damping being practically unchanged. As in Fig. 6.2, for the given aircraft, for $0 < m_w < 12.4$, this oscillation breaks up into a pair of subsidences, which, in the root-locus plot, are indicated by points on the $r$ axis. Similarly, the lines $DE$ and $FE$ show how the phugoid frequency varies; in practice it would be advisable to reproduce this part of the diagram to a larger scale to get a better degree of accuracy.

As shown above, for negative values of $m_w$ (i.e. for a statically unstable aircraft), there is a divergence (corresponding to points on $OG$, while, as $m_w$ decreases still further, a new damped oscillation appears (corresponding to points on $JK$ and $JL$).

A possible advantage of the root-locus plot is that the number of cycles to half-amplitude is easily obtained from it. Thus,

$$\text{the number of cycles to half-amplitude} = t_{\frac{1}{2}}/T = \frac{\log_e 2}{2\pi}\frac{s}{r} = 0.1103\ s/r.$$

## LONGITUDINAL DYNAMIC STABILITY OF HIGH SPEED AIRCRAFT

The stability and control characteristics are affected by the changes both in the aerodynamic loading and in the geometry of high speed aircraft (see ref. 5). One of the most important effects is that of the aft movement of the aerodynamic centre. For a wing in a two-dimensional flow, the aerodynamic centre is at the half-chord point in supersonic flow, as compared with the quarter-chord point in subsonic flow. This leads to a large increase in both the static and manoeuvre margins. This effect is lessened on sweptback wings, where aeroelastic bending can give a forward shift of the aerodynamic centre.

With increasing subsonic Mach number, both the lift curve slope and the tail downwash tend to increase, thus decreasing the effectiveness of the tailplane. At transonic and supersonic speeds there may be a considerable change in the downwash at the tail (depending on the location of the tail with respect to the wing downwash field).

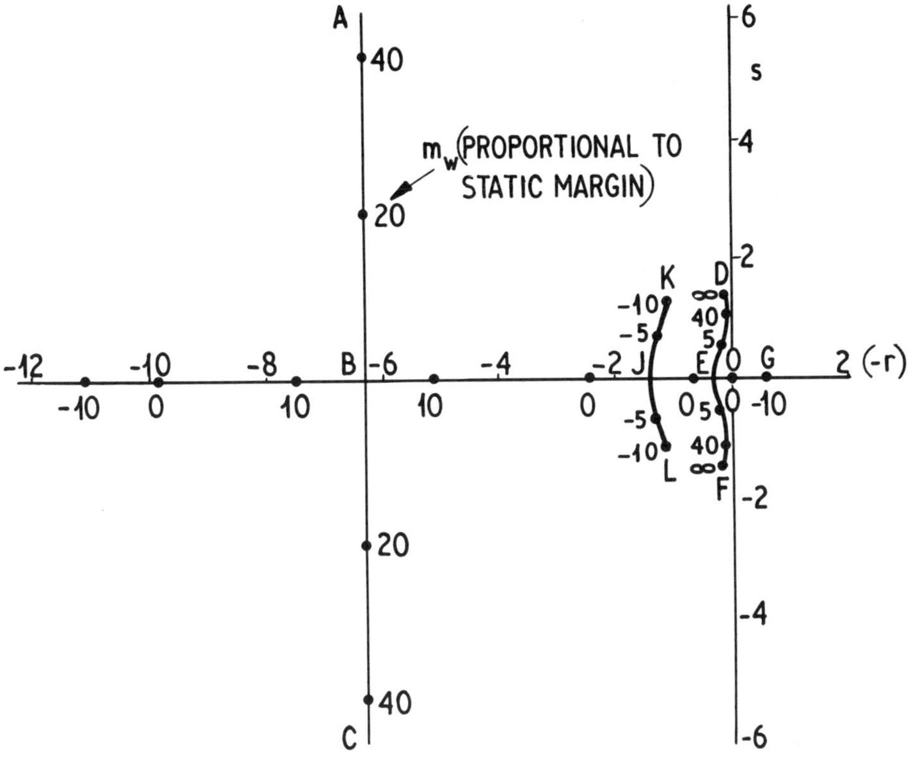


Fig. 6.4 Root-locus plot, $C_L = 1$. (Based on data in R. & M. 2078).

The static stability and control is also affected by the generally shorter tail arm, which often leads to the use of an all-moving tailplane (to provide the large changes in trim associated with the increase in static margin in the transonic speed range).

The long slender fuselage of many high speed aircraft increases the pitching inertia, which alters their longitudinal dynamic stability characteristics. The wings of these aircraft tend to be of low aspect ratio, and thus wing-body interference effects become more important.

Many aircraft (especially tail-less ones) suffer a loss of damping in pitch at transonic speeds. At these speeds, some aircraft have experienced a violent nose-up tendency at high angles of incidence; this is known as pitch-up, and is considered further in Part IV.

As shown in Chapter 5, the period of the short period oscillation decreases as the speed increases. This is partly off-set at supersonic speeds by a decrease in the lift curve slope. At low supersonic speeds, the phugoid damping may be low. This loss of damping is due to the decrease in $x_u$. From Eq. (3.16), if the variation of thrust is neglected,

$$x_u = -X_u = 2C_D + V_e \partial C_D / \partial V.$$

As can be shown by linearized theory, for a flat plate in two-dimensional supersonic flow, $x_u$ is negative for $M < \sqrt{2}$. Effects of finite aspect ratio modify this result, but it remains true that, where changes of $C_D$ with Mach number are large (e.g. at transonic speeds) phugoid instability may occur due to inadequate damping.

## REFERENCES


1. LYON, H.M., TRUSCOTT, P.M., AUTERSON, E.I. and WHATHAM, J. A theoretical analysis of longitudinal dynamic stability in gliding flight. R. & M. 2075 (1942).

2. FULLER, A.T. *Stability of Motion.* A collection of early scientific papers by Routh, Clifford, Sturm and Bocher. Taylor & Francis Ltd. (1975).

3. NEUMARK, S. The disturbed longitudinal motion of an uncontrolled aircraft and of an aircraft with automatic control. R. & M. 2078 (1943).

4. GREENSITE, A.L. *Elements of Modern Control Theory.* Spartan Books (1970).

5. KUCHEMANN, D. *The Aerodynamic Design of Aircraft.* Pergamon Press (1978).


## PROBLEMS

1. What is meant by the characteristic equation? Discuss the types of motion corresponding to the roots of that equation.

   A system with two degrees of freedom has the dynamical equations

$$4\ddot{x} + 2\dot{x} + 6x + \ddot{y} + \dot{y} - 4y = 0,$$
$$\ddot{x} + 2\dot{x} + 3x + 5\ddot{y} + 4\dot{y} + ky = 0,$$

   where $k$ is a constant. Find the characteristic equation and determine the value of $k$ in order that the system may have neutral stability. When $k$ has this value, show that the characteristic equation has the real root $\lambda = -1$, as well as the zero root. Find the two remaining roots. (Remove the known factors of the equation.)

2. Describe an approximate method of finding the factors of the characteristic equation for longitudinal stability. How can this approximation be improved? Find the roots of the characteristic equation given by

$$\lambda^4 + 29\lambda^3 + 249\lambda^2 + 70\lambda + 35 = 0.$$

3. For the data of the previous question, find the periods of oscillation and the time to half-amplitude, the aircraft mass being 20,000 kg, wing area 70 m$^2$, speed 200 m/s, altitude 5,000 m. Verify that the phugoid period is approximately $\pi\sqrt{2}\, V_e/g$ seconds.

4. Discuss the use of (i) stability diagrams and (ii) root-locus plots. Replot the stability diagrams given in reference 3 in the form of root-locus plots.

5. Discuss the influence of the performance of an aircraft on (i) its planform and (ii) its stability characteristics.

# Chapter 7
# LONGITUDINAL RESPONSE

## INTRODUCTION

In Chapter 6 the solution of the equations of longitudinal symmetric motion was discussed, together with the nature and significance of the roots of the characteristic equation. We saw how the effect on the roots of the variation of a given parameter could be shown by a stability diagram. However, such diagrams indicate only the damping factors and frequencies of the disturbed motion and do not enable us to follow the actual course of the motion, especially in its early stages. Thus the roots of the characteristic equation tell us nothing about the degree of 'overswing' which may occur following some disturbance.

In response theory we are concerned with the actual motion following a disturbance, e.g. an up-gust or a prescribed movement of the elevator. In this chapter we consider various theoretical methods of solving the equations of motion (the classical method and operational methods). An example of the complete solution of these equations is given. We consider in detail the response of an aircraft to application of the elevator. Finally we discuss the use of automatic controls ('active controls') and show how both the dynamic stability and the response can be improved by their use.

In response calculations we compute the complete solutions of the equations of motion and determine the components of motion ($u$, $w$, $\theta$ and $q$, for a longitudinal disturbance) as functions of time. As in the development of the equations of motion in Chapter 2, we assume that all the deviations are small. In the following paragraphs we shall discuss briefly various methods of solving the equations of motion (2.113) to (2.115), when the terms in $\eta'$ are zero, or some known function of $\hat{t}$ (the non-dimensional aerodynamic time).

## CLASSICAL METHOD OF SOLUTION

In the classical method (described in refs. 1 and 2) we express the solution as the sum of a particular integral and a complementary function.

For a set of linear equations such as (2.113) to (2.115), the complementary function can be expressed in the form

$$\hat{u} = \sum A_n e^{\lambda_n \hat{t}}\ , \quad \hat{w} = \sum B_n e^{\lambda_n \hat{t}}\ , \quad \theta = \sum C_n e^{\lambda_n \hat{t}}\ , \tag{7.1}$$

the summation being taken over all the roots $\lambda_n$ ($n = 1$ to 4) of the characteristic equation (6.3). $A_n$, $B_n$ and $C_n$ are arbitrary constants.

The form of the particular integral will depend on the forcing function, represented by the terms in $\eta'$. If $\eta'$ is a constant or a simple function of time, the particular integral can easily be found (see refs. 1 and 2).

The arbitrary constants are finally found from the initial conditions. We see that this requires a knowledge of the roots of the characteristic equation.

If the roots $\lambda_n$ are complex, we may replace the complementary function, given in Eq. (7.1), by expressions such as

$$\hat{u} = \alpha_1 e^{-r_1 \hat{t}} \cos(s_1 t + \varepsilon_1) + \alpha_2 e^{-r_2 \hat{t}} \sin(s_2 t + \varepsilon_2), \tag{7.2}$$

where the roots of the characteristic equation are $-r_1 \pm is_1$, $-r_2 \pm is_2$ and $\alpha_1$, $\alpha_2$, $\varepsilon_1$, $\varepsilon_2$ are arbitrary constants.

## OPERATIONAL METHODS

In these methods the differential equations are first transformed to a set of simultaneous algebraic equations in the transformed variables. These equations (which involve the initial conditions) are readily solved for each of the transformed variables, and the final step is to apply an inverse transformation to determine the behaviour of the real variables (such as $\hat{u}$, $\hat{w}$ and $\theta$) as functions of $\hat{t}$.

The Laplace transform method is discussed in reference 3. For a known function $f(\hat{t})$, the Laplace transform $\bar{f}(p)$ is defined by

$$\bar{f}(p) = \int_0^\infty e^{-p\hat{t}} f(\hat{t})\, d\hat{t} \tag{7.3}$$

Consider a system satisfying the linear differential equation

$$a_n \frac{d^n x}{d\hat{t}^n} + a_{n-1} \frac{d^{n-1} x}{d\hat{t}^{n-1}} + \ldots + a_1 \frac{dx}{d\hat{t}} + a_0 x = f(\hat{t}), \quad \hat{t} > 0, \tag{7.4}$$

where $a_0$, $a_1$, ..., $a_n$ are constants. We require the solution which has $x_0$, $\hat{D}x_0$, ... for the values of $x$, $\hat{D}x$, ... when $\hat{t} = 0$, where $\hat{D} = d/d\hat{t}$.

Let $\phi(\hat{D}) \equiv a_n \hat{D}^n + a_{n-1}\hat{D}^{n-1} + \ldots + a_1\hat{D} + a_0.$

Multiplying Eq. (7.4) by $e^{-p\hat{t}}$ and integrating from 0 to $\infty$, using Eq. (7.3), we find, if $p$ is a positive constant,

$$\begin{aligned} \phi(p)\bar{x} &= a_1 x_0 + a_2(p x_0 + \hat{D}x_0) + \ldots \\ &\quad + a_n(p^{n-1}x_0 + p^{n-2}\hat{D}x_0 + p^{n-3}\hat{D}^2 x_0 + \ldots) + \bar{f}(p). \end{aligned} \tag{7.5}$$

Equation (7.5) is the transformed (or subsidiary) equation corresponding to the given differential equation with the given initial conditions. If $f(\hat{t})$ is a simple function of $\hat{t}$, its transform $\bar{f}(p)$ can easily be found as a rational function of $p$.

Tables of such transforms are given in reference 3.

From Eq. (7.5), $\bar{x}$ can be expressed as a rational algebraic function of $p$, which can be resolved into a number of partial fractions. The corresponding equation for $x$ as a function of $\hat{t}$ can then be found by applying the inverse transformation to each of these partial fractions.

We have considered a single differential equation. The same procedure applies to a set of linear differential equations with constant coefficients. The final solution will, of course, be identical with that obtained by the classical method, but the work involved is usually much shorter.

Another very similar operational method is that due to Heaviside. In this method the transform $F(D)$ of a known function $f(\hat{t})$ is given by

$$F(D) = D\int_0^\infty e^{-D\hat{t}} f(\hat{t})\, dt\ . \tag{7.6}$$

In all the above methods it is necessary to determine the roots of the characteristic equation. Various methods for finding these roots are given in Appendix 2.

## RESPONSE OF AN AIRCRAFT TO A SIMPLE INITIAL SYMMETRIC DISTURBANCE

Consider the response to an initial disturbance $u = u_0$ (corresponding to an initial change in forward speed), the initial values of the other variables $w$, $\theta$ and $q$ being zero. Applying the Laplace transform method to Esq. (2.113) to (2.115), we obtain the subsidiary equations

$$\left.\begin{aligned} (p + x_u)\bar{u} + (x_{\dot{w}}p + x_w)\bar{w} + (x_q p + \hat{g}_1)\theta &= \hat{u}_\circ - x_\eta\bar{\eta}' \\ z_u\bar{u} + [(1 + z_{\dot{w}})p + z_w]\bar{w} + [(z_q - 1)p + \hat{g}_2]\bar{\theta} &= -z_\eta\bar{\eta}' \\ m_u\bar{u} + (m_{\dot{w}}p + m_w)\bar{w} + (p^2 + m_q p)\bar{\theta} &= -m_\eta\bar{\eta}' \end{aligned}\right\} \tag{7.7}$$

where $\bar{u}$, $\bar{w}$, $\bar{\theta}$ and $\bar{\eta}'$ are the Laplace transforms of $\hat{u}$, $\hat{w}$, $\theta$ and $\eta'$, and $\hat{u}_0 = u_0/V_e$, $V_e$ being the aircraft speed in the undisturbed flight. Now the elevator is kept fixed, i.e. $\bar{\eta}' = 0$. Therefore,

$$\frac{\bar{u}}{\Delta_1} = \frac{\bar{w}}{\Delta_2} = \frac{\bar{\theta}}{\Delta_3} = \frac{\hat{u}_0}{\Delta}\ , \tag{7.8}$$

where

$$\Delta = \begin{vmatrix} p + x_u & x_{\dot{w}}p + x_w & x_q p + \hat{g}_1 \\ z_u & (1+z_{\dot{w}})p + z_w & (z_q-1)p + \hat{g}_2 \\ m_u & m_{\dot{w}}p + m_w & p^2 + m_q p \end{vmatrix} \tag{7.9}$$

and $\Delta_r$ ($r = 1$ to 3) are third order determinants derived from $\Delta$ by replacing the $r$th column of $\Delta$ by the coefficients of $\hat{u}_0$ appearing on the r.h.s. of Eq. (7.7) (i.e. by 1, 0, 0).

From Eq. (7.9) we see that $\Delta$ is a polynomial of the fourth degree in $p$. In fact, the equation $\Delta(p) = 0$ is identical with the determinantal or characteristic equation (6.2), $\lambda$ being replaced by $p$. If $p = \lambda_n$ ($n = 1$ to 4) are the roots of the equation $\Delta = 0$, we have, from Eq. (7.8),

$$\frac{\bar{u}}{\hat{u}_0} = \frac{\Delta_1(p)}{\Delta(p)} = \sum_{n=1}^{4} \frac{U_n}{p-\lambda_n} , \tag{7.10}$$

where $$U_n = \lim_{p\to\lambda_n} \frac{(p-\lambda_n)\Delta_1(p)}{\Delta(p)} = \frac{\Delta_1(\lambda_n)}{\Delta'(\lambda_n)} . \tag{7.11}$$

Now $$\int_0^\infty e^{-p\hat{t}} e^{\lambda_n \hat{t}}\, d\hat{t} = \frac{1}{p-\lambda_n}$$

and thus, taking inverse transforms, we find

$$\frac{u}{u_0} = \frac{\hat{u}}{\hat{u}_0} = \sum_{n=1}^{4} U_n e^{\lambda_n \hat{t}} , \tag{7.12}$$

which is the same form as Eq. (7.1). The corresponding expansions for $w/u_0$ and $V_e\theta/u_0$ can be obtained in like manner from Eq. (7.8).

For longitudinal motion, the roots of the determinantal equation $\Delta = 0$ are all complex. If $\lambda_1$ and $\lambda_2$ are a conjugate pair of complex roots, of the form $-r_1 \pm is_1$, we find that

$$U_1 = a_1 + ib_1 , \quad U_2 = a_1 - ib_1 ,$$

where $a_1$ and $b_1$ are real (this can be used as a check on the calculations). Then

$$U_1 e^{\lambda_1 \hat{t}} + U_2 e^{\lambda_2 \hat{t}} = 2(a_1 \cos s_1\hat{t} - b_1 \sin s_1\hat{t})\, e^{-r_1\hat{t}}$$

and similarly for the other pair of complex roots $\lambda_3$ and $\lambda_4$.

## EXAMPLE OF A COMPLETE SOLUTION

In reference 4, the equations have been solved for an aircraft subjected to simple initial disturbance, i.e. to initial disturbance $u_0$ in forward velocity or $w_0$ in downward velocity or $\theta_0$ in angle of pitch. In Fig. 7.1 (based on reference 4), $u/u_0$, $w/u_0$, $V_e\theta/u_0$ are plotted against the non-dimensional time $\hat{t}$, for an initial disturbance $u_0$. Similarly, in the same figure, $u/w_0$, $w/w_0$ and $V_e\theta/w_0$ are shown for an initial disturbance $w_0$, and $u/V_e\theta_0$, $w/V_e\theta_0$ and $\theta/\theta_0$ are shown for an initial disturbance $\theta_0$.

In this particular case, for slow flight ($C_L = 1$), the roots of the characteristic equation are

$\lambda = -6.33 \pm 5.30i$ (short period oscillation)

and $\lambda = -0.05 \pm 1.08i$ (lightly damped phugoid).

The coefficients for the various disturbances are given in Table 1.

The terms corresponding to the heavily damped short-period oscillation influence the behaviour only in the initial stages of the motion, after which the lightly damped phugoid oscillation persists. The amplitudes of the $u$ and $\theta$ curves are nearly equal in all cases, while that of the $w$ curves is much smaller. Thus the angle of incidence $w/V_e$ varies much less than the angle of pitch $\theta$ except in the initial response to the disturbance $w_0$. Larger variations in the angle of incidence may be expected with a smaller static margin. We note that the phase

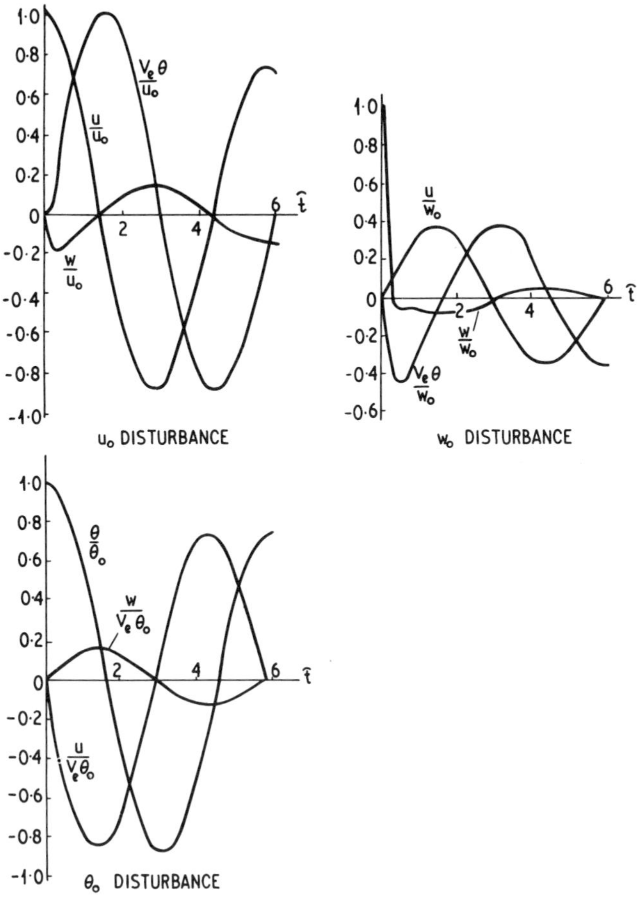


Fig. 7.1 Motion following an initial disturbance.
(Reproduced from R. & M. 2078 by S. Neumark). (Crown copyright).

Table 1

| | $e^{-6.33\hat{t}}$ $\cos 5.30\hat{t}$ | $e^{-6.33\hat{t}}$ $\sin 5.30\hat{t}$ | $e^{-0.05\hat{t}}$ $\cos 1.08\hat{t}$ | $e^{-0.05\hat{t}}$ $\sin 1.08\hat{t}$ |
|---|---|---|---|---|
| $u/u_0$ | +0.011 | -0.002 | +0.989 | -0.047 |
| $w/u_0$ | +0.179 | -0.167 | -0.179 | +0.004 |
| $V_e\theta/u_0$ | +0.160 | -0.030 | -0.160 | +1.078 |
| $u/w_0$ | +0.030 | +0.038 | -0.030 | +0.413 |
| $w/w_0$ | +0.993 | +0.337 | +0.007 | -0.074 |
| $V_e\theta/w_0$ | +0.440 | +0.545 | -0.440 | -0.120 |
| $u/V_e\theta_0$ | +0.001 | -0.001 | -0.001 | -0.914 |
| $w/V_e\theta_0$ | +0.004 | -0.029 | -0.004 | +0.165 |
| $\theta/\theta_0$ | +0.013 | -0.015 | +0.987 | +0.194 |

difference between $u$ and $w$ in the phugoid oscillation is nearly 180 degrees, while $\theta$ keeps nearly 90 degrees out of phase with either.

In this example we have assumed that, when an aircraft undergoes some sudden small disturbance, the aerodynamic forces immediately take on the values appropriate to steady flow conditions at the particular incidence. This is not strictly true for a wing meeting a sharp-edged up-gust; in that case, the flow is unsteady and the aerodynamic forces are no longer equal to their quasi-static values. This is discussed further in Chapter 8. As shown there, when unsteady flow effects are taken into account, there is a general reduction in the maximum value of the upward acceleration due to a given up-gust.

## RESPONSE OF AN AIRCRAFT TO APPLICATION OF THE ELEVATOR

When the elevator angle in changed from its initial trimmed position, a pitching moment acts on the aircraft. For a stable aircraft the response to application of the elevator can be divided into two stages. Firstly, there is a rapid change of incidence and rate of pitch while the speed remains practically unchanged, the aircraft finally settling down at a different trimmed incidence with a steady rate of pitch. This is followed by a lightly damped slow oscillation similar to the phugoid oscillation, in which there is little variation in incidence. Analysis of the initial rapid oscillation is of importance in determining how quickly the aircraft responds to a given movement of the elevator.

The response to a prescribed movement of the elevator can be found from the equations of motion (2.113) to (2.115), using the methods outlined earlier in this chapter. The elevator angle $\eta'$ is a given function of the non-dimensional time $\hat{t}$. We shall here adopt a simpler approximate method of analysis (assuming that the speed remains constant) and confine our attention to the first stage of the response. We shall assume that $z_q$ and $z_{\dot{w}}$ are zero, and that the term $\hat{g}_2\theta$ in Eq. (2.114) (arising from the gravity component) can be neglected in comparison with the other terms.

From Eqs. (2.114) and (2.115), omitting the terms in $\hat{u}$, we have

$$(\hat{D} + z_w)\hat{w} - \hat{q} + z_\eta\eta' = 0, \tag{7.13}$$

$$(m_{\dot{w}}\hat{D} + m_w)\hat{w} + (\hat{D} + m_q)\hat{q} + m_\eta\eta' = 0, \tag{7.14}$$

where $\hat{D} = d/d\hat{t}$, and $\eta'$ is the change in elevator angle.

The characteristic equation for this motion is the same as with controls fixed, and is given by Eq. (6.24),

$$\lambda^2 + B_1'\lambda + C_1' = 0, \tag{7.15}$$

$$\left.\begin{aligned} \text{where} \quad B_1' &= z_w + m_q + m_{\dot{w}} \\ \text{and} \quad C_1' &= z_w m_q + m_w \,. \end{aligned}\right\} \tag{7.16}$$

Thus the response of the aircraft to the application of a constant elevator deflection has the same period and damping as that of the short period motion.

The normal acceleration $ng$ (positive upwards) is, from Chapter 2, with $\Theta_e = 0$,

$$ng = -\dot{w} + qU_e = -\frac{g}{C_L}(\hat{D}w - \hat{q}).$$

From Eqs. (7.13), (7.14) and (7.16), we see that, for a stable aircraft subjected to application of the elevator, the final steady values of the incidence $\hat{w}$, the rate of pitch $\hat{q}$ and the normal acceleration $ng$ are given by

$$\hat{w} = -(m_\eta + z_\eta m_q)\ \Delta\eta/C_1', \tag{7.17}$$

$$\hat{q} = -(m_\eta z_w - m_w z_\eta)\ \Delta\eta/C_1' \tag{7.18}$$

and

$$ng = -g(m_\eta z_w - m_w z_\eta)\ \Delta\eta/C_L C_1', \tag{7.19}$$

where $\Delta\eta$ is the final steady elevator deflection and $C_1'$ is given by Eq. (7.16).

In Eq. (7.19), the term in $z_\eta$ is usually small compared with that in $m_\eta$ and thus

$$ng \simeq -\frac{g m_\eta z_w\ \Delta\eta}{C_L C_1'} = -\frac{\mu_1 g M_\eta Z_w\ \Delta\eta}{i_y C_L C_1'}. \tag{7.20}$$

Now, from Eqs. (3.19) and (3.43),

$$Z_w \simeq -\mathrm{d}C_L/\mathrm{d}\alpha \tag{7.21}$$

and

$$M_\eta = -a_2 \bar{V}_T. \tag{7.22}$$

Also, from the definition of the stick fixed manoeuvre margin $H_m$, given in Chapter 1,

$$H_m = -\bar{V} a_2\ \Delta\bar{\eta}/n\ C_L. \tag{7.23}$$

Therefore, from Eqs. (7.20)-(7.22), we find

$$C_1' = -\frac{\mu_1}{i_y}\frac{\mathrm{d}C_L}{\mathrm{d}\alpha}\, a_2 \bar{V}_T \frac{\Delta\eta}{nC_L},$$

i.e. on using Eq. (7.23) and neglecting the difference between $\bar{V}$ and $\bar{V}_T$,

$$C_1' \simeq \frac{\mu_1}{i_y}\frac{\mathrm{d}C_L}{\mathrm{d}\alpha} H_m. \tag{7.24}$$

From the characteristic equation (7.15), we should expect a divergence in pitch to occur when $C_1' < 0$, i.e. when the manoeuvre margin is negative. There would then be a rapid growth of the normal acceleration.

In reference 5 the response of an aircraft has been calculated for various prescribed movements of the elevator, for various values of $m_w$ (proportional to the static margin) and $m_q$. In Figs. 7.2 and 7.3 the change in incidence $w/V_e$ and the rate of pitch $q$ are plotted against $\hat{t}$ for various values of $m_w$ and $m_q$ for a linearly applied elevator (giving a linear growth in the applied pitching moment up to $\hat{t} = \frac{1}{2}$, the elevator angle being constant thereafter). We see that the greater the static stability of the aircraft, the sooner will the incidence reach its steady value. As would be expected, the greater the damping in pitch the sooner the rate of pitch reaches its steady value.

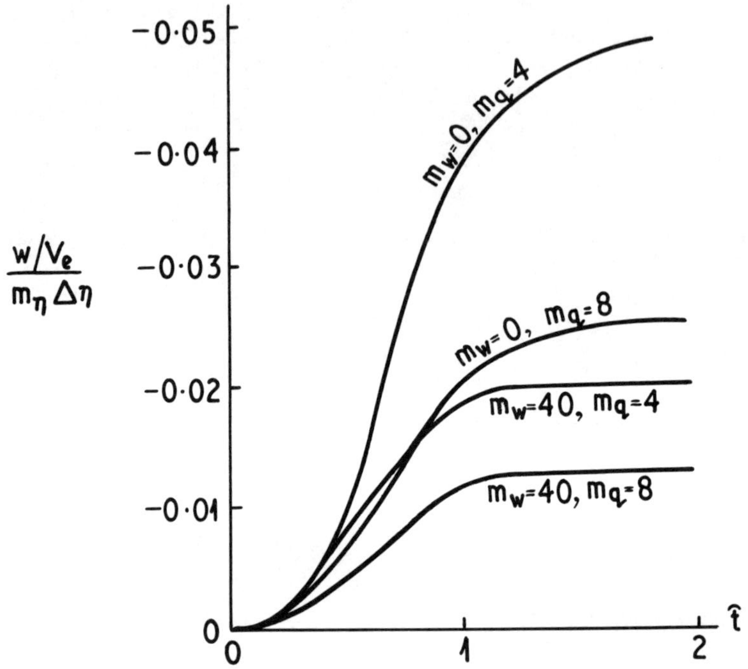


Fig. 7.2 Change in wing incidence due to application of elevator (linear increase of elevator deflection to $\Delta\eta$ at $\hat{t} = \frac{1}{2}$)

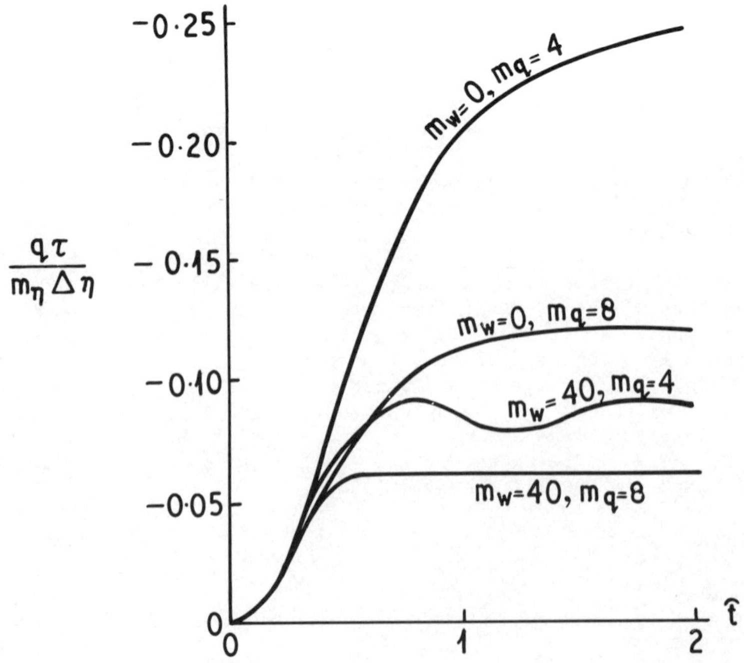


Fig. 7.3 Rate of pitch due to application of elevator (linear increase of elevator deflection to $\Delta\eta$ at $\hat{t} = \frac{1}{2}$)

## ARTIFICIAL STABILITY AND AUTOMATIC CONTROL

As shown both in this chapter and in the preceding one, the stability and response characteristics of an aircraft (without automatic control), at a given speed and height, are determined completely by the layout of the aircraft (including its mass distribution). There are, however, various ways in which both the stability and the response can be varied without further change of plan-form.

One way is by altering the mass distribution at various stages of the flight (e.g. by shifting the fuel); this affects the position of the c.g., and is thus a means of preventing the static margin from becoming unacceptably large (e.g. in the change from subsonic to supersonic speeds).

Another way is by means of an automatic control system in which the movement of the elevator is related to one or more components of the flight disturbance (e.g. forward speed, pitch) in such a way as to oppose the disturbance. In both of these methods, the aim is to improve artificially the stability and response of the aircraft.

Artificial stabilization is of importance whenever the natural stability is inadequate, for example, (i) for aircraft at flight speeds at which the static and manoeuvre margins may be negative, (ii) for tailless aircraft, for which the damping in pitch is often poor, and (iii) for aircraft with lightly damped (or undamped) phugoid modes. Conversely, the provision of such automatic controls (often called 'active controls') enables an aircraft to be designed with a greater range of c.g. positions, or with a smaller tailplane (thus reducing drag and increasing performance). The effect of such controls on aircraft design is discussed in reference 6.

## GENERAL THEORY OF AUTOMATIC CONTROL

In this chapter we have considered the response of an aircraft using the classical approach via the equations of motion. As shown in reference 4, the same approach can be used for automatically controlled aircraft by adding suitable control equations. We shall now consider the block diagram method used by 'systems engineers' in their analysis of automatic control systems; this method is particularly useful when the automatic control system is of a complicated nature (and the resulting characteristic equation is of high degree). The two approaches are complementary; thus, the classical approach can give a better idea of the transient motion (in all its components). In any case, a preliminary calculation to investigate possible simple control laws is advisable, further improvements in the control system being realized with the help of wind tunnel and flight test results.

## OPEN-LOOP SYSTEMS

So far we have only considered the case in which the magnitude of the control deflection did not depend upon the aircraft motion; this is an example of an open-loop system. Consider first the system shown in Fig. 7.4. This is a block diagram of a simple open-loop system in which input data $\theta_1$ (which might be signals from a gyroscope or accelerometer) are fed into a servo-system (e.g. an automatic control system which could include an amplifier and servo-motor); this produces an output $\theta_2$ (which might represent an elevator deflection). Such a system is an example of a *mechanism* and is termed open-loop because there is nothing in the mechanism which measures the output $\theta_2$ and takes some action if the result is not the desired one.

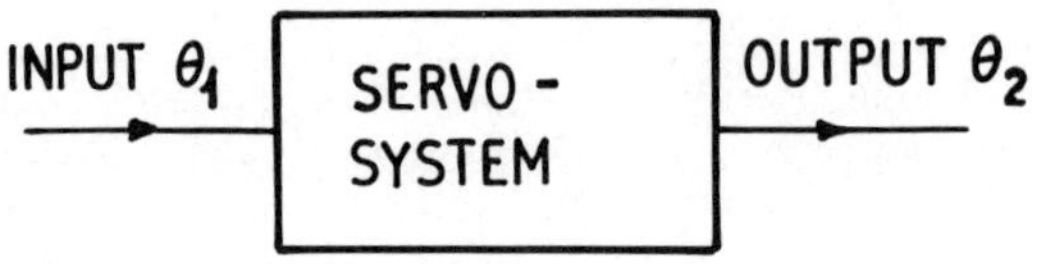


Fig. 7.4 Simple open-loop system

Both $\theta_1$ and $\theta_2$ will be functions of time. It is assumed that they are related by a 'control equation' of the form

$$a_n D^n \theta_2 + a_{n-1} D^{n-1} \theta_2 + \ldots + a_1 D\theta_2 + a_0 \theta_2 = b_n D^n \theta_1 + \ldots + b_0 \theta_1, \quad (7.25)$$

where $D = d/dt$, and all the $a$ and $b$ are constants. On taking Laplace transforms of both sides of Eq. (7.25), if the system starts from an undisplaced position at $t = 0$, we obtain

$$(a_n p^n + a_{n-1} p^{n-1} + \ldots + a_1 p + a_0)\bar{\theta}_2(p) = (b_n p^n + \ldots + b_0)\bar{\theta}_1(p), \quad (7.26)$$

where $p$ is the Laplace operator.

Equation (7.26) can be written in the form

$$\bar{\theta}_2(p) = G(p)\bar{\theta}_1(p), \quad (7.27)$$

where $$G(p) = (b_n p^n + b_{n-1} p^{n-1} + \ldots + b_0)/(a_n p^n + a_{n-1} p^{n-1} + \ldots + a_0). \quad (7.28)$$

$G(p)$ is the *transfer function* relating $\theta_1$ and $\theta_2$. Figure 7.5 is the symbolic representation of Eq. (7.27).

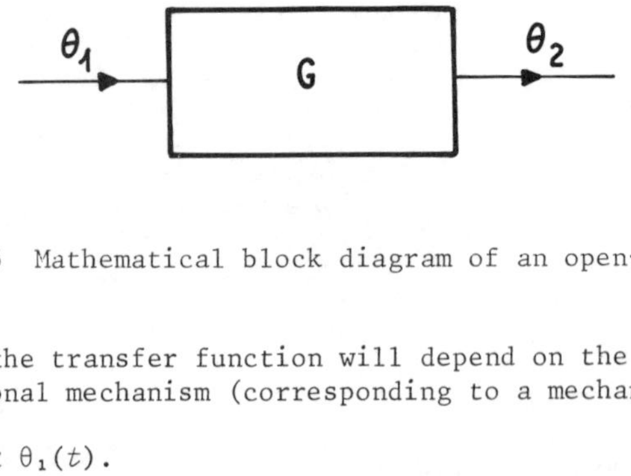


Fig. 7.5 Mathematical block diagram of an open-loop system

The precise form of the transfer function will depend on the type of servo-system. Thus, for a proportional mechanism (corresponding to a mechanical gearing),

$$\theta_2(t) = k\,\theta_1(t).$$

Taking Laplace transforms, we see that the equation becomes

$$\bar{\theta}_2(p) = k\,\bar{\theta}_1(p)$$

and thus $G = k$.

If two servo-systems are connected in cascade, as in Fig. 7.6, we have

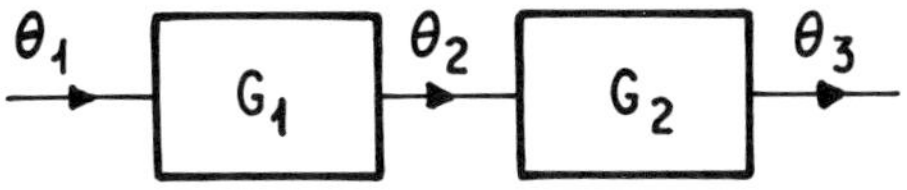


Fig. 7.6 Servo-systems in cascade

$$\bar{\theta}_2(p) = G_1(p)\,\bar{\theta}_1(p)\ ,$$

$$\bar{\theta}_3(p) = G_2(p)\,\bar{\theta}_2(p)$$

and thus $\bar{\theta}_3(p) = G_1G_2\,\bar{\theta}_1(p) = G_3\,\bar{\theta}_1(p),$ (7.29)

where $G_3 = G_1G_2$ .

The system shown in Fig. 7.6 can thus be represented by a single block diagram of the form of Fig. 7.5 with $\theta_2$ being replaced by $\theta_3$ and $G$ by $G_3$.

Figure 7.6 corresponds to the type of open-loop system we have considered above, in which $\theta_1$ could represent the pilot's stick deflection, $\theta_2$ the elevator deflection and $\theta_3$ the aircraft response (e.g. in pitch). $G_2$ is then the transfer function for the aircraft.

From Eq. (7.7), putting $u_0 = 0$, we find

$$\frac{\bar{u}}{\Delta_{1\eta}} = \frac{\bar{w}}{\Delta_{2\eta}} = \frac{\bar{\theta}}{\Delta_{3\eta}} = \frac{\bar{\eta}'}{\Delta}, \qquad (7.30)$$

where $\Delta$ is given by Eq. (7.9) and $\Delta_{r\eta}$ $(r = 1$ to $3)$ are third order determinants derived from $\Delta$ by replacing the $r$th column of $\Delta$ by the coefficients of $\bar{\eta}'$ appearing on the r.h.s. of Eq. (7.7) (i.e. by $-x_\eta$, $-z_\eta$, $-m_\eta$).

Equation (7.30) can be written in the alternative form

$$\left.\begin{aligned} \bar{u} &= T_{u\eta}\,\bar{\eta}'\ , \\ \bar{w} &= T_{w\eta}\,\bar{\eta}'\ , \\ \bar{\theta} &= T_{\theta\eta}\,\bar{\eta}'\ , \end{aligned}\right\} \qquad (7.31)$$

where $T_{u\eta}$, $T_{w\eta}$, $T_{\theta\eta}$ are the transfer functions relating $\bar{u}$, $\bar{w}$ and $\bar{\theta}$ with $\bar{\eta}'$.

Thus the aircraft response in pitch to an elevator angle $\eta$ can be represented by the block diagram (Fig. 7.7) where

$$T_{\theta\eta}(p) = \frac{\Delta_{3\eta}}{\Delta} = \frac{A_\theta p^2 + B_\theta p + C_\theta}{A_1p^4 + B_1p^3 + C_1p^2 + D_1p + E_1}\ . \qquad (7.32)$$

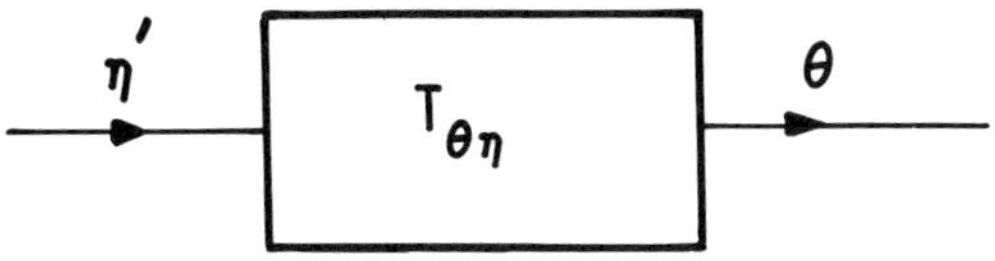


Fig. 7.7 Block diagram for aircraft response in pitch

In Eq. (7.32), the constants $A_\theta$, $B_\theta$ and $C_\theta$ are functions of the concise derivatives, as can be seen from Eq. (7.7); $A_1$, $B_1$, $C_1$, $D_1$ and $E_1$ are the coefficients occurring in the characteristic equation (6.3).

Similarly we find

$$T_{u\eta}(p) = \frac{\Delta_{1\eta}}{\Delta} = \frac{A_u p^3 + B_u p^2 + C_u p + D_u}{A_1 p^4 + B_1 p^3 + C_1 p^2 + D_1 p + E_1} \tag{7.33}$$

and

$$T_{w\eta}(p) = \frac{\Delta_{2\eta}}{\Delta} = \frac{A_w p^3 + B_w p^2 + C_w p + D_w}{A_1 p^4 + B_1 p^3 + C_1 p^2 + D_1 p + E_1} \,. \tag{7.34}$$

## CLOSED-LOOP SYSTEMS

In practice, whether under the control of a pilot or an auto-pilot, in many cases the control deflection applied (e.g. to restore the aircraft to a given steady state of flight) depends upon the deviation of the aircraft from the datum state, and the resulting system is known as a 'closed-loop' system, or a system with feed-back control. As shown below, a closed-loop flight control system can greatly improve the aircraft's flying qualities.

The essential requirement of closed-loop control is that the error between the state desired and the state existing is constantly measured, and action is taken to reduce it. A closed-loop system is thus an error-sensitive system.

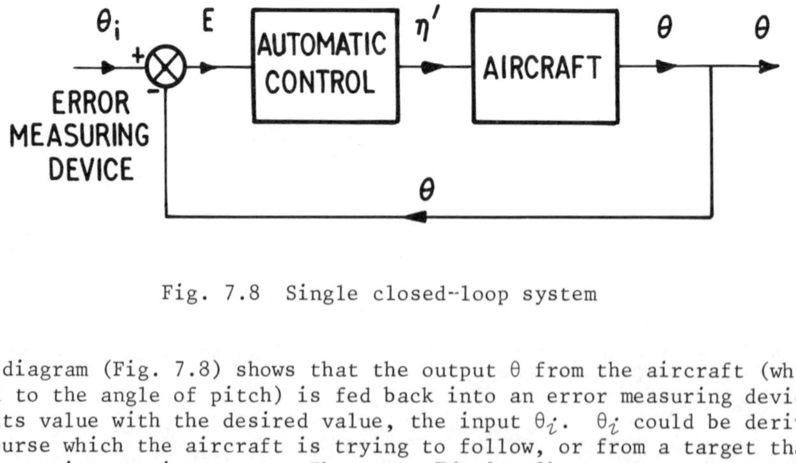


Fig. 7.8 Single closed-loop system

The block diagram (Fig. 7.8) shows that the output $\theta$ from the aircraft (which could correspond to the angle of pitch) is fed back into an error measuring device which compares its value with the desired value, the input $\theta_i$. $\theta_i$ could be derived from a fixed course which the aircraft is trying to follow, or from a target that the aircraft is trying to intercept. The error $E(= \theta_i - \theta)$ then becomes the new input to the control unit, which produces an output $\eta'$ (which could be the elevator angle). This, in turn, becomes the input for the aircraft system. The feed-back of the output $\theta$ to an earlier part of the system makes the system a closed-loop and provides the form of control that is the basic characteristic of any *servomechanism*. The control unit itself may have several components (and, possibly, its own inner feed-back loop) but these can all be grouped together in one box in the block diagram.

Treating each box as an open-loop system, we have (in terms of Laplace transforms)

$$\left.\begin{aligned} \bar{\eta}' &= G_c \bar{E} \\ \text{and} \qquad \bar{\theta} &= G_{\theta\eta} \bar{\eta}'. \end{aligned}\right\} \tag{7.35}$$

Thus $$\bar{\theta}/\bar{E} = G_{\theta\eta} G_c = G. \tag{7.36}$$

As shown above, $G$ is the open-loop transfer function.

Now $$E = \theta_i - \theta \tag{7.37}$$

and thus the output-input transfer function is

$$\frac{\bar{\theta}}{\bar{\theta}_i} = \frac{\bar{\theta}}{\bar{E} + \bar{\theta}} = \frac{G}{1 + G} . \tag{7.38}$$

Equation (7.38) can be put in the alternative form

$$(1 + G)\bar{\theta} = G \bar{\theta}_i. \tag{7.39}$$

We see also that

$$(1 + G)\bar{\eta}' = G_c \bar{\theta}_i . \tag{7.40}$$

A precisely similar analysis could be carried out using classical methods. Thus, for the control unit,

$$\phi_2(D)\eta' = \phi_1(D)E , \tag{7.41}$$

and, for the aircraft,

$$\phi_4(D)\theta = \phi_3(D)\eta', \tag{7.42}$$

where all the $\phi$ are polynomials in $D$ (= $d/dt$) with constant coefficients.

Therefore $\phi_2(D)\ \phi_4(D)\theta = \phi_2(D)\ \phi_3(D)\eta' = \phi_1(D)\ \phi_3(D)E$

and, from Eq. (7.37),

$$[\phi_2(D)\ \phi_4(D) + \phi_1(D)\ \phi_3(D)]\theta = \phi_1(D)\ \phi_3(D)\theta_i , \tag{7.43}$$

which is equivalent to Eq. (7.39).

To examine the motion of an automatically controlled aircraft set to fly with zero datum angle of pitch, we put $\theta_i = 0$. Then

$$[\phi_2(D)\ \phi_4(D) + \phi_1(D)\ \phi_3(D)]\theta = 0.$$

To solve this linear differential equation, put $\theta = \sigma e^{pt}$, where $\sigma$ and $p$ are constants. The characteristic equation is

$$\phi_2(p)\ \phi_4(p) + \phi_1(p)\ \phi_3(p) = 0. \tag{7.44}$$

Now, comparing Eq. (7.35) with Eqs. (7.41) and (7.42), we see that

$$G_c = \phi_1(p)/\phi_2(p)$$

and $$G_{\theta\eta} = \phi_3(p)/\phi_4(p).$$

Thus $$1 + G = 1 + G_c G_{\theta\eta} = [\phi_2(p)\phi_4(p) + \phi_1(p)\phi_3(p)]/\phi_2(p)\phi_4(p), \tag{7.45}$$

and, in the new notation, the characteristic equation for a closed-loop system is

$$\left.\begin{aligned} &1 + G(p) = 0, \\ \text{or}\quad &1 + G_c(p)G_{\theta\eta}(p) = 0. \end{aligned}\right\} \tag{7.46}$$

From Eq. (7.45), we see that, in general, the zeros of this equation are the same as those of Eq. (7.44).

## DYNAMIC STABILITY WITH SOME SIMPLE TYPES OF AUTOMATIC CONTROL

The main purpose of the longitudinal automatic control system is to maintain nearly constant values of speed, incidence and altitude in flight without human supervision. This is attained by relating the movement of the elevator to the components of the flight disturbance. As shown below, a suitable automatic control can greatly improve the damping of the phugoid motion.

We consider first some simple automatic controls in which the change in elevator angle $\eta'$ from the trimmed position is related to the angle of pitch $\theta$ (or rate of pitch) of the aircraft. From Eq. (7.35), with $\theta_i$ zero (the datum steady state), the control equation is

$$\bar{\eta}' = -G_c\bar{\theta}.$$

For simplicity we assume that $G_c$ is a linear function of $p$ (i.e. we consider proportional and rate controls). The control equation can then be written in the form

$$\bar{\eta}' = (g_\theta + g_{\dot{\theta}}\, p)\bar{\theta} , \tag{7.47}$$

where $g_\theta$ and $g_{\dot{\theta}}$ are autopilot parameters (gains or gearings) which are assumed to be constant for small deviations from steady flight conditions (but may vary with the steady state conditions).

The characteristic equation of the aircraft and automatic control system becomes

$$1 - (g_\theta + g_{\dot{\theta}}\, p)T_{\theta\eta} = 0 , \tag{7.48}$$

or, from Eq. (7.32),

$$\Delta(p) - (g_\theta + g_{\dot{\theta}}\, p)\Delta_{3\eta} = 0. \tag{7.49}$$

For the given type of automatic control, this is a quartic equation in $p$ of the form

$$\bar{A}_1 p^4 + \bar{B}_1 p^3 + \bar{C}_1 p^2 + \bar{D}_1 p + \bar{E}_1 = 0, \tag{7.50}$$

in which the coefficients differ from those of the characteristic equation (6.3) because of the terms in Eq. (7.49) due to the automatic control.

In the expressions for the coefficients of Eq. (7.50) all the terms arising from automatic controls contain products of the particular gain (or gearing ratio) $g$ and the elevator concise derivatives $x_\eta$, $z_\eta$ or $m_\eta$. Thus the control gain appropriate to a given aircraft depends upon the effectiveness of the elevator in the given flight condition; as shown below, it also depends upon the static margin of the aircraft.

On neglecting terms of small magnitude, we find

$$\bar{A}_1 = A_1, \tag{7.51}$$

and

$$\bar{B}_1 = B_1 + g_{\dot{\theta}}\, m_\eta . \tag{7.52}$$

Thus the value of $B_1$ is unaffected by a simple pitch attitude control (with $g_{\dot{\theta}} = 0$). Now $(-\bar{B}_1/\bar{A}_1)$ equals the sum of all the roots of Eq. (7.50), i.e. it equals the sum of all the damping factors. With such an automatic control, an increase in the damping of the long period oscillation is achieved at the expense of that of the short period one, making these two motions more nearly equally damped.

## STABILITY DIAGRAMS FOR SOME SIMPLE TYPES OF AUTOMATIC CONTROL

In reference 4, the effect of some simple types of automatic control is considered for an aircraft in slow horizontal flight ($C_L = 1.0$); the following discussion is based on the results of that reference.

The variation of the roots of the characteristic equation (7.50) with the strength of the control is shown by means of one-parameter stability diagrams, similar to those of Figs. 6.2 and 6.3. As in those figures, the real and imaginary parts of the roots $-r \pm is$ (i.e. the non-dimensional damping $r$ and the non-dimensional frequency $s$) are plotted in the lower and upper parts of Figs. 7.9 and 7.10. In alternative methods of presentation, such as root-locus plots, it is not always easy to see the critical value of any control gains.

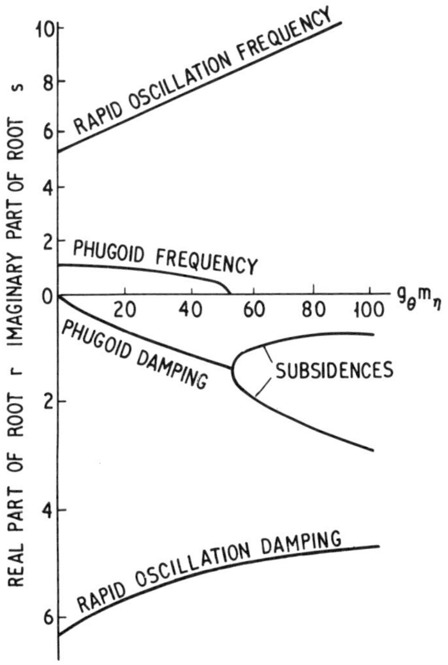


Fig. 7.9 Stability diagram for a statically stable aircraft with automatic control in θ. (Based on data in R. & M. 2078).

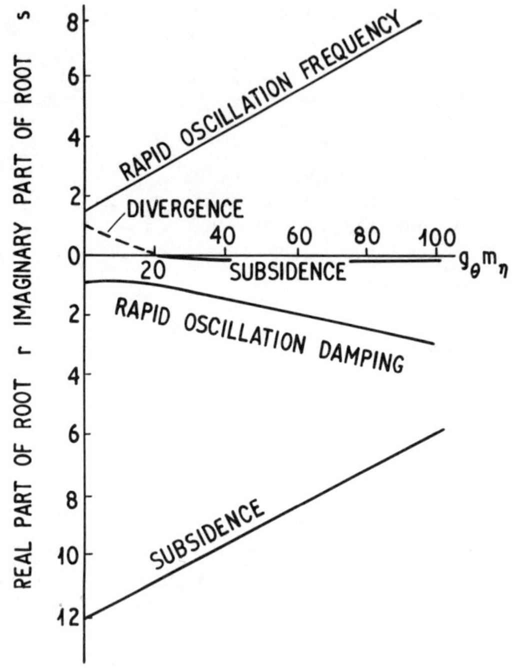


Fig. 7.10 Stability diagram for a statically unstable aircraft with automatic control in θ. (Based on data in R. & M. 2078).

## Simple pitch attitude control

We take $\eta' = g_\theta\ \theta$.

Figure 7.9 is drawn for slow flight of a statically stable aircraft. With increasing control strength (i.e. increasing values of $g_\theta m_\eta$), the damping of the short period oscillation decreases but there is a corresponding increase in the phugoid damping. Beyond a critical value of the control strength, the phugoid oscillation splits up into two subsidences, one of them showing a decrease in damping.

Figure 7.10 is drawn for a statically unstable aircraft. With no automatic control, the motion consists of a rapid oscillation, a subsidence and a divergence; as can be seen, the aircraft with automatic control becomes stable for moderate values of the control strength, the divergence being converted into a subsidence.

## Rate of pitch control

From the equations of motion, we find that the effect of a rate control such as

$$\eta' = g_{\dot\theta}\ \dot\theta$$

is the same as that of an increase in $m_q$, i.e. it increases the damping in pitch. This is a very effective control for an aircraft with deficient short period damping; however, the effect on the phugoid damping is not as marked as with a smple pitch or manometric control.

### Manometric control

The effect of feeding in the change of forward speed to the automatic control (a manometric type of control) can be analysed in a precisely similar manner to that already given.

We take $\eta' = g_u\,\hat{u} + g_{\dot{u}}\,d\hat{u}/d\hat{t}$

(where $g_u$ and $g_{\dot{u}}$ are both negative). The effect on the damping is very similar to that of the simple attitude control. This control (with both $u$ and $\dot{u}$ components) has a very beneficial effect on the phugoid damping, even for relatively small values of the control gain.

## RESPONSE WITH AUTOMATIC CONTROL

So far we have only considered the effect of the automatic control on the stability of the aircraft. Unlike many other control systems, an aircraft has more than one degree of freedom, and in longitudinal motion we are interested in the response in pitch, incidence and speed. The automatic control should be such that deviations from steady flight following some disturbance should be as small as possible. Thus, a properly designed automatic control should not produce a violent swing in pitch following a disturbance in forward speed.

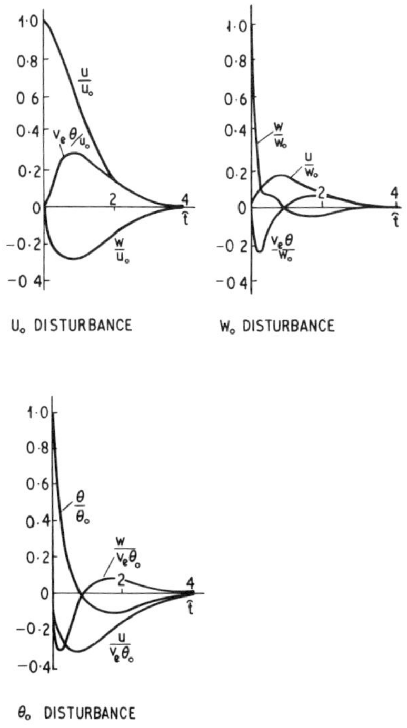


Fig. 7.11 Motion following an initial disturbance. Automatic control in θ. (Reproduced from R. & M. 2078 by S. Neumark). (Crown copyright).

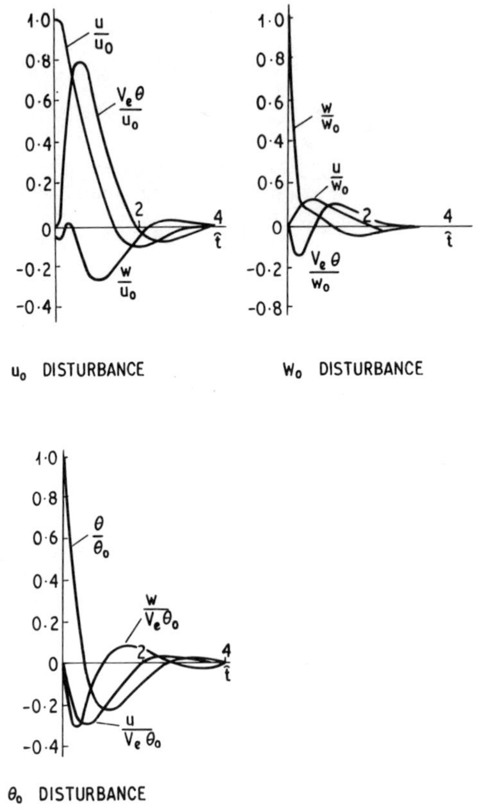


Fig. 7.12 Motion following an initial disturbance. Automatic control in $u$ and $\dot{u}$. (Reproducted from R. & M. 2078 by S. Neumark). (Crown copyright).

The response of an aircraft with automatic control can be calculated by the classical or operational methods outlined above. The responses to initial disturbances in $u$, $w$ and $\theta$ are shown in Fig. 7.11 for a simple attitude control (for $g_\theta m_\eta = 40$) and in Fig. 7.12 for a manometric control ($g_u m_\eta = g_{\dot{u}} m_\eta = -30$). The figures (based on data in reference 4) are drawn for slow flight of a statically stable aircraft (Fig. 7.1 gives the corresponding response for the aircraft without automatic control).

As already shown, the phugoid is highly damped. There are initial swings in $u$, $w$ and $\theta$, the course of these swings being different in the two types of control. We note particularly the initial swing in $\theta$ for the $u_0$ disturbance with manometric control; this type of control would give poor riding characteristics in bumpy weather with horizontal gusts. To overcome this defect, a combined attitude and speed control is sometimes used. The characteristics of such multi-loop control systems are discussed in reference 7.

## REFERENCES


1. INCE, E.L. *Ordinary Differential Equations*. Dover Publications (1956).

2. HEADING, J. *Ordinary Differential Equations*. Allen & Unwin (1971).

3. CARSLAW, H.S. and JAEGER, J.C. *Operational Methods in Applied Mathematics*. Oxford (1949).

4. NEUMARK, S. The disturbed longitudinal motion of an uncontrolled aircraft and of an aircraft with automatic control. R. & M. 2078 (1943).

5. BRYANT, L.W. and GANDY, R.W. The response of an aeroplane to application of the elevators. R. & M. 2275 (1950).

6. AGARD Conference Proceedings No. 260. *Stability and Control*. (1979).

7. McRUER, D., ASHKENAS, I. and GRAHAM, D. *Aircraft Dynamics and Automatic Control*. Princeton U.P. (1973).


## PROBLEMS

1. Derive formulae similar to those given in Eqs. (7.8) and (7.12) for the response of an aircraft to simple initial disturbances in $w$ and $\theta$.

2. Derive expressions for the response in incidence and in rate of pitch for an aircraft due to application of (i) a constant elevator deflection, and (ii) a linear deflection of the elevator up to the same value, the deflection being constant thereafter (the aircraft forward speed being assumed constant). Show that the response settles down to the same value (for a stable aircraft) in the two cases.

3. By considering the signs of the coefficients in the characteristic equation (6.3), show that instability can occur with a positive static margin if the manoeuvre margin is negative.

4. Using Eqs. (7.13) and (7.14), determine the response of an aircraft to sinusoidal oscillation of the elevator. Show that large amplitudes in both incidence and rate of pitch can occur if the damping of the short period mode is very small and the forcing frequency is close to that of the short period oscillation.

5. Draw the multi-loop block diagram for a closed-loop system in which both pitch $\theta$ and velocity $u$ are fed back into the automatic control. Hence determine the characteristic equation for the aircraft-automatic control system.

# Chapter 8
# RESPONSE TO GUSTS

## INTRODUCTION

When the longitudinal response of an aircraft was considered in Chapter 7, it was assumed that, when the aircraft underwent any disturbance (e.g. due to a horizontal or vertical gust, or to a pitching disturbance), the aerodynamic forces on the aircraft were determined by the instantanous incidence of the particular lifting surface. While this is approximately true for a gradually applied disturbance, it overestimates the loads for a sudden disturbance such as that due to a sharp up-gust. As shown in references 1 and 2, in such a disturbance there is a gradual growth of circulation, and hence of lift, the circulation finally reaching its steady state value. This leads in general to a reduction in the maximum value of the upward acceleration of the aircraft due to a given gust, and hence to a reduction in the load factor.

With the increase in aircraft speed and size, the loading due to gusts has become one of the important design criteria. The gust loading will, of course, depend on the structure of the gust, as well as on the response characteristics of the aircraft.

## SIMPLIFIED TREATMENT OF GUST LOADS, NEGLECTING UNSTEADY FLOW EFFECTS

We shall first neglect the pitching of the aircraft and its flexibility, and we shall consider an aircraft encountering a gradual gust, as shown in Fig. 8.1.

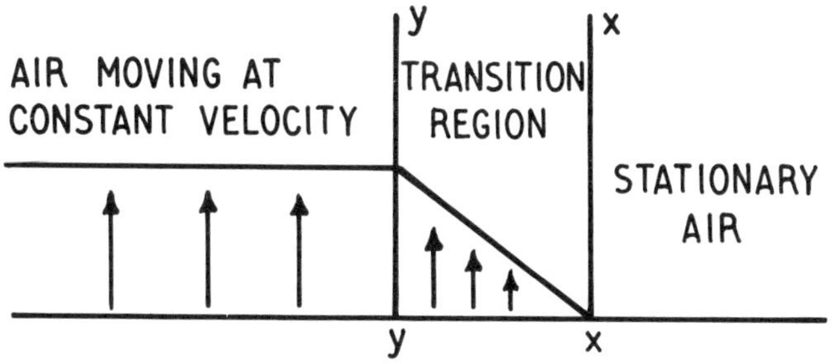


Fig. 8.1 A gradual gust

Here the air is assumed to be stationary to the right of $XX$, and to be moving with constant upward velocity to the left of $YY$; between $XX$ and $YY$, the velocity increases linearly from zero to its maximum value. We shall consider the gust to be two-dimensional, and we shall neglect the effects of the finite aspect ratio of the wing.

Thus we consider an aircraft, initially moving horizontally at constant forward speed $V_e$, encountering an up-gust $W$. Let $z$ be the vertical displacement (measured positive downward) of the c.g. of the aircraft from its initial position. Let $w$ be the downward velocity of the aircraft c.g.

Then the equation of vertical motion for the aircraft is

$$m\ddot{z} = m\dot{w} = -\Delta L, \tag{8.1}$$

where $m$ = mass of the aircraft
and $\Delta L$ = increment in lift due to gust.

The increase in the incidence of the wing is composed of two parts: (i) $W/V_e$ due to the gust, and (ii) $w/V_e$ due to the downward velocity $w$ of the aircraft.

If unsteady effects are neglected, the increment in lift is

$$\Delta L = \tfrac{1}{2}\rho_e V_e^2 Sa\left(\frac{W}{V_o} + \frac{w}{V_o}\right), \tag{8.2}$$

where $a$ is the lift curve slope of the aircraft in steady flight.

From Eqs. (8.1) and (8.2), the equation for the vertical motion of the aircraft is

$$m\ddot{z} = m\dot{w} = -\tfrac{1}{2}\rho_e V_e Sa(W + w)$$

or, in terms of the non-dimensional parameters defined in Chapter 2,

$$\frac{d\hat{w}}{d\hat{t}} = -a(\hat{W} + \hat{w}), \tag{8.3}$$

where
$\hat{w} = w/V_e$,
$\hat{W} = W/V_e$,
$\hat{t} = t/\tau$
and $\tau = m/\tfrac{1}{2}\rho_e V_e S$.

The downward vertical acceleration is given by

$$\ddot{z} = \frac{V_e}{\tau}\frac{d\hat{w}}{d\hat{t}}. \tag{8.4}$$

## Sharp-edged gust

In determining the gust load, we are mainly concerned with the maximum vertical acceleration developed by the aircraft due to a given gust. For a sharp-edged gust (i.e. a gust with no transition region),

$$W = W_{max}, \quad \text{a constant,}$$

and from Eq. (8.3), since $\hat{w}$ is zero initially,

$$\hat{w} = -\hat{W}_{max}(1 - e^{-a\hat{t}})$$

and
$$\frac{d\hat{w}}{d\tau} = -a\hat{W}_{max}e^{-a\hat{t}}. \tag{8.5}$$

Thus, for a sharp-edged gust, the maximum value of the acceleration occurs at the instant the aircraft meets the gust, and, from Eqs. (8.4) and (8.5),

$$\ddot{z}_{max} = -\frac{a}{\tau} W_{max}. \tag{8.6}$$

The increment $\Delta n$ in the load factor is given by

$$\Delta n = -\frac{\ddot{z}_{max}}{g} = \frac{a}{g\tau} W_{max} = \frac{\rho_e V_e S a}{2mg} W_{max} . \tag{8.7}$$

Gradual gust

We consider next the gradual gust (Fig. 8.1) and assume that

$$W = \frac{W_{max}}{\hat{t}_1}\hat{t}, \quad \hat{t} \le \hat{t}_1$$

and
$$W = W_{max}, \quad \hat{t} > \hat{t}_1.$$

The solution of Eq. (8.3) for the gradual gust is

$$\left.\begin{aligned} \frac{d\hat{w}}{d\hat{t}} &= -\frac{\hat{W}_{max}}{\hat{t}_1}(1 - e^{-a\hat{t}}), \quad \hat{t} \le \hat{t}_1 \\ \text{and} \quad \frac{d\hat{w}}{d\hat{t}} &= -\frac{\hat{W}_{max}}{\hat{t}_1}[e^{-a(\hat{t}-\hat{t}_1)} - e^{-a\hat{t}}], \quad \hat{t} > \hat{t}_1 \end{aligned}\right\} \tag{8.8}$$

The variation of the normal acceleration for a gradual gust (linear up to time $t_1$) is shown in Fig. 8.2. The maximum acceleration occurs when $t = t_1$ (corresponding to $\hat{t} = \hat{t}_1$), and is given by

$$\ddot{z} = -\frac{W_{max}}{\tau\hat{t}_1}(1 - e^{-a\hat{t}_1}). \tag{8.9}$$

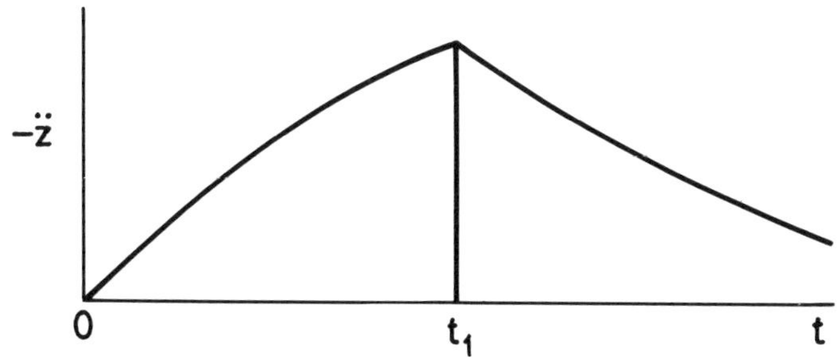


Fig. 8.2 Normal acceleration due to a gradual gust (linear to time $t_1$).

Gust alleviation factor

The gust alleviation factor $K$ is given by

$$K = \frac{\text{maximum downward acceleration of the aircraft for the given gust}}{\text{maximum downward acceleration in a sharp-edged gust of the same maximum value, no allowance being made for unsteady effects}}$$

$$= \frac{\text{maximum load}}{\frac{1}{2}\rho_e V_e S a\, W_{max}} \qquad (8.10)$$

From Eqs. (8.6) and (8.9), for a gradual gust (with no allowance for pitching or unsteady flow effects),

$$K = \frac{1}{a\hat{t}_1}\left(1 - e^{-a\hat{t}_1}\right) . \qquad (8.11)$$

The gust alleviation factor is plotted as a function of $a\hat{t}_1$ in Fig. 8.3.

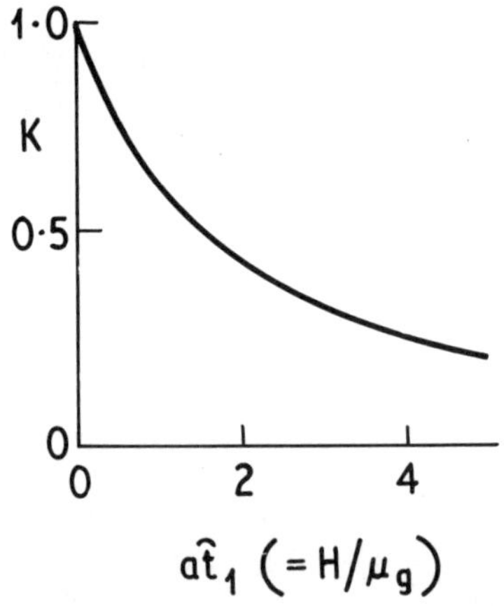


Fig. 8.3 Alleviation factor for response to a gradual gust (steady flow theory)

If $s_1$ is the gust length to attain its maximum intensity,

$$s_1 = V_e t_1$$

and

$$a\hat{t}_1 = \frac{a t_1}{\tau} = \frac{\rho_e S a \bar{\bar{c}}}{2m}\,\frac{s_1}{\bar{\bar{c}}} = \frac{H}{\mu_g} , \qquad (8.12)$$

where the density factor $\mu_g$ is given by

$$\mu_g = \frac{m}{\frac{1}{2}\rho_e S a \bar{\bar{c}}} , \qquad (8.13)$$

and $H = s_1/\bar{\bar{c}}$, the gust length to attain its maximum, in terms of the mean wing chord $\bar{\bar{c}}$. $H$ is sometimes called the gust gradient.

## GUST LOADS ALLOWING FOR THE EFFECTS OF UNSTEADY FLOW

In the above analysis we have not allowed for the effects of unsteady flow on the aerodynamic forces. Any change in the incidence of an aerofoil, or in its velocity, causes a change in circulation round the aerofoil, which, in turn, causes a vortex to be shed from the trailing edge of the aerofoil. These free vortices in the wake alter the flow round the aerofoil, and also the circulation.

These changes in circulation (and hence in lift) take place gradually, the circulation at any instant lagging behind that occurring in a steady flow. They also depend upon the time (or the distance travelled by the wing) since the change in incidence (or in velocity) took place. The theoretical treatment of the aerodynamic forces on a wing in non-uniform motion is summarized in reference 3.

When pitching is neglected and the aircraft is assumed to be rigid, the gust alleviation factor depends upon (i) the gust shape, (ii) the aspect ratio of the wing, and (iii) the density parameter $\mu_g$, defined by Eq. (8.13). In Fig. 8.4 (reproduced from reference 4), the gust alleviation factor $K$ is shown for a flat-topped gust, gust gradient $H$ $(=s_1/\bar{c}$, where $s_1$ is the gust length to attain its maximum value), for various values of $\mu_g$ for wings of aspect ratio 6. The broken curves are based on steady flow theory. It is seen that the unsteady flow effects are very important for sharp-edged gusts ($H = 0$) and for gusts of small gradient, but they become unimportant when the gust gradient is large.

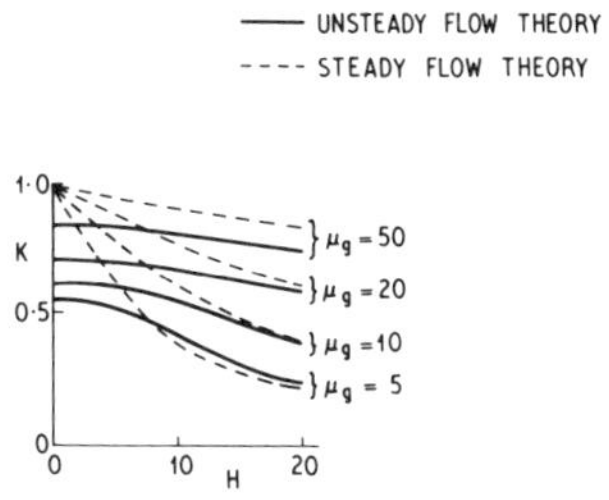


Fig. 8.4 Gust alleviation factor $K$ for a flat-topped gust (gust gradient $H$) for various values of $\mu_g (= m/\frac{1}{2}\rho_e Sa\bar{\bar{c}})$. (Reproduced from *J. Aeronaut. Sci.* 18, 33, 1951).

We note that $\mu_g$ is inversely proportional to the air density $\rho_e$. Thus, as the altitude of the aircraft increases, $\mu_g$ increases and the gust alleviation factor will increase. Reference 5 gives results for other types of gust (e.g. triangular gusts, which build up to a maximum and then fall to zero). For triangular gusts, the alleviation factor is very sensitive to the gust gradient, and there may be large reductions in $K$ for small values of $H$. As with the flat-topped gust, unsteady flow effects become unimportant when the gust gradient is large.

## EFFECT OF PITCHING

In the above analysis we have neglected the pitching motion of the aircraft. When an aircraft penetrates into a vertical up-gust, the gust acting on the forward part of the fuselage produces a small lift, and a nose-up pitching moment; this is followed by the forces and moments from the wing when it enters the gust. The pitching moment from the wing can be nose-up or nose-down depending on the position of the c.g. of the aircraft with respect to the wing. Finally, the gust reaches the tailplane and produces a corresponding nose-down pitching moment. At the same time, the changes in downwash (due to change in wing lift) produce further changes in the tail load and moment. In general, the effect of pitching is small in comparison with the unsteady flow effects. However, as shown below, the pitching mode can be of importance in the response of an aircraft to oscillatory vertical gusts, especially if the damping in pitch is low.

## RESPONSE TO SINUSOIDAL GUSTS

We shall finally study the response of an aircraft to a sinusoidal gust, of the form

$$\left.\begin{aligned} W &= W_{\max} \sin \Omega x \\ &= W_{\max} \sin \Omega V_e t \ , \end{aligned}\right\} \tag{8.14}$$

where $W_{\max}$ is the maximum amplitude of the vertical gust, and $\Omega$ is its space frequency, i.e. the gust wavelength is $2\pi/\Omega$.

Let $$\hat{W} = W/V_e \tag{8.15}$$

and $$\omega_g = \Omega V_e \tau = \Omega \mu_1 \bar{\bar{c}} \ , \tag{8.16}$$

where $\omega_g$ is the non-dimensional gust frequency.

Then Eq. (8.14) can be written

$$\hat{W} = \hat{W}_{\max} \sin \omega_g \hat{t} \ . \tag{8.17}$$

For simplicity, we assume that the aircraft speed is constant; we shall also neglect the effects of unsteady flow. As shown above, due to an up-gust $W$, the incidence of the aircraft in the disturbed motion will be increased from $w/V_e$ to $(w+W)/V_e$, and, from Eqs. (7.13) and (7.14), the equations of motion become

$$(\hat{D} + z_w)\hat{w} - \hat{q} + z_w\hat{W} = 0, \tag{8.18}$$

$$(m_{\dot{w}}\hat{D} + m_w)\hat{w} + (\hat{D} + m_q)\hat{q} + m_{gT}\hat{D}\hat{W} + m_w\hat{W} = 0, \tag{8.19}$$

where $\hat{D} \equiv d/d\hat{t}$. The term involving $m_{gT}$ arises from the lag in the gust reaching the tailplane. It can be shown that, to a good degree of approximation,

$$m_{gT} = -m_{qT} + m_{\dot{w}} \ , \tag{8.20}$$

where the suffix $T$ stands for the tailplane contribution.

From Eqs. (8.18) and (8.19), eliminating $\hat{q}$, we see that

$$(\hat{D}^2 + B_1'\hat{D} + C_1')\hat{w} + [(\hat{D} + m_q)z_w + m_{gT}\hat{D} + m_w]\hat{W} = 0, \tag{8.21}$$

where $$B_1' = z_w + m_q + m_{\dot{w}}$$

and $$C_1' = z_w m_q + m_w \ .$$

We can write Eq. (8.21) in the form

$$\hat{w} = T_w \hat{W} \ , \tag{8.22}$$

where $T_w$ is the transfer function relating the downward velocity $w$ of the aircraft to the up-gust $W$. From Eqs. (8.21) and (8.22), we see that

$$T_w = -\frac{F\hat{D} + C_1'}{\hat{D}^2 + B_1'\hat{D} + C_1'} \tag{8.23}$$

where $F = z_w + m_{gT}$.

Similarly we find

$$\hat{q} = T_q \hat{W},$$

where
$$T_q = -\frac{m_{gT}\hat{D}^2 + G\hat{D}}{\hat{D}^2 + B_1'\hat{D} + C_1'}$$

and
$$G = m_w + z_w(m_{gT} - m_{\dot{w}}) = m_w - z_w m_{qT}.$$

FREQUENCY RESPONSE FUNCTIONS

The effect of the frequency of the gust on the aircraft response is most easily found by using the frequency response method (reference 6). Let the response in downward velocity by given by

$$\begin{aligned}\hat{w} &= A_w \hat{W}_{max} \sin(\omega_g\hat{t} + \varepsilon_w)\\ &= A_w \hat{W}_{max} (\sin \omega_g\hat{t} \cos \varepsilon_w + \cos \omega_g\hat{t} \sin \varepsilon_w)\end{aligned} \tag{8.24}$$

and that in rate of pitch by

$$\begin{aligned}\hat{q} &= A_q W_{max} \sin(\omega_g\hat{t} + \varepsilon_q)\\ &= A_q W_{max} (\sin \omega_g\hat{t} \cos \varepsilon_q + \cos \omega_g\hat{t} \sin \varepsilon_q),\end{aligned} \tag{8.25}$$

where $A_w$, $A_q$, $\varepsilon_w$ and $\varepsilon_q$ are constants.

$A_w$ is the ratio of the maximum amplitude of the motion in $w$ to that of the gust, and $\varepsilon_w$ is the phase difference between the two motions, and similarly for $A_q$ and $\varepsilon_q$.

On substituting Eq. (8.24) into (8.21) and equating coefficients of $\sin \omega_g t$ and $\cos \omega_g t$ on both sides, we obtain

$$A_w\{(-\omega_g^2 + C_1') \cos \varepsilon_w - B_1'\omega_g \sin \varepsilon_w\} = -C_1'$$

and
$$A_w\{(-\omega_g^2 + C_1') \sin \varepsilon_w + B_1'\omega_g \cos \varepsilon_w\} = -F\omega_g.$$

Squaring and adding these equations, we find that

$$A_w = \left\{\frac{F^2\omega_g^2 + C_1'^2}{(\omega_g^2 - C_1')^2 + B_1'^2\omega_g^2}\right\}^{\frac{1}{2}} \tag{8.26}$$

We see that $A_w = |T_w(i\omega_g)|$.

Similarly, $$A_q = |T_q(i\omega_g)| = \omega_g \left\{\frac{(m_{gT})^2 \omega_g^2 + G^2}{(\omega_g^2 - C_1')^2 + B_1'^2\omega_g^2}\right\}^{\frac{1}{2}} \tag{8.27}$$

Now, when pitching is taken into account, the downward acceleration of the aircraft (parallel to $Oz$) is

$$\ddot{z} = \dot{w} - V_e q = \frac{V_e}{\tau}(\hat{D}\hat{w} - \hat{q}) = -z_w \frac{V_e}{\tau}(\hat{w} + \hat{W}),$$

i.e.
$$\ddot{z} = -\frac{aV_e}{\tau}(\hat{w} + \hat{W}), \tag{8.28}$$

since, from Eq. (3.19), $z_w = -Z_w \simeq a$, where $a$ is the lift curve slope. The increment $\Delta n$ in the load factor is given by

$$\Delta n = -\frac{\ddot{z}_{\max}}{g}. \tag{8.29}$$

From Eqs. (8.20) and (8.21),

$$(\hat{D}^2 + B_1'\hat{D} + C_1')(\hat{w} + \hat{W}) = (\hat{D} + m_q + m_{qT})\hat{D}\hat{W}. \tag{8.30}$$

Thus, writing

$$\ddot{z} = -A_z \frac{aV_e}{\tau} W_{\max} \sin(\omega_g \tau + \varepsilon_z),$$

we find that

$$\Delta n = A_z \frac{aV_e}{\tau} \hat{W}_{\max} = A_z \frac{\rho_e V_e S a}{2mg} W_{\max}, \tag{8.31}$$

where, from Eqs. (8.28) and (8.30),

$$A_z = \omega_g \left\{ \frac{\omega_g{}^2 + (m_q + m_{qT})^2}{(\omega_g{}^2 - C_1')^2 + B_1'^2 \omega_g{}^2} \right\}^{\frac{1}{2}}. \tag{8.32}$$

Comparing Eqs. (8.10) and (8.31), we see that, for this oscillatory motion, the gust alleviation factor $K$ is given by

$$K = A_z. \tag{8.33}$$

From Eqs. (8.26) and (8.27), we see that, for small values of $\omega_g$, $A_w \simeq 1$ and $A_q$ is proportional to $\omega_g$; for large values of $\omega_g$, $A_w \to 0$ and $A_q \to m_{qT}$. Thus the effect of pitching is negligible for gusts of low frequency (large wavelength) but can be of importance for gusts of moderate and high frequency.

In Fig. 8.5 (reproduced from ref. 7), the amplitude ratio $A_z$ is plotted against the non-dimensional gust frequency $\omega_g$ for a particular aircraft. It is seen that $A_z = 0$ at $\omega_g = 0$, and $A_z$ tends to unity as $\omega_g \to \infty$. From Eqs. (8.26), (8.27) and (8.32), we see that large values of all the amplitude ratios will occur when the damping of the short period mode is very small and the frequency of the gust is close to that of the short period oscillation.

The response to oscillatory vertical gusts is treated in reference 8, allowance being made for unsteady flow effects. It is shown that, for a conventional aircraft at low speeds, the unsteady flow effects are not important; for practical applications, unless the damping of the short period mode is very small (e.g. at transonic speeds), the preceding analysis is sufficiently accurate.

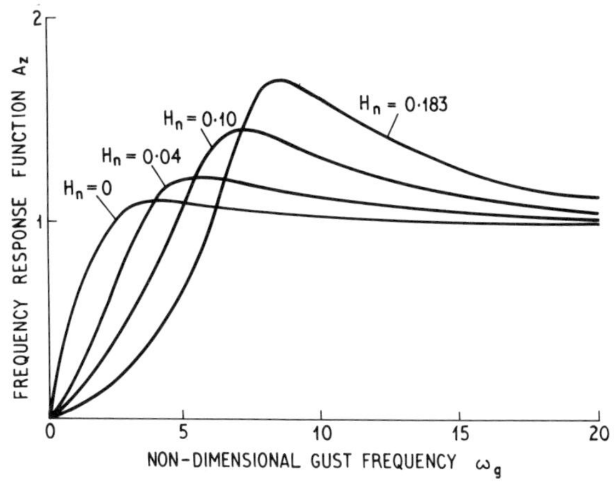


Fig. 8.5 Frequency response diagram for a sinusoidal gust (Crown copyright)

## AIR TURBULENCE

In the above analysis, we have considered the response of an aircraft to gusts of simple known forms. In general, isolated large gusts are of more importance in determining the maximum loads that an aircraft has to bear; the response in turbulent air is of importance both in assessing (i) whether the aircraft has satisfactory flying characteristics, and (ii) the fatigue life of the airframe.

Fig. 8.6 shows a typical variation of up-gusts with time. The intensity of the turbulence will, of course, vary with altitude and with weather conditions. The general pattern of the gust structure is similar to that of small-scale turbulence in wind tunnels, and to that of noise in electrical systems. Thus the gust structure can be defined only in a statistical manner, e.g. in terms of the standard deviation, or the probability distribution, of the gust strengths, both taken over a given time.

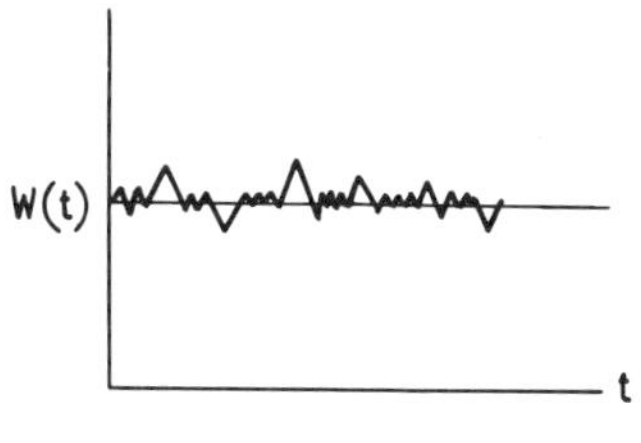


Fig. 8.6 Variation of up-gusts with time

The response of an aircraft to continuous random gusts is considered in reference 7. It is shown that the standard deviation $\sigma_n$ of the aircraft response in vertical acceleration is related both to the frequency response function $A_z$ and to the energy content of the gust at a given frequency (the latter can become very large at low values of the gust space frequency $\Omega$). As shown in Fig. 8.5, for such values of the gust frequency, $A_z$ increases as the static margin decreases. Thus the low frequency gust spectrum is especially important for aircraft having small static margins.

From Eq. (8.16), we see that, as the aircraft size increases (i.e. as $\bar{\bar{c}}$ increases), the value of $\omega_g$ corresponding to a given gust frequency $\Omega$ increases. The larger aircraft (with a lower natural frequency) is more sensitive to the low frequency gusts (which have a higher energy level). Thus $\sigma_n$ increases as the aircraft size increases. The increase in the gust loads with large aircraft may be of importance in affecting the fatigue life of the airframe.

## REFERENCES

1. WAGNER, H. The production of the dynamic lift on wings. *Z. angew. Math. Mech.* 5, 17 (1925).

2. KUSSNER, H.G. Stresses produced in aircraft wings by gusts. NACA Tech. Memo 654 (1932).

3. LYON, H.M. A review of theoretical investigations of the aerodynamic forces on a wing in non-uniform motion. R. & M. 1786 (1937).

4. BISPLINGHOFF, R.L., ISAKSON, G. and O'BRIEN, T.F. Gust loads on rigid aircraft with pitching neglected. *J. Aeronaut. Sci.* 18. 33 (1951).

5. ZBROZEK, J.K. Gust alleviation factor. R. & M. 2970 (1958).

6. BROWN, G.S. and CAMPBELL, D.P. *Principles of Servomechanisms*. Wiley (1948).

7. ZBROZEK, J.K. A study of the longitudinal response of aircraft to turbulent air.

8. ZBROZEK, J.K. Longitudinal response of aircraft to oscillatory vertical gusts (frequency analysis including the effect of unsteady aerodynamics).

## PROBLEMS

1. Solve Eqs. (8.18) and (8.19) for the case of a sharp-edged gust. Hence show that the contribution of pitching to the gust load factor is small, provided that the longitudinal inertia in pitch and the damping are not very low.

2. Give the physical reasons for the gradual growth of lift on a wing after a sudden change of incidence. The change in the circulation $\Delta\Gamma$ (for a flat plate in a two-dimensional flow) following a change in downward velocity $\Delta w$ is given by $\Delta\Gamma = \frac{1}{2}\pi k(s/c).\Delta w.c$, where $s$ is the distance travelled by the plate (chord $c$) after the sudden change of incidence. Give a physical interpretation of $k$ in terms of the unsteady lift. If $k = 1$ at $s/c = 0$, show the expected variation of $k$ with $s/c$.

3. Determine the phase difference $\varepsilon_w$, given in Eq. (8.24), as a function of $\omega_g$, and show that if the gust wavelength is large, $\varepsilon_w = 180°$. Give a physical interpretation of this result in terms of the incidence of the aircraft in the disturbed motion.

4. By considering the nature of the terms in $B_1'$ and $C_1'$ in Eq. (8.21), show that, with increasing frequency, the effect of inertia forces increases and that of aerodynamic forces decreases.

5. Discuss the effect of variation in the longitudinal stability characteristics on the response of an aircraft to atmospheric turbulence. How could wing spoilers reduce the gust alleviation factor?

# Part III

# LATERAL DYNAMIC STABILITY AND RESPONSE

# Chapter 9

# BASIC LATERAL MOTIONS

## INTRODUCTION

In Part I we saw that, for small disturbances, the lateral motion of an aircraft, involving disturbances in bank, yaw and sideslip, could be treated separately from the longitudinal motion. The equations of lateral asymmetric motion (for small disturbances from steady trimmed flight) were derived in Chapter 2. Before obtaining the complete solution of these equations, we shall consider three simple approximate lateral motions: the yawing oscillation, the pure rolling motion and the slow spiral motion. We shall assume that the asymmetric disturbances are small, and that the controls are kept fixed.

## THE YAWING OSCILLATION

Consider the motion of an aircraft with forward speed $V_e$, which is oscillating in yaw about its centre of gravity $O$. As in Chapter 2, we take axes $Ox$, $Oy$, $Oz$ which are fixed in the aircraft, $Ox$ being in the forward direction and $Oy$ to starboard (Fig. 9.1). In this approximate treatment, we take $Oz$ to be fixed in direction;

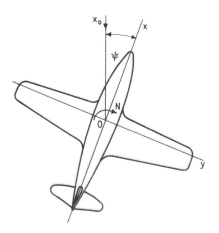

Fig. 9.1 An aircraft in yawed flight

the aircraft thus has one degree of freedom, in yaw, and is thus similar to a weathercock (or to a model pivoted in a wind tunnel, the direction of the relative wind being parallel to $Ox_0$). The relative wind thus has a component $V_e \sin\psi \simeq V_e\psi$ from port, where $\psi$ is the angle of yaw (assumed small).

With the usual sign convention (measuring *relative* sideslip positive from starboard) we see that the angle of sideslip $\beta$ of the aircraft is given by

$$\beta = v/V_e = -\psi \tag{9.1}$$

where $v$ is the velocity of sideslip.

As stated in Chapter 2, this relation between angle of sideslip and angle of yaw only holds in the particular case in which the direction of the relative wind is unaffected when the aircraft is yawed.

In the yawed position, there will be a yawing moment $N$ about $Oz$ due to the aerodynamic forces. This yawing moment will be the sum of two terms, one proportional to the rate of yaw $r(=\dot{\psi})$ and one to the velocity of sideslip. In the notation of Chapter 2,

$$N = \mathring{N}_r r + \mathring{N}_v v,$$

i.e. from Eq. (9.1), $N = \mathring{N}_r\dot{\psi} - \mathring{N}_v V_e\psi.$ (9.2)

In Eq. (9.2), the term in $\mathring{N}_v$ arises from the static moment that acts on an aircraft in yawed flight. Thus the condition for directional (or weathercock) static stability is that this moment should oppose the yawing motion, i.e. $\mathring{N}_v > 0$, or in terms of the non-dimensional derivative defined in Chapter 4,

$$N_v > 0. \tag{9.3}$$

If $I_z$ is the moment of inertia of the aircraft about $Oz$, the equation of the yawing motion is

$$I_z\ddot{\psi} = N. \tag{9.4}$$

From Eqs. (9.2) and (9.4),

$$I_z\ddot{\psi} - \mathring{N}_r\dot{\psi} + \mathring{N}_v V_e\psi = 0. \tag{9.5}$$

Substituting $\psi = \sigma e^{\mu t}$, (9.6)

where $\sigma$ and $\mu$ are constants, we have, from Eq. (9.5),

$$I_z\mu^2 - \mathring{N}_r\mu + \mathring{N}_v V_e = 0,$$

or, in terms of the non-dimensional parameters defined in Chapter 2,

$$i_z\mu^2 - N_r\mu/\tau + \mu_2 N_v/\tau^2 = 0, \tag{9.7}$$

where $\tau = m/\tfrac{1}{2}\rho_e V_e S$ (9.8)

and $\mu_2 = m/\tfrac{1}{2}\rho_e S b.$ (9.9)

For the oscillation to be stable, the coefficients of all the terms in Eq. (9.7) must be positive, i.e. $N_v > 0$ and $N_r < 0$. We see that the first inequality is that for static directional stability, given by Eq. (9.3); the second inequality ensures that the oscillation is damped.

The roots of Eq. (9.7) can be written in the form

$$\mu = \frac{1}{2i_z\tau}\left[N_r \pm i\sqrt{4\mu_2 N_v i_z - N_r^2}\right]. \tag{9.10}$$

Substituting in Eq. (9.6), we see that the complete solution is

$$\psi = \sigma_1 e^{(N_r/2i_z\tau)t}\sin\sqrt{\frac{\mu_2 N_v}{i_z} - \frac{N_r^2}{4i_z^2}}\,(t/\tau) +$$

$$+\ \sigma_2 e^{(N_r/2i_z\tau)t}\cos\sqrt{\frac{\mu_2 N_v}{i_z} - \frac{N_r^2}{4i_z^2}}\,(t/\tau) \tag{9.11}$$

where $\sigma_1$ and $\sigma_2$ constants, determined by the initial conditions. This corresponds to a damped oscillation (if $4\mu_2 N_v i_z > N_r^2$), the time to half-amplitude being given by

$$\frac{1}{2} = e^{(N_r/2i_z\tau)t_{\frac{1}{2}}},$$

i.e.

$$t_{\frac{1}{2}} = -\frac{2i_z\tau\log_e 2}{N_r},$$

or, from Eq. (2.119),

$$t_{\frac{1}{2}} = \frac{2\tau}{n_r}\log_e 2\,. \tag{9.12}$$

The period $T$ in seconds is

$$T = 2\pi\tau\left(\frac{\mu_2 N_v}{i_z} - \frac{N_r^2}{4i_z^2}\right)^{-\frac{1}{2}},$$

i.e. from Eq. (2.119),

$$T = 2\pi\tau\left(-n_v - \frac{n_r^2}{4}\right)^{-\frac{1}{2}} \tag{9.13}$$

We note that, in the present notation, the concise derivative $n_v$ ($= -\mu_2 N_v/i_z$) is negative for an aircraft with positive weathercock stability.

From Eqs. (9.12) and (9.13) we see that both the period and the damping are proportional to $\tau$ and are thus *inversely* proportional to the forward speed of the aircraft.

For an aircraft with large weathercock stability, we have, from Eq. (9.13),

$$T \simeq 2\pi\tau(-n_v)^{-\frac{1}{2}} = 2\pi\sqrt{\left(\frac{i_z b C_L}{g N_v\cos\Theta_e}\right)}, \tag{9.14}$$

where $b$ is the wing span.

We see that the period of the yawing oscillation is increased by increasing the wing span, the inertia in yaw or $C_L$, and is decreased by increasing $N_v$. For a given $C_L$ the period is independent of wing loading and height. The period $T$ is of the order of 3 to 10 seconds.

The analysis of the yawing oscillation is analogous to that of the short period longitudinal oscillation (given in Chapter 5). However, the fin sidewash is far less important than the tailplane downwash.

## THE PURE ROLLING MOTION

We shall consider next the pure rolling motion of an aircraft, with no sideslip or yaw. As shown in Chapter 2, when an aircraft is rolling there are rolling moments, yawing moments and side forces due to the aerodynamic forces. The rolling moment due to rolling is by far the most important, and we shall, for the present, neglect the yawing moment and side forces.

If $I_x$ is the moment of inertia of the aircraft about $Ox$, the rolling axis, the equation of motion is

$$I_x \dot{p} = L, \tag{9.15}$$

where $p$ is the rate of roll and $L$ is the rolling moment due to the aerodynamic forces.

Assuming the rate of roll is small, we can write

$$L = \mathring{L}_p\, p, \tag{9.16}$$

since both sideslip and yaw are zero, $\mathring{L}_p$ being constant. From Eqs. (9.15) and (9.16),

$$I_x \dot{p} = \mathring{L}_p p .$$

Hence

$$p = \sigma_3 e^{\mathring{L}_p t/I_x} , \tag{9.17}$$

where $\sigma_3$ is a constant.

Now for all incidences below the stall, $\mathring{L}_p$ is negative (from Chapter 4) and, from Eq. (9.17), we see that the motion is a subsidence, the time $t_{\frac{1}{2}}$ to half-amplitude being given by

$$t_{\frac{1}{2}} = -\frac{I_x}{\mathring{L}_p}\log_e 2 = -\frac{i_x \tau}{L_p}\log_e 2 , \tag{9.18}$$

i.e. from Eq. (2.119),

$$t_{\frac{1}{2}} = \frac{\tau}{l_p}\log_e 2 . \tag{9.19}$$

The pure rolling motion is a highly damped subsidence (provided the rate of roll is small).

## THE SLOW SPIRAL MOTION

Consider next an aircraft in a banked turn (Fig. 9.2) in which the angles of bank, yaw and sideslip are varying with the time. We suppose that both the radius of the spiral path and the rate of roll are changing so slowly that their rates of change can be neglected. We also neglect the side forces due to rates of bank, yaw and sideslip and we assume that the angles of bank, yaw and sideslip are small.

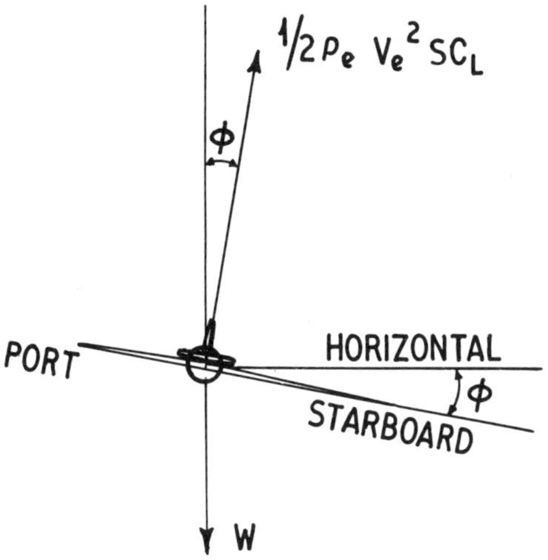


Fig. 9.2 Forces on an aircraft in a banked turn

If $V_e$ is the aircraft forward speed and $r$ is the rate of yaw about the axis $Oz$ through the aircraft c.g., the horizontal radius $R$ of the turn is given by

$$R = \frac{V_e}{r \cos \phi} \tag{9.20}$$

where $\phi$ is the angle of bank.

The aircraft (weight $W$) has an inward radial acceleration $V_e{}^2/R$ acting horizontally. Resolving horizontally,

$$\tfrac{1}{2}\rho_e V_e{}^2 S C_L \sin \phi = \frac{W V_e{}^2}{gR} . \tag{9.21}$$

Resolving vertically,

$$\tfrac{1}{2}\rho_e V_e{}^2 S C_L \cos \phi = W. \tag{9.22}$$

From Eqs. (9.20)-(9.22), as $\phi$ is small,

$$g\phi = V_e{}^2/R = V_e r. \tag{9.23}$$

The rate of roll $p$ is given by

$$p = \dot{\phi} .$$

Hence, differentiating Eq. (9.23) with respect to $t$, we find

$$gp = V_e \dot{r} . \tag{9.24}$$

Since we are neglecting the rate of change of the radius of the spiral path and the rate of change of the angular velocity in roll, the rolling and yawing equations become

$$\mathring{L}_p p + \mathring{L}_r r + \mathring{L}_v v = 0,$$

$$\mathring{N}_p p + \mathring{N}_r r + \mathring{N}_v v = 0,$$

or in terms of the non-dimensional derivatives defined in Chapter 4,

$$L_p p + L_r r + L_v v/b = 0, \tag{9.25}$$

$$N_p p + N_r r + N_v v/b = 0. \tag{9.26}$$

From Eqs. (9.24)-(9.26), we see that the solution is of the form

$$\left.\begin{aligned} p &= \sigma_4 e^{\mu t} \\ r &= \sigma_5 e^{\mu t} \\ v &= \sigma_6 e^{\mu t} \end{aligned}\right\} \tag{9.27}$$

where $\sigma_4$, $\sigma_5$, $\sigma_6$ and $\mu$ are constants.

Substituting in Eqs. (9.24)-(9.26) and eliminating $\sigma_4$, $\sigma_5$, $\sigma_6$, we have

$$\begin{vmatrix} g & -V_e\mu & 0 \\ L_p & L_r & L_v \\ N_p & N_r & N_v \end{vmatrix} = 0$$

i.e.
$$\mu = -\frac{g}{V_e}\,\frac{L_v N_r - L_r N_v}{L_v N_p - L_p N_v}\,. \tag{9.28}$$

We see that the spiral motion involves yaw, bank and sideslip. As shown in Chapter 4, for typical values of the derivatives, $L_r$ and $N_v$ are positive and $L_v$, $L_p$, $N_p$ and $N_r$ are negative. Thus $(L_v N_p - L_p N_v)$ is positive, but $(L_v N_r - L_r N_v)$ may be either positive or negative.

If $L_v N_r > L_r N_v$, the spiral motion is a subsidence, the time to half-amplitude being given by

$$t_{\frac{1}{2}} = -\frac{1}{\mu}\log_e 2\,. \tag{9.29}$$

If $L_v N_r < L_r N_v$, the spiral motion is a divergence, the time $t_d$ to double amplitude being given by

$$t_d = \frac{1}{\mu}\log_e 2. \tag{9.30}$$

In this case, the aircraft, on commencing to turn to starboard owing to some small disturbance, begins to sideslip inwards (towards the centre of the turn), to over-bank itself and to start a spiral dive.

In practice $(L_v N_r - L_r N_v)$ is usually numerically much smaller than $(L_v N_p - L_p N_v)$, and thus the spiral motion is usually either a slowly decreasing subsidence or a slowly increasing divergence, $t_{\frac{1}{2}}$ or $t_d$ being of the order of one minute or more. This spiral instability is not serious since the pilot has time to apply controls to correct the motion. We see that if $(-L_v/N_v)$ is large, i.e. if the aircraft has high effective dihedral in comparison to its directional stability, the spiral motion will be stable. On the other hand, if the directional stability is high, i.e. $N_v$ large, the spiral motion will be unstable.

PROBLEMS

1. What is meant by weathercock stability? What condition must be satisfied for an aircraft to be directionally stable? Show that the weathercock stability is (i) increased by increasing fin size, and (ii) reduced by moving the aircraft c.g. aft.

2. A 'V' tail is fitted to an aircraft. Use strip theory to determine the contribution of the tailplane to the weathercock stability.

3. Analyse the equations of motion for an aircraft with two degrees of freedom (in yaw and sideslip) but with rolling suppressed. Side forces due to gravity and to rate of yaw can be neglected. Show that the characteristic equation is a quadratic, and compare the damping and frequency of the motion with that of the simple yawing oscillation.

4. By considering the pure rolling motion of an aircraft, neglecting the effects of sideslip and yawing, show that when the ailerons are undeflected the motion following an initial disturbance is a subsidence, and find the time to half-amplitude. When the ailerons are deflected in a steady roll show that the rate of roll per unit aileron angle is $(-2V_eL_\xi/bL_p)$. Obtain an expression for the rate of roll when an aileron angle $\xi_1$ is suddenly applied to an aircraft without roll, this aileron angle being kept constant. Show that the aircraft finally has a rate of roll equal to the steady rate of roll due to $\xi_1$.

5. Analyse the equations of motion for an aircraft with two degrees of freedom (in roll and sideslip) but with yawing suppressed. The inertia terms in the rolling moment equation can be neglected and also the side force due to rate of roll. Show that the characteristic equation is a quadratic, and determine the period and time to half-amplitude of the oscillatory motion.

# Chapter 10
# LATERAL DYNAMIC STABILITY

## INTRODUCTION

In Chapter 9 we considered various particular lateral motions, e.g. the yawing oscillation, the pure rolling motion and the slow spiral motion. We analysed these motions when one or more of the lateral degrees of freedom were suppressed, obtaining in this manner a simple physical picture of these motions and of the parameters on which they depend.

We shall now return to the equations of lateral asymmetric motion given in Chapter 2. As shown in that chapter, for small disturbances of a symmetric aircraft, the lateral asymmetric motion can be separated from the longitudinal symmetric motion; the equations of lateral motion then reduce to a set of linear differential equations with constant coefficients (2.121)-(2.125), in terms of $v$ (the velocity of sideslip), $\phi$ (the angle of bank) and $\psi$ (the angle of yaw), and their derivatives with respect to $\hat{t}$ (the non-dimensional aerodynamic time). The general solution of these equations is similar to that for the equations of longitudinal symmetric motion, given in Chapter 6.

We shall now establish the conditions that must apply for the lateral motion to be stable for small disturbances, with stick fixed. We shall show how the stability criteria can be presented in a simple manner in the form of stability diagrams; these show the effect on the stability of changes in the aircraft design.

## STICK FIXED DYNAMIC STABILITY

The equations of motion (2.121)-(2.123) are three linear differential equations in the variables $\hat{v}$, $\phi$ and $\psi$, the non-dimensional rates of roll $\hat{p}$ and of yaw $\hat{r}$ being related to $\phi$ and $\psi$ by Eqs. (2.124) and (2.125). To determine the stick fixed lateral dynamic stability of the aircraft, we put $\xi = \zeta = 0$ in Eqs. (2.121)-(2.123). In the usual way of solving such a system of linear differential equations with constant coefficients we assume that there is a solution of the form

$$\hat{v} = \rho_1 e^{\lambda\hat{t}}, \quad \phi = \rho_2 e^{\lambda\hat{t}}, \quad \psi = \rho_3 e^{\lambda\hat{t}}, \tag{10.1}$$

where $\rho_1$, $\rho_2$, $\rho_3$ and $\lambda$ are constants, and $\hat{t}$ is the non-dimensional time given by Eq. (2.100). The determinantal, or characteristic, equation for $\lambda$ is obtained as in Part II (Chapter 6).

From Eqs. (2.124), (2.125) and (10.1),

$$\left.\begin{aligned} \hat{p} &= \lambda\rho_2 e^{\lambda\hat{t}} \\ \text{and} \qquad \hat{r} &= \lambda\rho_3 e^{\lambda\hat{t}}. \end{aligned}\right\} \qquad (10.2)$$

From Eqs. (2.121)-(2.123), (10.1) and (10.2), eliminating $\rho_1$, $\rho_2$ and $\rho_3$, we find that the characteristic equation for $\lambda$ is given by

$$\begin{vmatrix} \lambda + y_v & y_p\lambda - \hat{g}_1 & (1 + y_r)\lambda - \hat{g}_2 \\ l_v & \lambda^2 + l_p\lambda & e_x\lambda^2 + l_r\lambda \\ n_v & e_z\lambda^2 + n_p\lambda & \lambda^2 + n_r\lambda \end{vmatrix} = 0 \qquad (10.3)$$

This is a quintic equation in $\lambda$, in which the constant term is zero, and it is written in the form

$$A_2\lambda^5 + B_2\lambda^4 + C_2\lambda^3 + D_2\lambda^2 + E_2\lambda = 0. \qquad (10.4)$$

Cancelling throughout by $\lambda$, we see that the characteristic equation is given by

$$A_2\lambda^4 + B_2\lambda^3 + C_2\lambda^2 + D_2\lambda + E_2 = 0, \qquad (10.5)$$

where $A_2$, $B_2$, $C_2$, $D_2$ and $E_2$ are constants given by

$$A_2 = 1 - e_x e_z \,, \qquad (10.6)$$

$$B_2 = l_p + n_r - e_x n_p - e_z l_r + (1 - e_x e_z) y_v \,, \qquad (10.7)$$

$$\begin{aligned} C_2 = {} & l_p n_r - l_r n_p + (l_p + n_r - e_x n_p - e_z l_r) y_v + \\ & + [e_z(1 + y_r) - y_p] l_v - [1 + y_r - e_x y_p] n_v, \end{aligned} \qquad (10.8)$$

$$\begin{aligned} D_2 = {} & (l_p n_r - l_r n_p) y_v + [n_p(1 + y_r) - n_r y_p + \hat{g}_1 - e_z\hat{g}_2] l_v - \\ & - [l_p(1 + y_r) - l_r y_p - \hat{g}_2 + e_x\hat{g}_1] n_v \end{aligned} \qquad (10.9)$$

$$E_2 = (\hat{g}_1 n_r - \hat{g}_2 n_p) l_v - (\hat{g}_1 l_r - \hat{g}_2 l_p) n_v \,. \qquad (10.10)$$

We note that, as in the analysis of longitudinal stability, the characteristic equation (10.5) is a quartic equation. Also, since $e_x e_z$ ($= I_{zx}^2/I_x I_z$) is small compared with unity, from Eq. (10.6), $A_2 > 0$.

## TYPES OF MOTION CORRESPONDING TO THE ROOTS OF THE CHARACTERISTIC EQUATION

As shown in Part II (Chapter 6), four types of motion may occur, depending on the nature of the roots of the characteristic equation. From Eq. (10.1) we see that, when $\lambda$ is real and positive, the constituent ($\hat{v}$, $\phi$, $\psi$ or their derivatives with respect to $\hat{t}$) of the disturbed motion increases steadily with time and tends to infinity; this is called a *divergence*. When $\lambda$ is real and negative, the constituent decreases with time, tending asymptotically to zero; this is called a *subsidence*. When $\lambda$ is complex with real part negative, the constituent of the disturbed motion is a *damped oscillation* tending to zero. When $\lambda$ is complex with real part positive, the constituent is an *increasing oscillation* tending to $\pm\infty$ as $\hat{t} \to \infty$. When $\lambda$ is zero, the original displacement persists undamped; when $\lambda$ is complex with zero real part, the motion is simple harmonic. These two cases are said to be neutral or critical conditions.

If the roots of the characteristic equation are written in the form

$$\lambda = -r \pm is,$$

where $r$ and $s$ are real, then, as shown in Part II, the constituents corresponding to this mode of motion are given by

$$\hat{v} = \sigma_1 e^{-r\hat{t}} \cos s\hat{\tau} + \sigma_2 e^{-r\hat{t}} \sin s\hat{\tau}, \tag{10.11}$$

where $\sigma_1$ and $\sigma_2$ are constants, and similarly for $\phi$ and $\psi$. The period $T$ (in seconds) is given by

$$T = \frac{2\pi}{s}\tau = \frac{2\pi}{s}\frac{V_e C_L}{g\cos\Theta_e}, \tag{10.12}$$

and the time $t_{\frac{1}{2}}$ (in seconds) to half-amplitude is

$$t_{\frac{1}{2}} = \frac{\log_e 2}{r}\tau = \frac{\log_e 2}{r}\frac{V_e C_L}{g\cos\Theta_e}. \tag{10.13}$$

When $r$ is negative (in an undamped oscillation), the time $t_d$ to double amplitude is

$$t_d = \frac{\log_e 2}{(-r)}\tau. \tag{10.14}$$

It should be noted that, as originally derived, in the form of Eq. (10.4), the characteristic equation was a quintic having one root zero, corresponding to the solution

$$\hat{v} = \rho_1, \quad \phi = \rho_2, \quad \psi = \rho_3,$$

$\rho_1$, $\rho_2$, $\rho_3$ being constants, i.e. corresponding to flight with constant angles of sideslip, bank and yaw. Substituting in Eqs. (2.121)-(2.123), we see that in such a motion, with controls fixed in their neutral positions,

$$\hat{v} = 0$$

and $$\hat{g}_1\phi + \hat{g}_2\psi = 0,$$

i.e. from Eq. (2.117),

$$\phi\cos\Theta_e + \psi\sin\Theta_e = 0. \tag{10.15}$$

From Eq. (2.26) we see that the component of gravity $Y_g$ along $Oy$ is then zero, i.e. the aircraft is flying with wings level and without sideslip, but with small constant angles of bank and yaw. The lateral aerodynamic forces and moments on the aircraft depend upon the velocity of sideslip and the angular velocities of roll and yaw, but not upon the *angles* of bank or yaw. An aircraft thus has neutral stability in yaw (i.e. in azimuth); this must not be confused with directional (or weathercock) stability. The neutral stability in yaw does not depend on the aerodynamic characteristics of the aircraft; it follows from the fact that an aircraft, when flying steadily in a certain direction, will continue in that direction unless it is subsequently disturbed.

We shall now analyse the characteristic equation in the form given by Eq. (10.5).

## ANALYSIS OF THE ROOTS OF THE CHARACTERISTIC EQUATION

As shown in Part II (Chapter 6), the conditions for stability are that *all* the real roots of the characteristic equation (10.5) and the real parts of *all* the complex roots must be negative. The disturbed motion is said to be dynamically stable if it is compounded of subsidences or damped oscillations, and dynamically unstable if it contains a divergence or increasing oscillation.

Various methods for determining the roots of the characteristic equation are given in Appendix 2. The coefficients $A_2$, $B_2$, $C_2$, $D_2$ and $E_2$ depend on non-dimensional parameters which in turn depend on the steady flight conditions (e.g. speed and height), and thus we should investigate the stability of the aircraft under all conditions of flight.

### The rolling subsidence

For conventional aircraft, the coefficient $A_2$ is approximately unity and $B_2$ is much greater than unity. As shown in Appendix 2, the characteristic equation has a large negative root, given approximately by

$$\lambda = -B_2 \simeq -l_p = L_p/i_x \,, \tag{10.16}$$

where we have neglected terms which are usually small. This corresponds to the rolling subsidence (Chapter 9), the time to half-amplitude being given by

$$t_{\frac{1}{2}} = -\frac{i_x\tau}{L_p}\log_e 2 \,, \tag{10.17}$$

in agreement with Eq. (9.18).

The rapid damping of this mode is due to the large damping in roll of an aircraft (large negative $L_p$). As shown in Chapter 4, the damping comes almost entirely from the wings.

### The slow spiral motion

For conventional aircraft, the coefficient $E_2$ in the characteristic equation (10.5) is numerically much smaller than $D_2$. $E_2$ may be negative for certain flight conditions, but $D_2$ is positive for normal values of the aerodynamic derivatives. Considering small values of $\lambda$, we see that the characteristic equation for lateral stability has an approximate root

$$\lambda = -E_2/D_2 . \tag{10.18}$$

From Eqs. (10.9) and (10.10), if the steady flight path is horizontal, on neglecting terms which are usually small, we find that $D_2$ and $E_2$ are given approximately by

$$D_2 \simeq l_v n_p - l_p n_v \tag{10.19}$$

and

$$E_2 \simeq \hat{g}_1(l_v n_r - l_r n_v). \tag{10.20}$$

Now, from Eq. (2.117), $\hat{g}_1 = C_L$ . (10.21)

Thus, from Eqs. (10.18)-(10.21), the small root of the characteristic equation is given by

$$\lambda = -C_L \frac{l_v n_r - l_r n_v}{l_v n_p - l_p n_v}$$

i.e.
$$\lambda = -C_L \frac{L_v N_r - L_r N_v}{L_v N_p - L_p N_v} \qquad (10.22)$$

This corresponds to the slow spiral motion (Chapter 9).

If $E_2$ is positive, i.e. if $l_v n_r > l_r n_v$, the spiral motion is a subsidence, the time to half-amplitude being given by

$$t_{\frac{1}{2}} = \frac{\log_e 2}{(-\lambda)} \tau ,$$

i.e. from Eq. (2.101), with $\Theta_e = 0$,

$$t_{\frac{1}{2}} = \frac{V_e}{g} \frac{L_v N_p - L_p N_v}{L_v N_r - L_r N_v} \log_e 2 , \qquad (10.23)$$

in agreement with Eqs. (9.28) and (9.29).

If $E_2$ is negative, i.e. if $l_v n_r < l_r n_v$, the spiral motion is a divergence, the time to double amplitude being given by

$$t_d = \frac{V_e}{g} \frac{L_v N_p - L_p N_v}{L_r N_v - L_v N_r} \log_e 2 , \qquad (10.24)$$

in agreement with Eqs. (9.28) and (9.30).

As shown in Chapter 9, the spiral motion involves yaw, bank and sideslip. From Eqs. (10.23) and (10.24) we see that the damping of this mode depends upon the non-dimensional derivatives $L_p$, $L_r$, $L_v$, $N_p$, $N_r$ and $N_v$, which in turn depend on the layout of the aircraft, notably upon the effective dihedral and the fin volume. We shall consider this in more detail when we discuss the significance of the critical condition $E_2 = 0$.

## The lateral oscillation

The other pair of roots of the characteristic equation (10.5) is complex and corresponds to the lateral oscillation (Chapter 9), or Dutch roll. This oscillation increases or decreases as the real part of these complex roots is positive or negative. It is this oscillation which is referred to when an aircraft is said to have lateral oscillatory stability. The lateral oscillation was treated approximately in Chapter 9 by considering only the yawing motion. However, as shown in reference 1, the actual lateral oscillation involves yaw, bank and sideslip. The period and damping depend in a complicated manner on many of the non-dimensional derivatives (both inertial and aerodynamic), which in turn depend on the layout of the aircraft. We shall consider this in more detail when we discuss the significance of the critical condition $R = 0$, where $R$ is Routh's discriminant, given by

$$R = B_2 C_2 D_2 - B_2^2 E_2 - A_2 D_2^2 . \qquad (10.25)$$

## Dynamic stability criteria

We shall now consider the criteria for dynamic stability and we shall see how these can be expressed in terms of $L_v$ (proportional to the effective dihedral) and $N_v$

(proportional to the directional stability). Finally we shall consider the relation between the period and damping of both the lateral oscillation and the spiral motion in terms of these two parameters.

As shown in Part II (Chapter 6), for the quartic equation (10.5) in which $A_2 > 0$, the simplest set of stability criteria is

$$B_2 > 0, \tag{10.26}$$

$$D_2 > 0, \tag{10.27}$$

$$E_2 > 0, \tag{10.28}$$

and

$$R = B_2C_2D_2 - B_2^2E_2 - A_2D_2^2 > 0. \tag{10.29}$$

These criteria for stability are also derived in Appendix 2. For typical ranges of values of the aerodynamic derivatives, $B_2$ and $D_2$ are positive, and the critical criteria are $E_2 > 0$, $R > 0$.

## Critical stability criteria

As shown in Part II (Chapter 6), if the characteristic equation has a pair of equal and opposite roots, $R = 0$. If $B_2$ and $D_2$ are both positive and $R = 0$, the characteristic equation has a conjugate pair of imaginary roots $\lambda = \pm is$. For oscillatory stability the real part of the complex roots of the characteristic equation must be negative, which corresponds to $R > 0$. If $B_2$, $D_2$ and $E_2$ are positive, an aircraft is oscillatory stable if $R > 0$, and oscillatory unstable if $R < 0$.

As shown in Part II (Chapter 6), when $E_2 < 0$, the characteristic equation has at least one positive real root, representing a divergence. When $E_2 = 0$, the characteristic equation has a zero root, representing a state of neutral stability. As stated above, the characteristic equation for lateral stability usually has a small real root (since $E_2$ is generally numerically small compared with $D_2$). The aircraft is stable in the spiral mode if this small real root is negative. Now the coefficients $A_2$, $B_2$, $C_2$ and $D_2$ of the characteristic equation (10.5) are positive for typical values of the aerodynamic derivatives. Hence the condition for spiral stability is $E_2 > 0$. Now, from Eq. (10.10), using Eq. (2.117), we find

$$E_2 = C_L\{(l_v n_r - l_r n_v) - \tan\Theta_e(l_v n_p - l_p n_v)\}, \tag{10.30}$$

and the condition for spiral stability is

$$l_v n_r > l_r n_v + \tan\Theta_e(l_v n_p - l_p n_v)$$

or, from Eq. (2.119), in terms of the non-dimensional derivatives defined in Chapter 4,

$$L_v N_r > L_r N_v + \tan\Theta_e(L_v N_p - L_p N_v). \tag{10.31}$$

For horizontal flight $\Theta_e = 0$, and the condition for spiral stability becomes

$$L_v N_r > L_r N_v. \tag{10.32}$$

Now, as shown in Chapter 4, $L_r$ is positive and $N_r$ is negative (in low speed flight). Thus, for spiral stability,

$$(-L_v/N_v) > (-L_r/N_r). \tag{10.33}$$

As noted in Chapter 9, if $(-L_v/N_v)$ is large, i.e. if the aircraft has a high effective dihedral in comparison with its directional stability, the spiral motion will be stable. On the other hand, if the directional stability is high, i.e. $N_v$ is large, the spiral motion will be unstable.

## STABILITY DIAGRAMS

As shown in Part II (Chapter 6), it is often useful to investigate the dependence of the stability of an aircraft upon some parameter (or parameters). Now the rotary derivatives $L_p$, $N_p$ and $L_r$ depend mainly on the wing plan-form, and this will be determined by considerations of performance rather than by stability. When the general layout of the aircraft has been settled, the designer still has freedom to choose the dihedral and the fin size mainly from stability considerations. As shown in Chapter 4, $L_v$ is proportional to the effective dihedral and $N_v$ is proportional to the directional stability (and thus depends on the fin size).

We shall therefore consider a two-parameter stability diagram, showing the curves $E_2 = 0$ (the divergence boundary) and $R = 0$ (the Routhian boundary) as functions of $L_v$ and $N_v$. As the divergence boundary is crossed from its positive to its negative sides, one root of the characteristic equation becomes positive, corresponding to a divergence. As the Routhian boundary is crossed, the damping of an oscillatory mode changes sign and a previously stable oscillation becomes unstable. Thus an aircraft will be stable only when the values of the variables are such that the corresponding point on the stability diagram is on the positive side of both the divergence and the Routhian boundaries.

In Chapter 4 it was shown that both $N_v$ and $N_r$ have important contributions from the fin; we can write

$$N_v = N_v(\text{no fin}) + N_v(\text{fin}), \tag{10.34}$$

$$N_r = N_r(\text{no fin}) + N_r(\text{fin}), \tag{10.35}$$

where, from Eqs. (4.19) and (4.38),

$$N_v(\text{fin}) = a_1\bar{V}_F \tag{10.36}$$

and

$$N_r(\text{fin}) = -a_1\bar{V}_F l_F/b = -N_v(\text{fin})\, l_F/b. \tag{10.37}$$

The fin volume ratio $\bar{V}_F$ is given by

$$\bar{V}_F = S_F l_F/Sb, \tag{10.38}$$

where $S_F$ = fin area,
$S$ = wing area,
$l_F$ = distance of the aerodynamic centre of the fin aft of the centre of gravity of the aircraft,
and $b$ = wing span.

From Eqs. (10.34)-(10.37),

$$N_r = N_r(\text{no fin}) - \{N_v - N_v(\text{no fin})\}\, l_F/b. \tag{10.39}$$

The two-parameter stability diagrams are drawn with $N_v$ and $L_v$ as the abscissa and ordinate, the other non-dimensional stability derivatives being kept constant (for a given value of $C_L$) except $N_r$, which is given in terms of $N_v$ by Eq. (10.39).

From Eqs. (10.30) and (10.31) we see that the divergence boundary $E_2 = 0$ is independent of $\mu_2$, the lateral relative density parameter, given by

$$\mu_2 = m/\tfrac{1}{2}\rho_e S b, \tag{10.40}$$

where $m$ is the mass of the aircraft and $\rho_e$ is the air density. This boundary is also independent of the rolling and yawing inertia parameters $i_x$ and $i_z$. The Routhian boundary $R = 0$ will vary with $\mu_2$, $i_x$ and $i_z$. Both boundaries will vary with $C_L$.

## Analysis of the stability diagrams

The two-parameter stability diagrams (Figs. 10.1 and 10.2) are reproduced from reference 2. They are drawn for typical values of the aerodynamic and inertial parameters, for high and low speed flight. In this connection, the term high speed is meant to imply low $C_L$; similarly low speed is meant to imply high $C_L$. No compressibility effects are included in Figs. 10.1 and 10.2, or in the present discussion. It must also be remembered that, while the general trend of the boundaries is fairly typical, the positions of the boundaries will vary for aircraft of very different plan-forms and inertia distributions, especially if separation of flow over the wing takes place at a moderate value of $C_L$. The Routhian boundary is drawn for $\mu_2$ = 20, 40 and 100. As can be seen from Eq. (10.40), for a given aircraft, $\mu_2$ increases as $\rho_e$ decreases, i.e. as the height increases. In Figs. 10.1 and 10.2, the arrows show the stable sides of the two boundaries.

## High speed characteristics

Fig. 10.1 is drawn for $C_L = 0.1$, corresponding to the high speed conditions. For a low value of $\mu_2$ (=20), there is no danger of oscillatory instability for typical values of $L_v$ of -0.03 to -0.12, for an aircraft with weathercock stability ($N_v$ positive). Spiral instability, too, will not be encountered for the above range of $L_v$. As the lateral relative density increases, the position of the Routhian boundary is changed, and we see that, for a given value of $L_v$ (effective dihedral), an aircraft with a higher lateral relative density (higher value of $\mu_2$) will require a larger value of $N_v$ (proportional to the directional stability) to possess oscillatory stability. As shown in Chapter 4, $N_v$ can be increased by increasing the size of fin.

We must remember that the stability diagrams merely show the critical stability boundaries. For the lateral motions to be adequately damped, the values of $L_v$ and $N_v$ for the aircraft should correspond to a point well inside the stable region

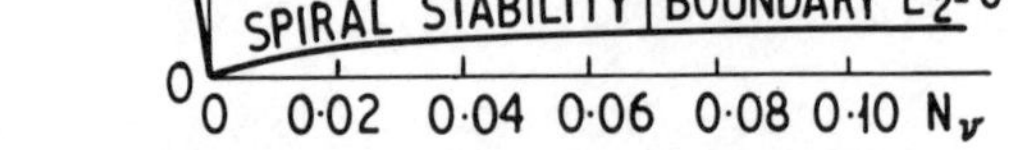

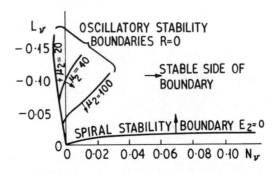

Fig. 10.1 Two-parameter stability diagram (high speed, $C_L = 0.1$). (Reproduced from R. & M. 1989 by E. Priestley). (Crown copyright).

bounded by the curves $R = 0$ and $E_2 = 0$. From Fig. 10.1 we see that even for very large values of $\mu_2$ there is an appreciable region between the Routhian boundary and the spiral stability (or divergence) boundary, for low values of $C_L$.

## Low speed characteristics

Figure 10.2 is drawn for $C_L = 1.0$, corresponding to the low speed conditions. The spiral stability boundary has now become much more important. However, as we shall see below, provided the value of $N_v$ is not excessive, the growth of the spiral motion is slow (the time to double amplitude may be as much as 3 min.), and the pilot has ample time to apply the controls to correct this motion. Thus spiral instability is not, in general, serious for piloted aircraft. It must, of course, be taken into account for pilotless aircraft (e.g. guided missiles); this can be done by means of an automatic pilot. We see from Fig. 10.2 that the oscillatory

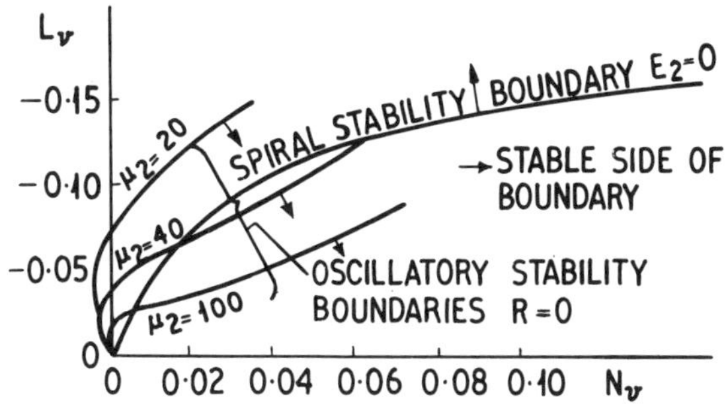


Fig. 10.2 Two-parameter stability diagram (low speed, $C_L = 1.0$). (Reproduced from R. & M. 1989 by E. Priestley) (Crown copyright)

stability boundaries (for the various values of $\mu_2$) have also shifted in an unfavourable manner for the higher value of $C_L$, a still larger $N_v$ (i.e. a larger fin area) being necessary for a given value of $L_v$, i.e. for a given dihedral. As for the high speed conditions, the fin area required to ensure that the aircraft has oscillatory stability is greater the larger the value of $\mu_2$. This change in the position of the Routhian boundary for high values of $C_L$ is very important, since an aircraft should have adequate oscillatory stability under all conditions of flight. The position is particularly serious for highly loaded aircraft near the ceiling (with large $\mu_2$). Another serious case is that of an aircraft with sweptback wings, for which, as shown in Chapter 4, $(-L_v)$ increases with $C_L$. From Fig. 10.2 we see that for such an aircraft (with a high value of $L_v$ at the high value of $C_L$), a large value of $N_v$ will be necessary to ensure both adequate oscillatory stability and not too much spiral instability, particularly if the aircraft has a high lateral relative density. The value of $(-L_v)$ can always be decreased by decreasing the effective dihedral, but for a sweptback wing aircraft this may well lead to a very low value of $(-L_v)$ at high speeds, leading to spiral instability. It may well be preferable to increase the lateral stability of the aircraft artificially by means of an automatic pilot (e.g. a yaw damper), as shown in Chapter 11.

## THE PERIOD AND DAMPING OF THE LATERAL MOTIONS

So far we have discussed only the determination of the critical stability boundaries and their illustration by means of stability diagrams. These boundaries separate stable from unstable regions and enable us to say whether a given aircraft is stable or unstable. As shown in Part II (Chapter 6), the periods and the damping of the motions can also be exhibited on these stability diagrams. The Dutch roll oscillation and the spiral motion are the only lateral motions for which the damping may be critical, and these are the two motions which we shall now consider.

If $\lambda = -r + is$ is a root of the characteristic equation, then, from Eqs. (10.12) and (10.13), the time to half-amplitude and the period are inversely proportional to $r$ and $s$ respectively. As shown in reference 2, two families of curves (of constant $r$ and constant $s$) can be drawn, in terms of $L_v$ and $N_v$, for the lateral oscillation, and another family of curves (of constant $r$) for the damping of the spiral motion. The Routhian and divergence boundaries are particular cases of these curves for $r = 0$.

## Analysis of the period and damping of the lateral motions

The period and damping of the lateral motions are shown in Figs. 10.3 - 10.5, plotted against $N_v$ and $L_v$, as in the case of the stability diagrams. Figures 10.3 and 10.4 show the curves of constant damping ($r$ = constant) and constant period ($s$ = constant) for the lateral oscillation, Fig. 10.3 being drawn for $\mu_2 = 20$ and Fig. 10.4 for $\mu_2 = 100$. Both figures are drawn for low speed flight ($C_L = 1.0$), the values of the aerodynamic derivatives being the same as for the corresponding stability diagram (Fig. 10.2). In Figs. 10.3 and 10.4, the curve $r = 0$ corresponds to the oscillatory stability boundary; curves with $r$ positive correspond to damped oscillations, curves with $r$ negative to increasing oscillations. We see that, in general, increase of $N_v$ (e.g. by increasing the fin area) improves the

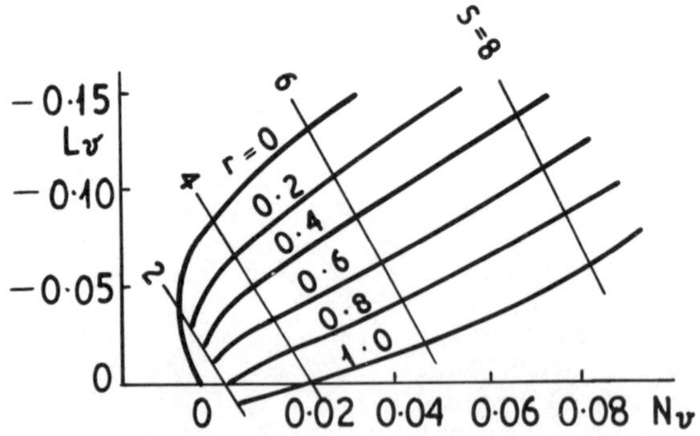


Fig. 10.3 Period and damping of the lateral oscillation ($\mu_2 = 20$). (Reproduced from R. & M. 1989 by E. Priestley) (Crown copyright).

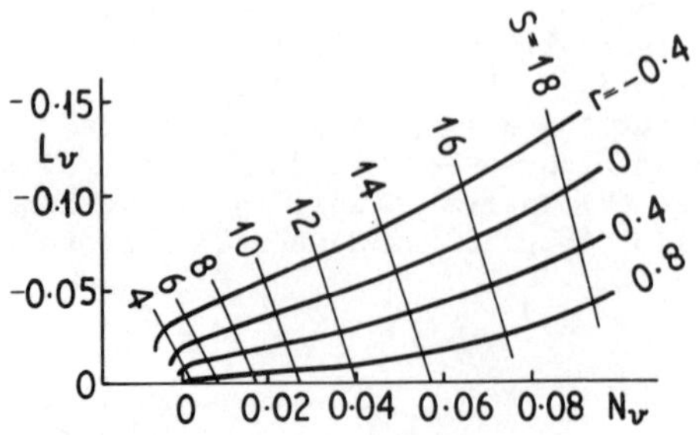


Fig. 10.4 Period and damping of the lateral oscillation ($\mu_2 = 100$). (Reproduced from R. & M. 1989 by E. Priestley) (Crown copyright).

oscillatory stability by increasing the damping; similarly for a decrease in $(-L_v)$, i.e. a decrease in effective dihedral. We note that the same damping can be obtained with a longer period by decreasing both $N_v$ and $(-L_v)$, i.e. decreasing both the fin area and the effective dihedral. This is important in order to avoid unpleasant sustained oscillations, i.e. oscillations in which the damping is small compared with the period. For satisfactory flying qualities an oscillation should be damped to (about) half-amplitude by the end of the first period (unless the period is very short). For a given period, the damping is increased by decreasing the effective dihedral; decrease of dihedral may, however, cause spiral instability. We see that the damping of the oscillatory motion is very sensitive to the effective dihedral.

As noted above, the effect of increasing $\mu_2$ from 20 to 100 is to shift the Routhian boundary to higher values of $N_v$ for a given value of $L_v$. From Figs. 10.3 and 10.4 we see that a given decrease in $(-L_v)$ has a greater effect on the damping at the higher value of $\mu_2$. For a moderate degree of damping of the lateral oscillation, say $r = 0.4$ to $0.8$, the lines of constant damping can be approximated to by straight lines through the origin, i.e. $L_v/N_v$ = constant. Thus the ratio $L_v/N_v$ gives a better idea of the damping than the absolute values of these derivatives. The non-dimensional frequency $s$ is approximately doubled in going from $\mu_2 = 20$ to $\mu_2 = 100$. For large values of $\mu_2$ and $N_v$, it is shown in reference 2 that the non-dimensional frequency of $s$ of the lateral (Dutch roll) oscillation is given approximately by

$$s = \sqrt{\left(\frac{\mu_2 N_v}{i_z}\right)}. \tag{10.41}$$

The period $T$ in seconds is given by

$$T = \frac{2\pi}{s}\,\tau = 2\pi\tau\left(\frac{\mu_2 N_v}{i_z}\right)^{-\frac{1}{2}} = \frac{2\pi}{\sqrt{g}}\sqrt{\left(\frac{i_z b C_L}{N_v \cos\Theta_e}\right)}, \tag{10.42}$$

where $b$ = wing span,

in agreement with Eq. (9.14). Thus, for large values of $\mu_2$ and $N_v$, the period is practically independent of $L_v$.

The rate of growth of the spiral motion is shown in Fig. 10.5, drawn for the case of low speed flight ($C_L = 1.0$). In Fig. 10.5, the curve $r = 0$ corresponds to the spiral stability boundary; curves with $r$ negative correspond to spiral divergence. The curves with $r$ negative are, theoretically, dependent on the value of $\mu_2$, but in practice the variation with $\mu_2$ is negligible. We see that the rate of spiral divergence is increased by increasing $N_v$ (e.g. by increasing the fin area) or by decreasing $(-L_v)$, i.e. decreasing the effective dihedral. However, even for large values of $N_v$, the rate of divergence $r$ does not increase rapidly as we decrease

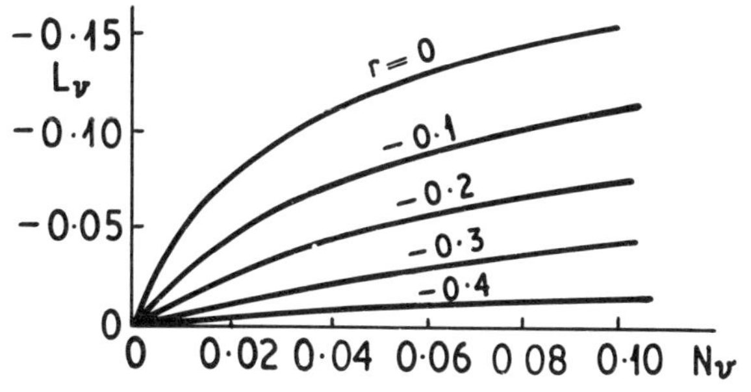


Fig. 10.5 Rate of growth of spiral motion.
(Reproduced from R. & M. 1989 by E. Priestley) (Crown copyright)

$(-L_v)$, and hence, even if the point on the stability diagram is well inside the region of spiral divergence, the rate of divergence will not be high. Thus, from Eq. (10.14), $r = 0.10$ corresponds to a time to double amplitude of 35 sec for an aircraft speed of 100 m/s at $C_L = 1.0$.

## FACTORS AFFECTING THE CHOICE OF $L_v$ AND $N_v$

We illustrated the lateral stability characteristics by means of stability diagrams, together with curves of constant damping and frequency, plotted against $N_v$ (proportional to the directional stability) and $L_v$ (proportional to the effective dihedral). The lateral stability characteristics also depend on the lateral relative density $\mu_2$, the rolling and yawing inertias and the other lateral non-dimensional stability derivatives, as well as on the flight conditions ($C_L$ and height, flaps up or down). For lateral stability, an aircraft must be directionally stable (i.e. $N_v$ positive); however, too high a value of $N_v$ may lead to spiral instability. Similarly, considering the effective dihedral, we see that too low a value of $(-L_v)$ will lead to spiral instability, while too high a value will lead to oscillatory instability. As shown above, these effects are most serious for (i) high values of $\mu_2 = m/\frac{1}{2}\rho_e S b$, (ii) low speeds, i.e. high $C_L$, (iii) aircraft with sweptback wings, for which there is an appreciable increase in $(-L_v)$ with $C_L$. As shown above, in the worst case, it may be necessary to provide artificial stability by means of an automatic pilot. We have seen too that, while spiral instability is not in general serious, the damping of the oscillatory mode is very sensitive to the ratio $L_v/N_v$.

There are many factors that affect the choice of $L_v$ and $N_v$ (i.e. the effective dihedral and the directional stability) for a new design. These factors come under three main headings: (i) safety precautions, (ii) rate of roll requirements, and (iii) stability requirements. In this connection, safety precautions are concerned with the maintenance of control after engine failure and fin stalling (see Chapter 11). Flight conditions after engine failure may well determine the value of $N_v$ required, and hence the size of fin. Rate of roll requirements dictate the aileron power. Finally, the above discussion has shown the relevance of the stability requirements.

In practice the designer is concerned with more than mere stability; the behaviour of the aircraft must be such that it is generally easy and pleasant to fly. Thus we have to consider the response of the aircraft to control movements and to gusts; this is considered in detail in Chapter 11. As long as the aircraft has weathercock stability, satisfactory flying characteristics can be obtained over a wide range of values of the ratio $L_v/N_v$.

## LATERAL DYNAMIC STABILITY OF HIGH SPEED AIRCRAFT

The lateral stability and control characteristics are affected by the changes both in the aerodynamic loading and in the geometry of high speed aircraft (see reference 3). As shown in Chapter 6, these changes depend on the flight Mach number, and would be expected to be most severe in the transonic range.

In general, the numerical values of the wing contribution to all the derivatives decrease as the supersonic Mach number increases, for wings with supersonic leading edges; thus the aerodynamic damping deteriorates, and the aircraft inertia parameters become correspondingly more important (especially at high altitudes). Adequate damping in yaw can be obtained by means of an auto-pilot (by which rudder angle is related to rate of yaw).

The stability and control characteristics are also affected by the very different mass distribution in a supersonic aircraft, which may have most of its fuel and equipment in a long slender fuselage, with a resulting increase in yawing inertia. Such an aircraft will probably have a rather larger proportion of the fuselage ahead of the wing than its subsonic counterpart, together with a much shorter fin arm. As can be seen from Chapter 4, there will be a correspondingly larger destabilizing moment from the fuselage (i.e. a more negative value of $N_v$); this will require a large fin to give the required positive value of $N_v$.

The effectiveness of the fin as a stabilizer increases at subsonic speeds (but this may be offset by aeroelastic distortion of the fuselage). However, the provision of positive directional stability may well be a difficult problem in the design of a supersonic aircraft. The contribution to $N_v$ due to the fin will decrease at supersonic speeds (roughly in proportion to the decrease in the lift curve slope of the fin). The destabilizing yawing moment from the fuselage is relatively insensitive to change of Mach number (since, apart from interference effects, it depends mainly on the Mach number of the 'cross flow'). The net effect is that $N_v$ may become very small (and even change sign) at some supersonic Mach number. A typical sketch of the variation of $N_v$ (and, thus, the aircraft directional stability) with Mach number is given in Fig. 10.6.

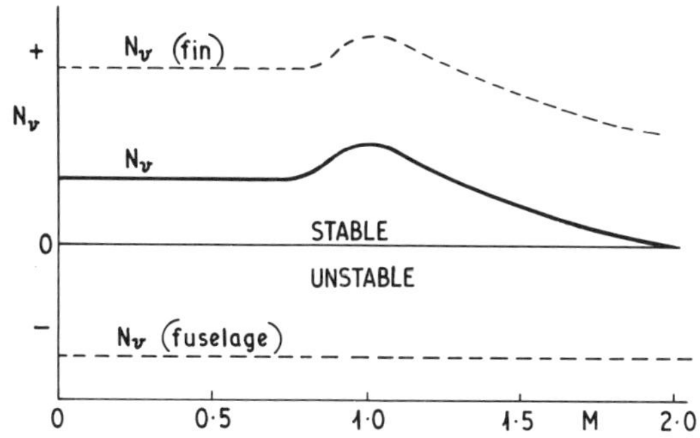


Fig. 10.6 Variation of directional stability with Mach number

As shown in Chapter 12, aeroelastic distortion of the fuselage can aggravate this effect. Positive directional stability can be obtained throughout the entire speed range if the aircraft has a sufficiently large fin (and a sufficiently rigid fuselage), but this may given an undesirably large $N_v$ at low speeds. The only solution to this problem may be to use an auto-pilot to improve the directional stability at supersonic speeds.

Large changes in the aerodynamic loading, and hence in the effective dihedral, can occur at Mach numbers for which the flow perpendicular to the wing leading edge is sonic. Thus, for delta wings with no dihedral, the wing contribution to $L_v$ and $N_v$ changes sign at that Mach number. Such changes could lead to spiral divergence; they also have important effects on the lateral response of the aircraft (as shown in Chapter 11). A positive effective dihedral is desirable, to ensure that an aircraft rolls in the correct way in response to rudder.

## REFERENCES


1. BRYANT, L.W. and HOPWOOD, M.L. Calculation of the damping of the lateral oscillation of an aircraft. R. & M. 1956 (1942).

2. PRIESTLEY, E. A further investigation of lateral stability. R. & M. 1989 (1941).

3. KUCHEMANN, D. *The Aerodynamic Design of Aircraft*. Pergamon Press (1978).


## PROBLEMS

1. What is the physical significance of the zero root of the characteristic equation for lateral stability written as a quintic?

2. Discuss briefly the modes of motion of an aircraft slightly disturbed laterally from steady flight. The lateral stability quartic for a certain aircraft is $\lambda^4 + 12\lambda^3 + 52\lambda^2 + 640\lambda + E_2 = 0$. Find the value of $E_2$ required for neutral stability of the oscillatory mode. What is then the value of $\lambda$ corresponding to the spiral mode?

3. Give the formulae for the non-dimensional lateral stability derivatives $L_p$, etc., in terms of $\mathring{L}_p$, etc., and state which parts of the aircraft contribute to each of these derivatives.

   An aircraft with a stalling speed of 25 m/s has a characteristic equation for lateral stability $f(\lambda) = \lambda^4 + B_2\lambda^3 + C_2\lambda^2 + D_2\lambda + E_2 = 0$. The values of $B_2$, $C_2$, $D_2$ and $E_2$ for various speeds of the aircraft are given in the following table:

| Speed (m/s) | $B_2$ | $C_2$ | $D_2$ | $E_2$ |
|---|---|---|---|---|
| 50 | 26 | 58 | 375 | 2 |
| 27 | 10 | 19 | 58 | -7 |
| 25 | 2 | -28 | -50 | 12 |

   Using Newton's method (one application for each real root), find the approximate factors of $f(\lambda)$ for each speed. Discuss the stability and the physical characteristics of the lateral motions at the given speeds.

4. What is the basic difference between the stability requirements for a guided missile and those for an aircraft? Give examples of cases (i) in which instability can be accepted, and (ii) in which mere stability is not enough, describing the physical nature of the resulting motion.

5. How could the moments and products of inertia of a light aeroplane be experimentally determined from flight tests?

# Chapter 11
# LATERAL RESPONSE

## INTRODUCTION

In Chapter 10 we saw how the stick fixed lateral dynamic stability characteristics could be determined from the general equations of motion given in Chapter 2. We discussed the nature and the significance of the roots of the characteristic equation. The dynamic stability characteristics were studied by means of stability diagrams, showing the dependence of the stability characteristics on the aerodynamic and inertial characteristics of the aircraft, in particular upon $L_v$ (the effective dihedral), $N_v$ (the weathercock stability parameter) and $\mu_2$ (the lateral relative density).

The stability diagrams indicate only the damping and frequency of the disturbed motion; they do not, in general, enable us to follow the actual course of the motion, which may be a combination of several modes.

In response theory we are concerned with the actual motion following a disturbance, e.g. a side gust or a prescribed movement of the ailerons or rudder, or motion after engine failure on a multi-engined aircraft. In response calculations we compute the complete solutions of the equations of lateral asymmetric motion given in Chapter 2, thus obtaining the components of the motion (angle of sideslip $\beta$, angle of bank $\phi$, angle of yaw $\psi$ and their derivatives with respect to $t$) as functions of time. As in the development of the equations of motion in Chapter 2, we assume that all the deviations are small. In the following paragraphs we shall first discuss various methods of solving these equations and then we shall analyse the response due to certain simple disturbances or simple control movements. Finally we shall discuss the use of automatic controls to improve both the dynamic stability and response.

## METHODS OF SOLVING THE EQUATIONS OF MOTION

In Part II, Chapter 7, various methods of solving the equations of motion were considered when the aircraft is submitted to some forced motion, e.g. due to prescribed movement of the controls. We considered the classical method of solution and operational methods. In general, one of the operational methods is the easiest for computational purposes, especially when we are interested only in the motion following an arbitrary initial disturbance from equilibrium, with no other disturbing factors (e.g. disturbances due to sudden short gusts). The analysis is precisely analogous to that for the longitudinal case.

The methods can be applied equally well to include response to a continuous gust of varying strength or to a prescribed motion of the controls, but such complication causes a very large increase in the computations required. We shall consider a number of cases of lateral response corresponding to simple disturbances or simple control movements.

## RESPONSE TO A SIDE GUST

We shall consider first the response of an aircraft subjected to a simple initial disturbance $v_0$ in sideslip velocity (corresponding to a sharp-edged side gust). It is convenient to base our discussion on the aircraft used in references 1 and 2, as the subsequent discussion on response to controls is based on these references. As shown below, we investigate the response at both high speed (i.e. low $C_L$) and low speed (high $C_L$). No account is taken of the effects of compressibility. We consider level flight, and take $Y_p = Y_r = 0$.

### Range of variables covered

In references 1 and 2, a small aircraft was considered which had the following values of the inertial and aerodynamic parameters:

| | High speed | Low speed |
|---|---|---|
| $C_L$ | 0.20 | 1.00 |
| $i_x$ | 0.015 | 0.015 |
| $i_z$ | 0.03 | 0.03 |
| $i_{zx}$ | 0 | -0.0025 |
| $L_p$ | -0.21 | -0.21 |
| $L_r$ | 0.03 | 0.12 |
| $N_p$ | -0.015 | -0.024 |
| $N_r$ (no fin) | 0 | 0 |
| $N_v$ (no fin) | -0.024 | -0.024 |
| $Y_v$ | -0.40 | -0.40 |

As in references 1 and 2, we assume that

$$l_F = s = \tfrac{1}{2}b,$$

i.e. the fin arm = wing semi-span.

Then $$N_v = N_v(\text{no fin}) + N_v(\text{fin})$$

and, from Eq. (10.39),

$$N_r = N_r(\text{no fin}) + \tfrac{1}{2}\{N_v(\text{no fin}) - N_v\}.$$

The response of this aircraft is calculated for the following values of $\mu_2$, $L_v$, $N_v$ and $N_r$:

| $L_v$ | $N_v$ | $N_r$ | | | |
|---|---|---|---|---|---|
| | | $C_L$ | 0.2 | 0.2 | 1.0 |
| | | $\mu_2$ | 10 | 50 | 10 |
| | | | Response curve designated by | | |
| -0.06 | 0.024 | -0.024 | *a* | *a'* | $a_1$ |
| -0.12 | 0.024 | -0.024 | *b* | | $b_1$ |
| -0.06 | 0.096 | -0.06 | *c* | *c'* | $c_1$ |
| -0.12 | 0.096 | -0.06 | *d* | | $d_1$ |

Thus we consider two values of $L_v$ (the effective dihedral) and two values of $N_v$ (proportional to the directional stability). $\mu_2$ is inversely proportional to the air density $\rho_e$ and thus, for a given aircraft, $\mu_2$ will increase as the height increases.

## Stability diagrams

The stability diagrams for this aircraft are shown in Figs. 11.1 and 11.2, and the roots of the characteristic equation are given in the following table.

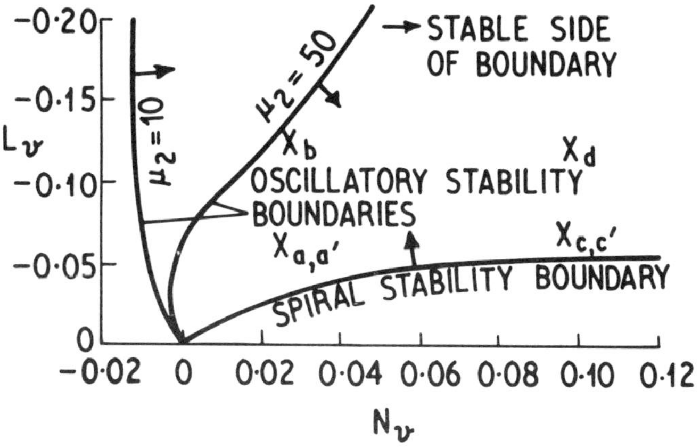


Fig. 11.1 Two-parameter stability diagram ($C_L = 0.1$)

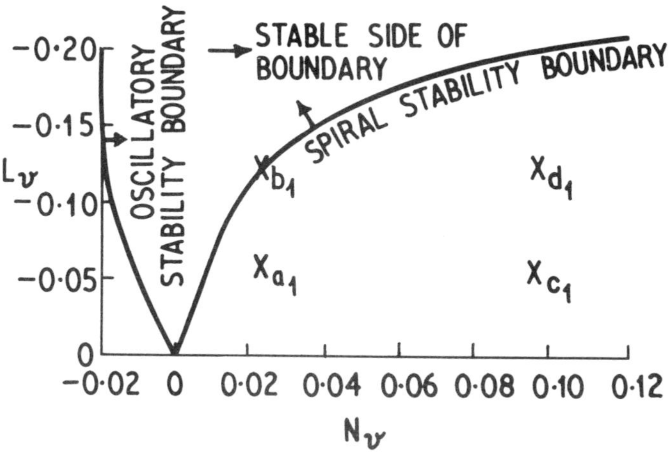


Fig. 11.2 Two-parameter stability diagram ($C_L = 1.0$, $\mu_2 = 10$)

Table 1 Roots of the characteristic equation

| Case | Large real root | Small real root | Complex roots |
|---|---|---|---|
| $a$ | -14.07 | -0.022 | -0.55 ± 3.15i |
| $b$ | -14.21 | -0.056 | -0.46 ± 3.44i |
| $c$ | -14.07 | -0.006 | -1.16 ± 5.77i |
| $d$ | -14.20 | -0.038 | -1.08 ± 5.91i |
| $a'$ | -14.53 | -0.022 | -0.32 ± 6.95i |
| $c'$ | -14.37 | -0.006 | -1.01 ± 12.83i |
| $a_1$ | -14.23 | +0.162 | -0.83 ± 3.64i |
| $b_1$ | -14.34 | 0 | -0.70 ± 4.23i |
| $c_1$ | -14.29 | +0.312 | -1.48 ± 6.11i |
| $d_1$ | -14.38 | +0.154 | -1.36 ± 6.45i |

Analysis of results

When an aircraft encounters a sharp-edged side gust, rolling and yawing moments and side forces act on the aircraft. These in turn will alter the angles of bank, yaw and sideslip, and angular velocities in roll and yaw will be developed. In Figs. 11.3 to 11.5, $v/v_0$, $\mu_2 pb/v_0$ $(=\hat{p}/\hat{v}_0)$ and $\mu_2 rb/v_0$ $(=\hat{r}/\hat{v}_0)$ are plotted against the non-dimensional aerodynamic time $\hat{t}$, for an initial disturbance $v_0$ for the high speed condition, and in Figs. 11.6 to 11.8 for the low speed condition, for a value of $\mu_2$ of 10. It can be seen that the behaviour of an aircraft at both high and low speeds is very sensitive to changes in fin area and wing dihedral.

As shown in Chapter 10, the lateral response is composed of three types of motion: a well damped rolling subsidence, a spiral mode (which is either a lightly damped subsidence or a slow divergence) and a lateral oscillation. From the above table and from Figs. 11.1 and 11.2 we see that the oscillatory motion (Dutch roll) is always damped; the aircraft has a small margin of spiral stability at high speeds, but is spirally unstable (or neutral, in case $b_1$) at low speeds.

In the algebraic expressions for $v/v_0$, $\mu_2 pb/v_0$ and $\mu_2 rb/v_0$, the terms corresponding to the well damped rolling subsidence only influence the behaviour of the aircraft in the initial stages of the motion, after which the oscillatory motion persists (together with a small component due to the spiral motion). From Eqs. (2.121) to (2.123), we see that, if $i_{zx} = 0$, the initial values of $d\hat{v}/d\hat{t}$, $d\hat{p}/d\hat{t}$ and $d\hat{r}/d\hat{t}$ are given by

$$\frac{d\hat{v}}{d\hat{t}} = -y_v\hat{v}_0 = Y_v\hat{v}_0, \tag{11.1}$$

$$\frac{d\hat{p}}{d\hat{t}} = -l_v\hat{v}_0 = \frac{\mu_2 L_v}{i_x}\hat{v}_0, \tag{11.2}$$

and

$$\frac{d\hat{r}}{d\hat{t}} = -n_v\hat{v}_0 = \frac{\mu_2 N_v}{i_z}\hat{v}_0. \tag{11.3}$$

Thus the magnitude (and sense) of the initial response in roll and yaw is mainly controlled by the values of $L_v$ and $N_v$ (as can be seen from Figs. 11.4, 11.5, 11.7 and 11.8). Following a sharp-edged side gust from starboard, an aircraft with positive effective dihedral (i.e. negative $L_v$) will start to roll with port wing down and to turn (in yaw) into the wind, thus reducing the angle of sideslip. The initial response in sideslip is relatively unaffected by $L_v$ and $N_v$ (except in so far as the period and damping are affected). From the above table, and from Figs. 11.3 to 11.8, we see that when the fin size is increased (curves $c$, $d$, $c_1$ and $d_1$),

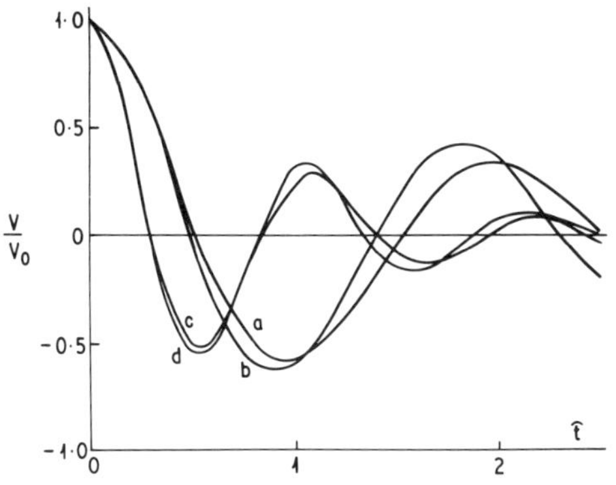


Fig. 11.3

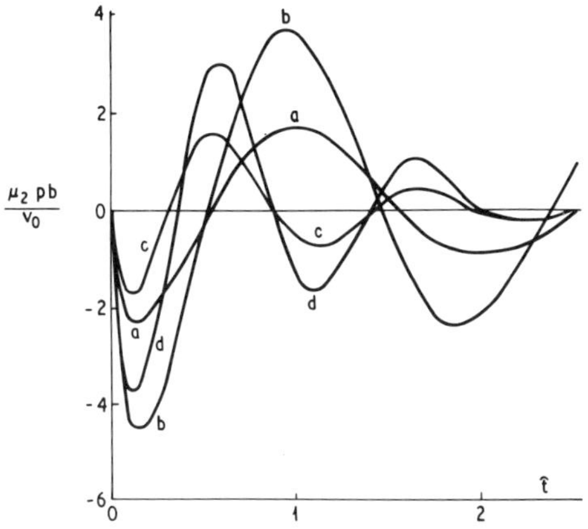


Fig. 11.4

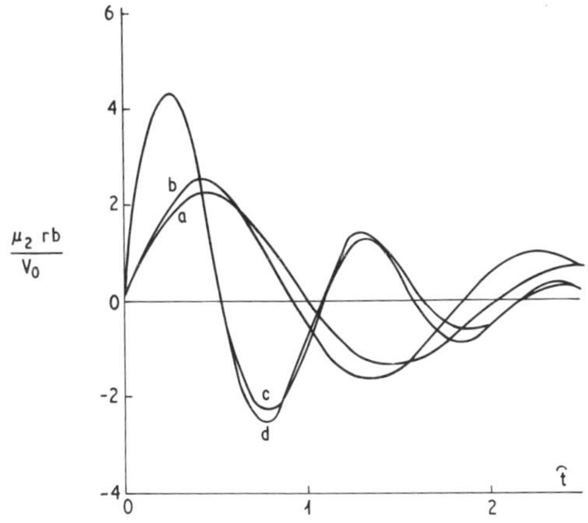


Fig. 11.5

Figs. 11.3-11.5 Motion following an initial disturbance in sideslip ($C_L$ = 0.2).

the frequency of the oscillation increases. For large values of $N_v$, the period $T$ (in seconds) of the lateral oscillation is, approximately, from Eq. (10.42),

$$T = \frac{2\pi\tau}{\sqrt{(\mu_2 N_v / i_z)}} = \frac{2\pi}{\sqrt{g}} \sqrt{\left(\frac{i_z b C_L}{N_v}\right)}, \tag{11.4}$$

for level flight, where $b$ is the wing span.

We see that the period decreases with decrease of wing span or of $C_L$. Thus aircraft of small span will be liable to a lateral oscillation of very short period. At high speeds in gusty conditions this may give rise to uncomfortable flying conditions; for such aircraft the minimum acceptable period of oscillation may well provide an upper limit to $N_v$, and hence to fin size.

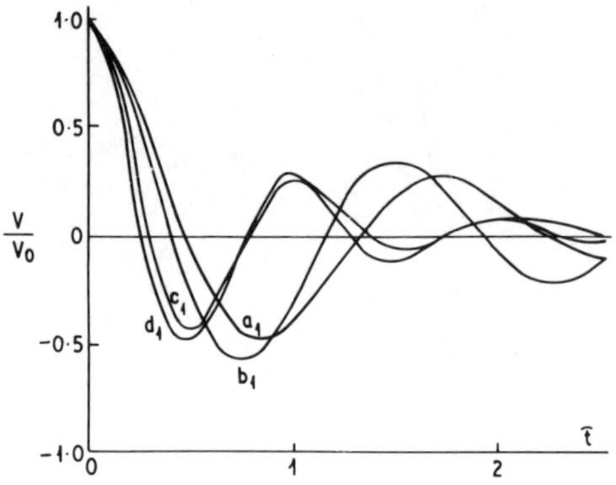


Fig. 11.6

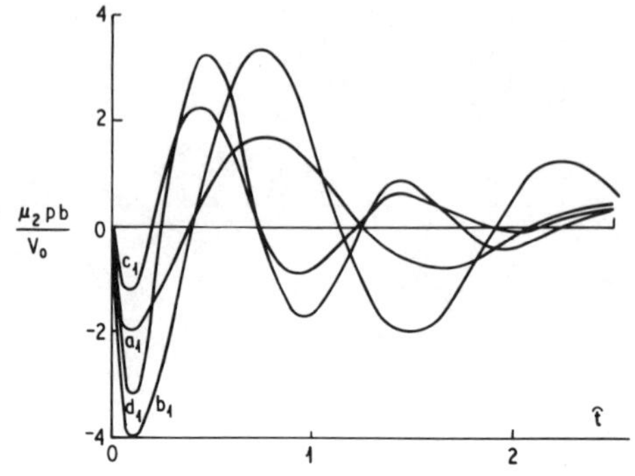


Fig. 11.7

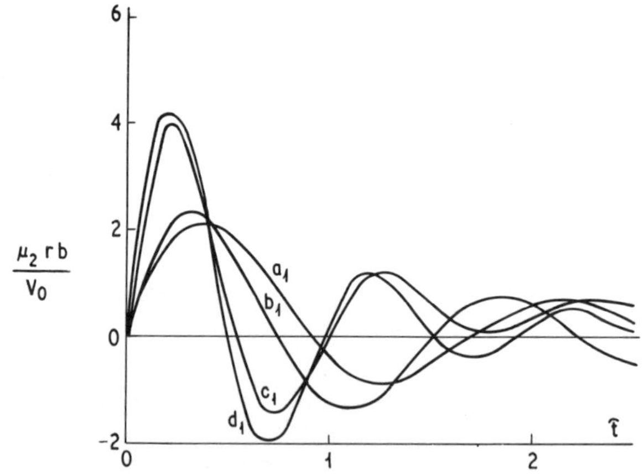


Fig. 11.8

Figs. 11.6-11.8 Motion following an initial disturbance in sideslip ($C_L$ = 1.0).

As can be seen from Eqs. (11.2) and (11.3), the effect of an increase in $\mu_2$ is to increase the initial response in $\hat{p}$ and $\hat{r}$, but, since both of these parameters are proportional to $\mu_2$ (for a given aircraft speed), the magnitude of the initial response in rate of roll (and in rate of yaw) is not greatly changed. However, as can be seen from the above table and from Eq. (11.4), the principal effect of an increase in $\mu_2$ is to increase the frequency of the lateral motion approximately as $\sqrt{\mu_2}$, measured in units of $\hat{t}$. The frequency in cycles per second is practically unchanged if the change in $\mu_2$ is due to change in altitude.

## RESPONSE OF AN AIRCRAFT TO APPLICATION OF THE AILERONS AND RUDDER

When the aileron angle or rudder angle are changed from their initial values in steady trimmed level flight, rolling and yawing moments act on the aircraft. These moments will alter the angles of bank and yaw, and angular velocities in roll and yaw will be developed. These in turn will generate other aerodynamic forces, and, as shown in Chapter 2, the resulting motion will involve sideslip, bank and yaw. The nature of the ensuing motion (i.e. of the response of the aircraft to application of the asymmetric controls) will depend very much on the aerodynamic and inertial characteristics of the aircraft, as well as upon the nature of the roots of the characteristic equation. Analysis of this motion is of importance in determining whether the aircraft has any undesirable tendencies, due to the coupling between these motions. For example, as shown below, the combination of small $N_v$ and large dihedral results in poor response in roll (due partly to such an aircraft having a poorly damped lateral oscillation), the rate of roll oscillating about a mean value. The response of an aircraft to the application of asymmetric controls is very sensitive at both high and low speeds to variations in fin area and wing dihedral.

The response to a prescribed movement of the ailerons and rudder can be found from the equations of motion (2.121)-(2-123), using the methods outlined in Part II (Chapter 7). In these equations, the aileron angle $\xi$ and the rudder angle $\zeta$ (both taken to be small) are given functions of the non-dimensional time $\hat{t}$. The analysis which follows is based on that of references 1 and 2, and applies to the aircraft considered above in the discussion of the response to a side gust. As above, we shall consider the effects of dihedral and fin size on the response characteristics.

It is convenient to define the following non-dimensional rolling and yawing moment coefficients due to controls:

$$C_l(\hat{t}) = \frac{\mathring{L}(t)}{\frac{1}{2}\rho_e V_e{}^2 Sb} = L_\xi \xi + L_\zeta \zeta, \tag{11.5}$$

$$C_n(\hat{t}) = \frac{\mathring{N}(t)}{\frac{1}{2}\rho_e V_e{}^2 Sb} = N_\xi \xi + N_\zeta \zeta. \tag{11.6}$$

We neglect the side forces due to rudder and ailerons.

### Response in roll due to an applied rolling moment

For simplicity, we shall first consider the case of 'simple rolling', supposing the rolling motion to be unaffected by the other components of motion. We assume that constant aileron angle $\xi_1$ is applied, with ailerons having zero yawing moment. Eq. (2.122) then becomes

$$(\hat{D} + l_p)\hat{p} + l_\xi \xi_1 = 0 \tag{11.7}$$

where $\hat{D} = \dfrac{d}{d\hat{t}}$ .

The solution for an instantaneously applied constant rolling moment $C_{l_1}$ (due to aileron angle $\xi_1$) is

$$\hat{p} = -\frac{l_\xi \xi_1}{l_p}(1 - e^{-l_p \hat{t}}) \tag{11.8}$$

or, in terms of the non-dimensional aerodynamic derivatives defined in Chapter 4,

$$\hat{p} = -\frac{\mu_2 L_\xi \xi_1}{L_p}(1 - e^{L_p \hat{t}/i_x}),$$

i.e. $$\frac{pb}{V_e}\frac{i_x}{C_{l_1}} = -\frac{i_x}{L_p}(1 - e^{L_p \hat{t}/i_x}). \qquad (11.9)$$

The limiting value of the rate of roll (as $\hat{t} \to \infty$) is

$$\hat{p} = -\frac{l_\xi \xi_1}{l_p},$$

i.e. $$p = -\frac{V_e}{b}\frac{L_\xi}{L_p}\xi_1. \qquad (11.10)$$

From Eqs. (11.7) and (11.10), we see that the limiting rate of simple rolling is equal to the steady rate of roll due to applying the given aileron angle $\xi_1$.

The response in roll of the given aircraft to an applied rolling moment is shown in Figs. 11.9 and 11.10. Up to the first maximum, the rate of roll differs little from that for simple rolling.

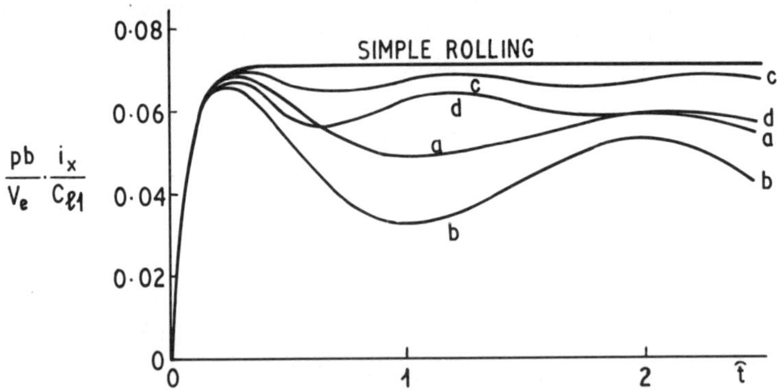


Fig. 11.9 Rate of roll due to instantaneous application of rolling couple $C_{l_1}$ ($C_L = 0.2$). (Based on R. & M. 1915 by R.W. Gandy).

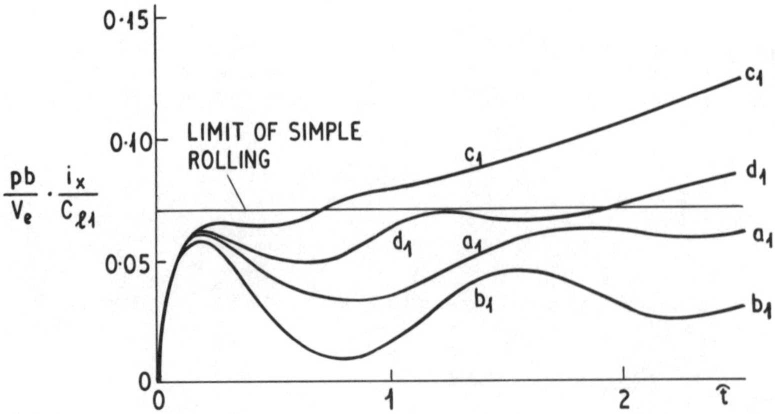


Fig. 11.10 Rate of roll due to instantaneous application of rolling couple $C_{l_1}$ ($C_L = 1.0$). (Based on R. & M. 1915 by R.W. Gandy).

It can be seen that the best response in roll is obtained by having a small dihedral ($-L_v$) and a large fin ($N_v$), as in case *c*; the response is then similar to that for simple rolling. At low speeds, however, the rate of roll in this case continues to increase with time indefinitely, due to spiral instability. Increase of fin size as a means of improving rolling response is more effective when the dihedral is large (cases *b* and *d*).

## Response in yaw and sideslip due to an applied rolling moment

The response in yaw is shown in Figs. 11.11 and 11.13, and that in sideslip in Figs. 11.12 and 11.14. During the early part of the motion the rate of yaw is negative, but a change of sign occurs and thereafter the rate of yaw remains positive. Increasing the fin area ($N_v$) reduces the negative rate of yaw in the early stages of the motion.

The sideslip developed is greatest when both the dihedral ($-L_v$) and the fin area ($N_v$) are small (curve *a*). Increase of fin area leads to a very marked reduction in sideslip velocity during the early stages of the motion, though subsequently the various curves are not widely separated. Increase of dihedral also reduces the sideslip velocity, especially if $N_v$ is small.

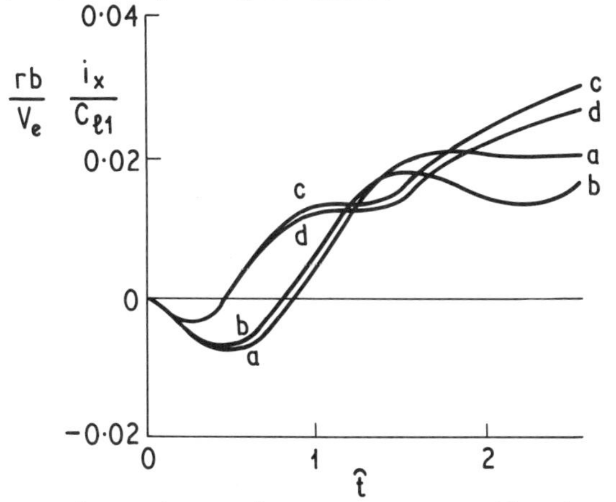


Fig. 11.11 Rate of yaw due to instantaneous application of rolling couple $C_{l_1}$ ($C_L = 0.2$). (Based on R. & M. 2272 by R.W. Gandy).

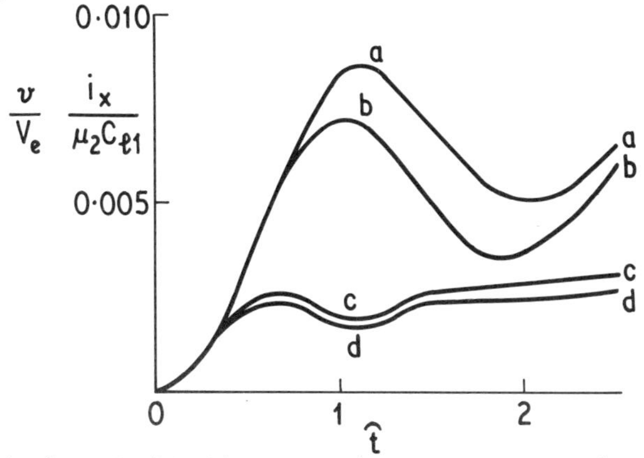


Fig. 11.12 Velocity of sideslip due to instantaneous application of rolling couple $C_{l_1}$ ($C_L = 0.2$). (Based on R. & M. 2272 by R.W. Gandy).

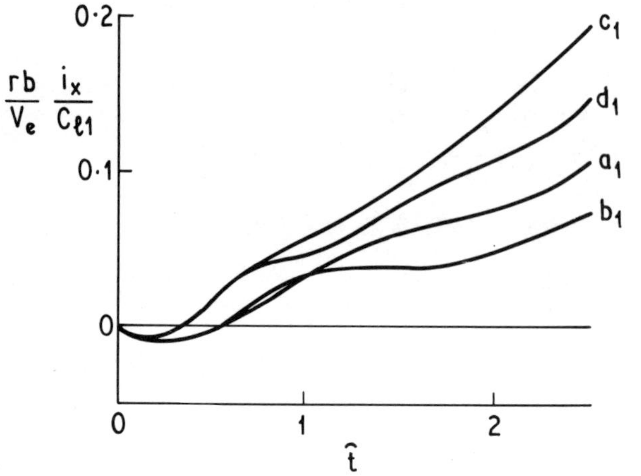


Fig. 11.13 Rate of yaw due to instantaneous application of rolling couple $C_{l_1}$ ($C_L = 1.0$). (Based on R. & M. 2272 by R.W. Gandy).

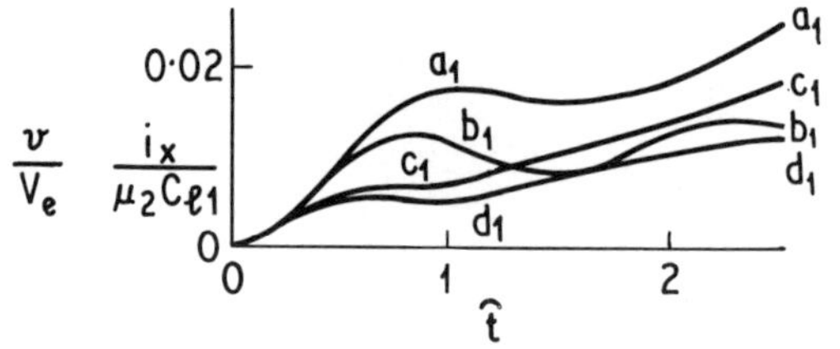


Fig. 11.14 Velocity of sideslip due to instantaneous application of rolling couple $C_{l_1}$ ($C_L = 1.0$). (Based on R. & M. 2272 by R.W. Gandy).

The response in yaw and sideslip can be explained by considering the equations of motion (2.121)-(2.123). Positive rolling motion causes a positive response in sideslip. As shown in Figs. 11.9 and 11.10, the rate of roll is appreciably reduced by increase in ($-L_v$), especially if $N_v$ is small (curves *a* and *b*), and a corresponding reduction in the rate of sideslip is therefore to be expected (curve *b*, Figs. 11.12 and 11.14). Now, since $N_p$ is negative, a positive rate of roll gives a negative yawing moment and hence the rate of yaw is negative in the early stages of the motion. From Eq. (2.121) we see that a negative rate of yaw will increase the sideslip; later, when the rate of yaw is positive, the effect is to decrease sideslip. It is the contribution of the yawing motion which accounts for the marked effect on sideslip of variations in $N_v$ (Figs. 11.12 and 11.14). Most of the low speed cases exhibit spiral instability, both sideslip and rate of yaw eventually becoming increasingly positive.

## Response in roll due an applied yawing moment

From Figs. 11.15 and 11.16, we see that the application of a positive yawing moment produces an initial positive rate of roll which increases to a maximum and thereafter fluctuates. The values of $L_v$ and $N_v$ are even more important in determining the nature of the response in roll due to an applied yawing moment than they are in the case of applied rolling moments. The combination of small dihedral ($-L_v$) and large fin ($N_v$), case *c*, keeps the response in roll small, but a small fin, especially if associated with a large dihedral (case *b*), results in a rate of roll which rapidly increases to a maximum and thereafter fluctuates with a large amplitude of oscillation.

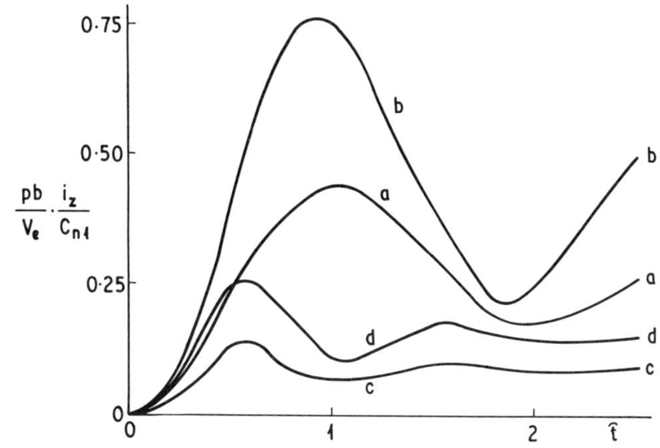


Fig. 11.15 Rate of roll due to instantaneous application of yawing couple $C_{n_1}$ ($C_L = 0.2$). (Based on R. & M. 1915 by R.W. Gandy).

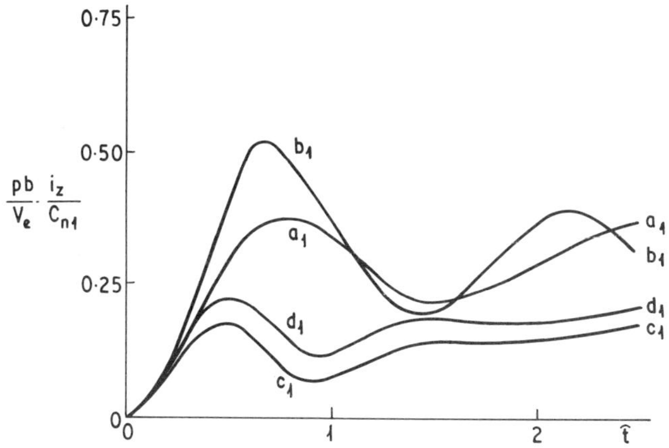


Fig. 11.16 Rate of roll due to instantaneous application of yawing couple $C_{n_1}$ ($C_L = 1.0$). (Based on R. & M. 1915 by R.W. Gandy).

This is particularly important in relation to the sudden occurrence of large yawing moments on an aircraft, as for example when one engine fails or in a cross-wind take-off or landing. An aircraft with large dihedral and a small fin would tend to roll heavily, and, since it is just such an aircraft which has the poorest response to the application of rolling moment, the pilot might not be able to provide adequate control by applying the ailerons.

Response in yaw and sideslip due to an applied yawing moment

The response in yaw and sideslip is shown in Figs. 11.17-11.20. Positive yawing moment produced positive yaw and negative sideslip. During the early stages of the motion the angle of sideslip is approximately equal (and opposite in sign) to the angle of yaw. Thus the sideslip does not at first produce sideways motion of the centre of gravity. As would be expected, for a given yawing moment the effect of a large fin (curves *c* and *d*) is to reduce very markedly the response in both yaw and sideslip; in addition, the oscillatory mode is less prominent and is more

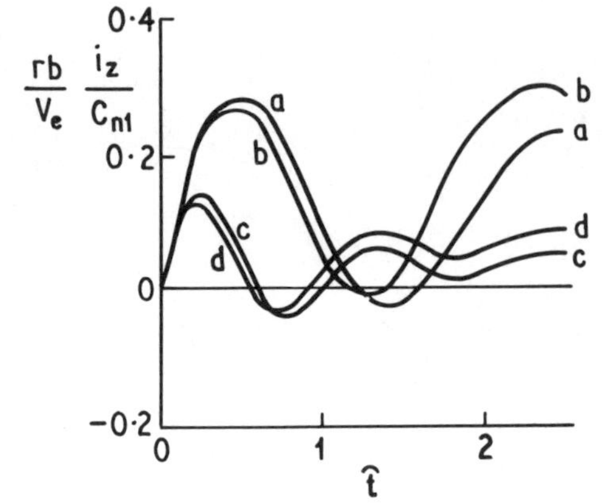


Fig. 11.17 Rate of yaw due to instantaneous application of yawing couple $C_{n_1}$ ($C_L = 0.2$). (Based on R. & M. 2272 by R.W. Gandy).

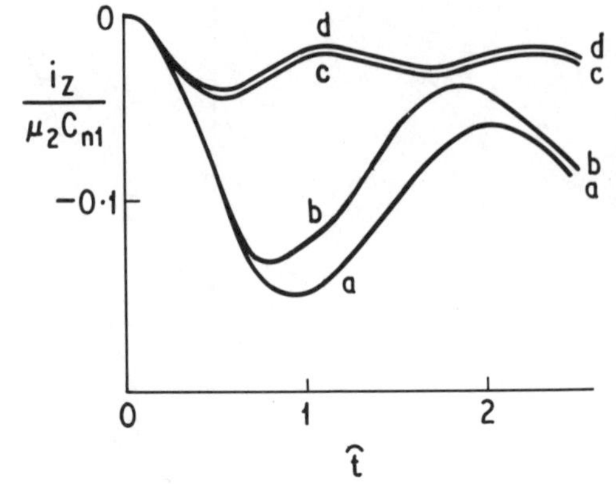


Fig. 11.18 Velocity of sideslip due to instantaneous application of yawing couple $C_{n_1}$ ($C_L = 0.2$). (Based on R. & M. 2272 by R.W. Gandy).

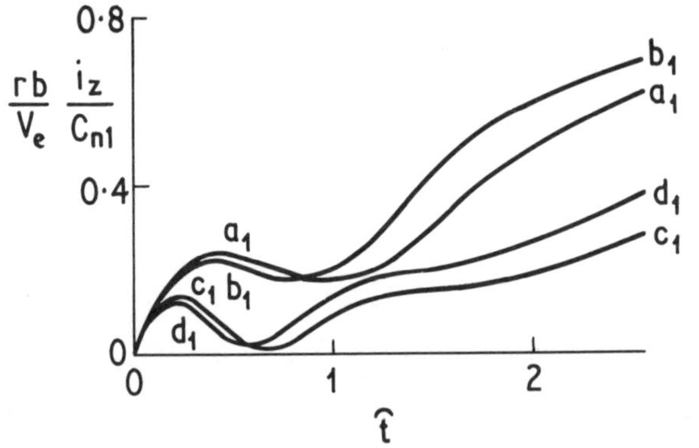


Fig. 11.19 Rate of yaw due to instantaneous application of yawing couple $C_{n_1}$ ($C_L = 1.0$). (Based on R. & M. 2272 by R.W. Gandy).

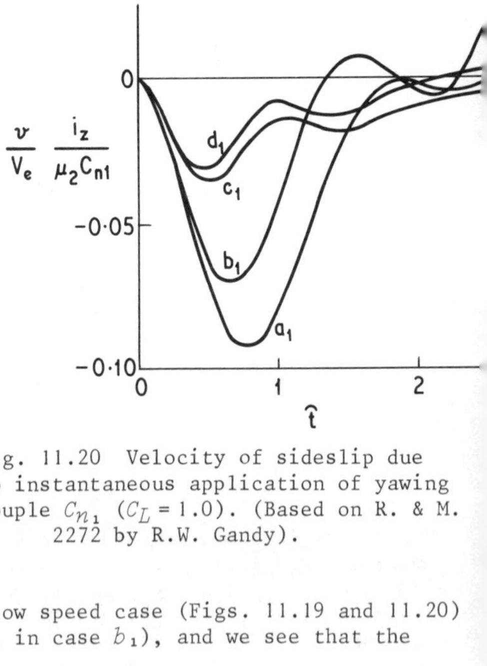


Fig. 11.20 Velocity of sideslip due to instantaneous application of yawing couple $C_{n_1}$ ($C_L = 1.0$). (Based on R. & M. 2272 by R.W. Gandy).

heavily damped, as shown in Table 1. In the low speed case (Figs. 11.19 and 11.20) the aircraft is spirally unstable (or neutral, in case $b_1$), and we see that the rate of yaw increases indefinitely.

Increase of dihedral (curves $b$ and $d$) reduces the response in sideslip. As shown above, with large dihedral there is a high rate of roll, especially when $N_v$ is small. As the positive bank develops, the gravitational component in Eq. (2.121) tends to reduce the negative rate of sideslip.

It would seem, therefore, that the problem of keeping direction by means of the rudder, as for example in a dive, is eased by the provision of fairly large fin area, since the motion is then least erratic. Large dihedral is slightly beneficial if regard is paid only to the response in yaw and sideslip, but this is more than offset by the large and erratic rolling motion which ensues. These conclusions, to some extent, support the conclusions with regard to rolling manoeuvres: a combination of a large fin and small dihedral gives satisfactory manoeuvring qualities, while the combination of a small fin and large dihedral is to be avoided.

## Response to combined rolling and yawing moments

As shown in Chapter 4, ailerons of conventional design commonly produce a negative yawing moment in association with a positive rolling moment. From the above figures we see that the response in roll to this yawing moment will be negative and will therefore reduce the effectiveness of the ailerons as a rolling device. From Figs. 11.9 and 11.15 we see that the adverse yawing moment will give a substantial reduction of response in roll when $(-L_v)$ is large and $N_v$ small (case *b*). This may be offset by use of the rudder, and in this way a wide range of yawing moment is available for a given rolling moment. For ailerons with favourable yawing moments, the average rate of roll is greater than the limit for simple rolling.

The corresponding motions in sideslip and yaw can be deduced from Figs. 11.11, 11.12, 11.17 and 11.18. The response in yaw and sideslip associated with a given rolling moment will be increased when negative yawing moment is applied as well. On the other hand, the use of the rudder to give positive yawing moment can result in a virtual elimination of sideslip, although the rate of yaw will tend to oscillate and may subsequently become negative for a short time.

## FIN STALLING

In considering the response of the aircraft we have to ensure that the fin and rudder will not stall as a result of applying ailerons or rudder, or as a result of the application of an asymmetric yawing moment due to engine failure on a multi-engined aircraft. From Fig. 11.12, the smallness of the values of $(v/V_e)(i_x/\mu_2 C_{l_1})$ shows that there is no risk of fin stalling for moderate aileron angles at high speeds. For example, taking representative values of $i_x = 0.015$, $\mu_2 = 10$, $C_{l_1} = -0.4\xi$, we see that the maximum value of the angle of sideslip $v/V_e$ in Fig. 11.12 is approximately $-2\xi$. For a heavily loaded aircraft at low speeds, fin stalling could be caused by aileron deflection, especially if the fin were small (Fig. 11.14). By increasing the size of the fin, the response in sideslip takes longer to reach appreciable values and the pilot would have time to apply the rudder.

Considering the response to applying the rudder we have, taking

$$i_z = 0.03, \quad \mu_2 = 10, \quad C_{n_1} = N_\zeta \zeta = -\frac{a_2}{a_1} N_v(\text{fin})\zeta ,$$

$$\frac{i_z}{\mu_2 C_{n_1}} = -\frac{0.003}{(a_2/a_1)N_v(\text{fin})\zeta} = -\frac{0.003}{(a_2/a_1)(N_v + 0.024)\zeta} .$$

Now, for an aircraft sideslipping with velocity $v$ and having a rate of yaw $r$, the local incidence at the fin is

$$-\frac{v}{V_e} + \frac{l_F}{V_e} r = -\frac{v}{V_e} + \frac{1}{2}\frac{rb}{V_e} .$$

From Figs. 11.17 - 11.20, on substituting the above values, we see that the maximum fin incidence is reduced by increasing $N_v$, in spite of the increased rudder moment. With the larger fin, the maximum fin incidence is about $2(a_2/a_1)\zeta$, and thus there is a danger of fin stalling for large rudder angles unless $a_2/a_1$ is very small.

## EFFECT OF ENGINE FAILURE; MINIMUM CONTROL SPEED

In the case of engine failure, the yawing moment $C_{n_1}$ is independent of $N_v$, and there is every advantage in having the larger fin. We see that, for engine failure at very low speeds, the adverse yawing moment to be overcome by applying the rudder will require a large rudder angle, since the rudder yawing moment will vary as $V_e{}^2\zeta$; this large rudder angle may stall the fin and rudder. There is thus a *minimum control speed* $V_{MCA}$ at which, if, in initially steady conditions, sudden engine failure occurs, it is possible to recover control and maintain steady straight flight. The current British Civil Airworthiness Requirements stipulate that, in recovering control, the rudder pedal force must not exceed 150 lb. $V_{MCA}$ must not exceed 1.2 times the stalling speed.

## EFFECT OF VARIATIONS IN $\mu_2$, THE LATERAL RELATIVE DENSITY

As with the response to a side gust, the principal effect of an increase in $\mu_2$ is to increase the frequency of the lateral motion. The value of the first maximum rate of roll is reduced, the reduction being greatest for small values of $N_v$, but the average rate of roll is not much changed. The initial response in yaw is markedly reduced by increasing $\mu_2$, but in the later stages of the motion there is little variation due to $\mu_2$. These effects are considered in detail in references 1 and 2.

## GENERAL CONCLUSIONS

The behaviour of an aircraft at both high and low speeds is very sensitive to variations in fin area and $L_v$ (effective wing dihedral). Rolling response is improved by increasing $N_v$; the combination of small $N_v$ and large effective dihedral is to be avoided since it results in poor rolling response; the same combination leads to a poorly damped lateral oscillation.

At high speeds in gusty conditions, the lateral oscillation may give rise to uncomfortable flying conditions if the period is low, as may be the case with small aircraft. For such aircraft the slowing down of this oscillation may be a paramount consideration, giving an upper limit to $N_v$.

On multi-engined aircraft, the engine failure conditions will determine the size of the rudder to ensure adequate control both immediately after engine failure and in the subsequent flight.

## FREQUENCY RESPONSE ANALYSIS

As in Part II (Chapter 8), the frequency response method can be used to determine the response to sinusoidal gusts, and to turbulent air (see reference 3). Yawing and rolling moments on the aircraft result from gradients of horizontal and vertical gusts, and thus the problem is rather more complicated than that for longitudinal response. It is assumed that the turbulence is isotropic, i.e. the spectrum of the side gusts is identical to that of the vertical gusts; the spectra of the yawing and rolling moments can then be related to the spectrum of the side gusts. This is discussed in detail in references 4 and 5.

## ARTIFICIAL STABILITY AND AUTOMATIC CONTROL

As shown in Chapter 10, the provision of adequate lateral stability imposes very severe limitations on the design of a sweptback wing aircraft; for such aircraft $(-Lv)$ increases with $C_L$, with the consequent possibility of oscillatory (Dutch roll) instability at low speeds. It is important for satisfactory flying conditions that the oscillatory motion be adequately damped.

To overcome all these difficulties the designer is often forced to consider some means of automatic control, i.e. the controls are geared to one or more of the components of the flight disturbance (e.g. sideslip, bank, yaw or their rates of change with time) in such a way as to oppose the disturbance.

As shown in Part II (Chapter 7), the use of an automatic control system can increase artificially the stability of an aircraft and improve its response. Conversely (as shown in reference 6), the provision of such active controls enables an aircraft to be designed with a small fin (thus reducing drag and increasing performance).

## OPEN AND CLOSED LOOP SYSTEMS

The general theory of automatic control was given in Part II (Chapter 7). So far in this chapter, we have only considered open-loop systems, in which the magnitude of the control deflection does not depend upon the aircraft motion.

Consider the response to rudder, with ailerons fixed, the initial values of the other variables $v$, $\phi$ and $\psi$ being zero. Applying the Laplace transform method to Eqs. (2.121) - (2.123), with $\xi = 0$, we obtain, on solving the subsidiary equations,

$$\frac{\bar{v}}{\Delta_{1\zeta}} = \frac{\bar{\phi}}{\Delta_{2\zeta}} = \frac{\bar{\psi}}{\Delta_{3\zeta}} = \frac{\bar{\zeta}}{\Delta}, \tag{11.11}$$

where $\Delta = \begin{vmatrix} p + y_v & y_p p - \hat{g}_1 & (1 + y_r)p - \hat{g}_2 \\ l_v & p^2 + l_p p & e_x p^2 + l_r p \\ n_v & e_z p^2 + n_p p & p^2 + n_r p \end{vmatrix}$

and $\Delta_{r\zeta}$ ($r$ = 1 to 3) are third order determinants derived from $\Delta$ by replacing the $r$th column of $\Delta$ by the coefficients of $\zeta$ appearing in Eqs. (2.121) - (2.123), with their signs changed (i.e. by $-y_\zeta$, $-l_\zeta$, $-n_\zeta$). Note that in the present analysis, $p$ is the Laplace operator.

Eq. (11.11) can be written in the alternative form

$$\left.\begin{aligned} \bar{v} &= T_{v\zeta}\bar{\zeta} \\ \bar{\phi} &= T_{\phi\zeta}\bar{\zeta} \\ \bar{\psi} &= T_{\psi\zeta}\bar{\zeta} \end{aligned}\right\} \tag{11.12}$$

where $T_{v\zeta}$, $T_{\phi\zeta}$ and $T_{\psi\zeta}$ are the transfer functions relating $\bar{v}$, $\bar{\phi}$ and $\bar{\psi}$ with $\bar{\zeta}$. We find

$$\left.\begin{aligned}
T_{v\zeta}(p) &= \frac{\Delta_{1\zeta}}{\Delta} = \frac{A_{v\zeta}p^3 + B_{v\zeta}p^2 + C_{v\zeta}p + D_{v\zeta}}{A_2p^4 + B_2p^3 + C_2p^2 + D_2p + E_2} \\
T_{\phi\zeta}(p) &= \frac{\Delta_{2\zeta}}{\Delta} = \frac{A_{\phi\zeta}p^3 + B_{\phi\zeta}p^2 + C_{\phi\zeta}p + D_{\phi\zeta}}{p(A_2p^4 + B_2p^3 + C_2p^2 + D_2p + E_2)} \\
T_{\psi\zeta}(p) &= \frac{\Delta_{3\zeta}}{\Delta} = \frac{A_{\psi\zeta}p^3 + B_{\psi\zeta}p^2 + C_{\psi\zeta}p + D_{\psi\zeta}}{p(A_2p^4 + B_2p^3 + C_2p^2 + D_2p + E_2)}
\end{aligned}\right\} \tag{11.13}$$

In Eq. (11.13), the constants $A_{v\zeta}$, ..., $D_{\psi\zeta}$ are functions of the concise derivatives; $A_2$, $B_2$, $C_2$, $D_2$ and $E_2$ are the coefficients occurring in the characteristic equation (10.5). Precisely similar equations can be obtained for the response to ailerons.

We now use these transfer functions to analyse a single closed-loop system in which the yaw $\psi$ is fed back to an earlier part of the control system. Figure 11.21 shows the block diagram representation of the system; the input $\psi_i$ is the required angle of yaw which, in this analysis, is taken to be zero.

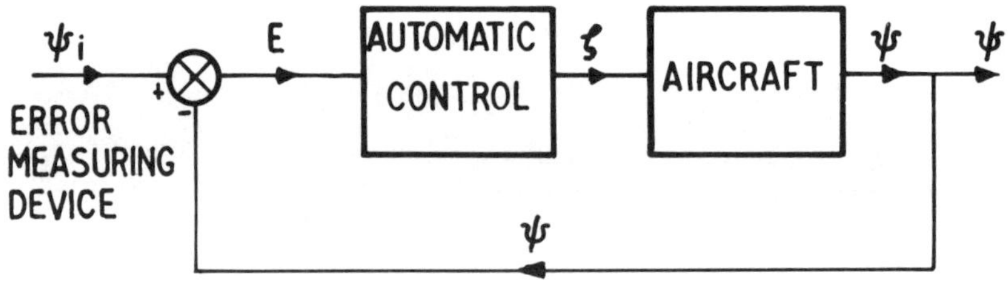


Fig. 11.21 Single closed-loop system

## DYNAMIC STABILITY WITH SOME SIMPLE TYPES OF AUTOMATIC CONTROL

The main purpose of a lateral automatic control system is to suppress any disturbance from steady flight conditions (zero sideslip, bank and yaw) as quickly and efficiently as possible. Thus a properly designed automatic control should not produce a violent swing in bank following a side gust. A suitable automatic control can greatly improve the damping of the lateral oscillation.

We consider first some simple types of automatic control, in which the change in rudder angle $\zeta$ is related to the angle of yaw $\psi$ (or rate of yaw) of the aircraft. The control equation is assumed to be (in terms of Laplace transforms)

$$\bar{\zeta} = (g_\psi + g_{\dot\psi}\, p)\,\bar{\psi}\ , \tag{11.14}$$

where $g_\psi$ and $g_{\dot\psi}$ are autopilot parameters (gains or gearings), which are assumed to be constant for small deviations from steady flight (but they may vary with the steady state conditions).

By analogy with Eq. (7.48), the characteristic equation of the aircraft and automatic control system is

$$1 - (g_\psi + g_{\dot\psi}\, p)\, T_{\psi\zeta} = 0, \tag{11.15}$$

or, from Eq. (11.13),

$$\Delta(p) - (g_\psi + g_{\dot\psi}\, p)\,\Delta_{3\zeta} = 0. \tag{11.16}$$

For the given type of automatic control, this is a quintic equation of the form

$$\bar{A}_2 p^5 + \bar{B}_2 p^4 + \bar{C}_2 p^3 + \bar{D}_2 p^2 + \bar{E}_2 p + \bar{F}_2 = 0, \tag{11.17}$$

in which the coefficients differ from those of the characteristic equation, in the form of Eq. (10.4), because of the terms in Eq. (11.16) due to the automatic control. In the expressions for the coefficients of Eq. (11.17), all the terms arising from automatic controls contain products of the particular gain (or gearing ratio) $g$ and the rudder concise derivatives $y_\zeta$, $l_\zeta$ or $n_\zeta$. Thus the gain appropriate to a given aircraft depends upon the aerodynamic effectiveness of the control in the given flight condition.

On neglecting terms of small magnitude, we find

$$\bar{A}_2 = A_2 , \tag{11.18}$$

$$\bar{B}_2 = B_2 + g_{\dot{\psi}} n_\zeta \tag{11.19}$$

and

$$\bar{F}_2 = g_\psi \hat{g}_1 (l_v n_\zeta - n_v l_\zeta). \tag{11.20}$$

We note that, if $g_\psi \neq 0$, the quintic characteristic equation has a non-zero real root, since the controlled aircraft is no longer neutrally stable in yaw (see Chapter 10).

## SIMPLE YAW ATTITUDE CONTROL

We take $\quad \zeta = g_\psi \psi.$

From Eq. (11.19) we see that the value of $\bar{B}_2$ is unaffected by a simple yaw attitude control (with $g_{\dot{\psi}} = 0$), i.e. the sum of the damping factors of all the modes of oscillation is unaltered. We find that such a control stabilizes any divergent spiral motion; the new root introduced by the automatic control combines with the small real root to give a lightly damped long period oscillation. However, the damping of the Dutch roll and of the rolling subsidence are practically unaltered.

### Rate of yaw control

By considering the equations, we find that the effect of a rate control such as

$$\zeta = g_{\dot{\psi}} \dot{\psi}$$

is the same as that of an increase in $n_r$, the other derivatives remaining almost unchanged. For an aircraft without automatic control, while increase of fin area increases the damping in yaw, the response of the aircraft to side gusts can give rise to short period oscillations, with uncomfortable flying conditions. As shown above, this may set an upper limit to $N_v$, and hence to the fin area. We can see the great advantage of an automatic control which allows $n_r$ to be varied, while keeping all the other derivatives unaltered.

As in Chapter 10, the condition for spiral stability with such a control can be shown to be

$$l_v (n_r + n_\zeta g_{\dot{\psi}}) > l_r n_v .$$

With a rate of yaw control (or yaw damper), the damping of both the spiral motion and the Dutch roll oscillation can be greatly improved. This is particularly important for highly loaded aircraft with sweptback wings. Such a damper has little effect on the damping of the rolling subsidence.

## RESPONSE WITH AUTOMATIC CONTROL

In the above analysis we have only considered the effect of the automatic control on the stability and damping. As shown in Part II (Chapter 7), there are other important factors such as the overshoot in the initial stages of the motion. The situation is particularly difficult in lateral motion, due to the interaction of the aerodynamic effects of rolling, yawing and sideslipping. A good automatic control (like a good pilot) should coordinate the movements of the ailerons and rudder in response to roll.

In addition to the yaw damper, the use of cross-coupled controls (rudder geared to rate of roll, or ailerons to both rate of roll and rate of yaw) provides an effective means of reducing overswing in the transient motion. The design of such multi-loop control systems is discussed in reference 7.

## REFERENCES

1. GANDY, R.W. The response of an aeroplane to the application of ailerons and rudders. Part I. Response in roll. R. & M. 1915 (1943).

2. GANDY, R.W. The response of an aeroplane to the application of ailerons and rudders. Part II. Response in yaw and sideslip. R. & M. 2272 (1949).

3. EGGLESTON, J.M. and PHILLIPS, W.H. A method for the calculation of the lateral response of airplanes to random turbulence. NACA Tech. Note 4196 (1958).

4. EGGLESTON, J.M. and DIEDERICH, F.W. Theoretical calculation of the power spectra of the rolling and yawing moments on a wing in random turbulence. NACA Report 1321 (1957).

5. DIEDERICH, F.W. The response of an airplane to random atmospheric disturbances. NACA Report 1345 (1958).

6. AGARD Conference Proceedings No. 157. Impact of active control technology on airplane design (1975).

7. AGARD Conference Proceedings No. 237. Advances in control systems (1974).

## PROBLEMS

1. Use the equations of lateral motion to find expressions for $\hat{v}$, $\hat{p}$ and $\hat{r}$ as power series in $\hat{t}$ for the case of a sharp-edged side gust (appropriate numerical values of the inertial and aerodynamic parameters can be taken). By retaining only the first three terms in the expansion for $\hat{v}$, derive the value of the overswing in $\hat{v}$ and compare the result with that given in Fig. 11.3.

2. What factors are of importance in ensuring that an aircraft has a rapid response in roll? Discuss the effect of reducing the effective dihedral.

3. From the equations of lateral motion, derive an expression for the ratio $\phi/\psi$ for the free motion of an aircraft (with controls fixed). Show that this expression contains only linear terms in the operator $\hat{D}$.

4. Use the rolling and yawing moment equations to obtain an expression for the ratio $\hat{p}/\hat{v}$, with controls fixed. Show that, if inertia effects are neglected,

$$\frac{\hat{p}}{\hat{v}} = -\frac{L_v N_r - L_r N_v}{L_p N_r - L_r N_p} .$$

Hence show that, for a spirally stable aircraft, a decrease in effective dihedral, or an increase in directional stability, will decrease the ratio of roll to sideslip, and will tend to promote a predominantly yawing motion.

5. If rudder is applied, how does the initial response in roll depend upon the magnitude of $L_v$? Show that this response could be reversed if the effective dihedral were negative.

# Part IV

# MODERN DEVELOPMENTS

# Chapter 12

# EFFECTS OF AEROELASTICITY, DYNAMIC COUPLING AND HIGH INCIDENCE

## INTRODUCTION

In all the previous chapters we have followed the traditionally accepted approach to stability and response theory, as applied to a rigid aircraft for which the longitudinal and lateral motions could be treated separately. We have also generally confined our attention to incidences below the stall, at which the flow is not separated. However, recent trends in aircraft design have led to more flexible structures in order to reduce weight; thus distortion, or 'aeroelastic' effects have become of increasing importance.

In developing the linearized equations of motion in Part I, the aircraft was assumed to be slightly disturbed from steady trimmed rectilinear motion; thus in the steady datum state the aircraft had no angular rotation. Under these conditions, it was shown that the longitudinal and lateral motions could be considered separately. However, if the steady motion of the aircraft differs from that assumed in Chapter 2, or if the deviations from the steady motion are not small, the longitudinal and lateral motions are, in general, coupled (as in the spin). Such a situation also occurs when an aircraft is slightly disturbed while possessing a high rate of roll. In this case, dynamic coupling occurs due to the increased importance of the gyroscopic couples resulting from the angular momentum of a rolling aircraft. As shown below, the high rate of roll greatly alters the prediction of the flying qualities of such an aircraft.

Flight at high incidence has been of vital interest since the earliest days of flying, as shown by the large amount of research done on the stalling and spinning of aircraft in the 1920's and 1930's. In recent years, substantial effort has been devoted to the development of aircraft capable of controlled flight at high angles of incidence, at which flow separation can occur. Under these circumstances large changes in incidence can occur, and the non-linear variation of the aerodynamic forces with incidence has to be taken into account. This is the subject of the last part of this chapter.

## AEROELASTICITY

In the preceding analysis, we have assumed that an aircraft was a rigid body which underwent no distortion due to the varying aerodynamic loads. This assumption is valid if the aircraft speed is low and if the stiffness of the structure is high.

However, at high speeds, with thin sweptback wings and a slender fuselage, the effects of distortion are of importance. In this chapter we consider these aero-elastic effects and their influence on aircraft dynamic stability. The structural distortion (such as wing bending and twisting, fuselage bending, tail unit bending and twisting) is caused by the loading of the various surfaces and will depend both upon the incidence of the particular surface element and on the dynamic pressure $\frac{1}{2}\rho_e V_e^2$. Thus the aeroelastic effects will vary with the aircraft speed independently of the effects of compressibility.

As pointed out by Collar (ref. 1), the field of aeroelasticity covers a wide range of phenomena, distributed over a range of frequencies — from high-frequency flutter to low-frequency oscillations in which the structural distortions occur relatively slowly. It is this latter type of oscillation with which we shall here be mainly concerned.

## THE EQUATIONS OF MOTION OF A DEFORMABLE AIRCRAFT

The equations of motion of a deformable aircraft have been derived in references 2 and 3. As for a rigid aircraft, the equations can be referred to a system of rectangular axes $Oxyz$, with $O$ at the centre of gravity of the aircraft and $Ox$ and $Oz$ in the plane of symmetry of the unstrained aircraft. The axes may be chosen to be either 'attached axes' (e.g. body axes of the aircraft in the equilibrium steady state) or 'mean axes'; the latter are chosen so that, at every instant, the linear and angular momenta of the motion of the deformable aircraft (relative to the axes) are identically zero.

With either set of axes, the coordinates of a given point $P(x,y,z)$ on the aircraft vary with time. The displacement of this point relative to its position in the aircraft in the equilibrium steady state can be defined by the equations

$$\left.\begin{aligned} \delta_x &= x - x_R\,, \\ \delta_y &= y - y_R\,, \\ \delta_z &= z - z_R\,, \end{aligned}\right\} \qquad (12.1)$$

where the suffix $R$ refers to the reference configuration. As in the classical theory of elasticity, the distortions of the structure are taken to be small in comparison with a typical overall linear dimension (wing chord or span) of the aircraft, the second and higher powers of the $\delta_x$, $\delta_y$, $\delta_z$ being neglected.

In many investigations, it can be assumed that the changes in the moments and products of inertia due to deformation of the structure are negligible. In these circumstances it is shown in reference 3 that, if second order terms are neglected, the equations of motion, Eqs. (2.7)-(2.14), for a symmetric aircraft slightly disturbed from steady trimmed rectilinear flight still hold true, the equations being referred to mean axes through the centre of gravity $O$. The aerodynamic forces and moments $X_a$, $Y_a$, $Z_a$, $L_a$, $M_a$ and $N_a$ will, however, depend on the deformation of the structure.

Eqs. (2.7)-(2.14) have now to be supplemented by equations relating the deformation to the normal modes and frequencies of vibration of the structure as an elastic body The latter equations can be expressed as

$$\left.\begin{aligned} \delta_x &= \sum_{i=1}^{\infty} \Delta_{xi}(x_U, y_U, z_U)\ \xi_i(t) \\ \delta_y &= \sum_{i=1}^{\infty} \Delta_{yi}(x_U, y_U, z_U)\ \xi_i(t) \\ \delta_z &= \sum_{i=1}^{\infty} \Delta_{zi}(x_U, y_U, z_U)\ \xi_i(t) \end{aligned}\right\} \tag{12.2}$$

where $\Delta$ are the natural mode shapes (e.g. in wing or fuselage bending), $\xi_i$ is the generalized coordinate for the given mode, and the suffix $U$ relates to the unstrained body.

As shown in reference 3, the generalized coordinates satisfy equations of motion of the form

$$M_j\ddot{\xi}_j + M_j\omega^2{}_j\xi_j = E_j \qquad (j = 1 \text{ to } \infty) \tag{12.3}$$

where $M_j$ and $E_j$ are respectively the generalized mass and incremental force of the system in the $j$th mode and $\omega_j$ is the corresponding frequency. In practical aeroelastic calculations, the elastic, continuous, infinite-degree-of-freedom system is replaced by an equivalent system having a finite number $n$ of degrees of freedom (together with the rigid body modes). As we are here restricting our attention to the effects of distortion on the stability of the aircraft, only those modes which have significant contributions from the overall body motion will be of interest (this contrasts with the analysis of flutter). In addition, the distributed mass is replaced by a number of concentrated masses $m_i$ at discrete points, the incremental loads (components $X_i$, $Y_i$, $Z_i$) due to distortion being taken to act at these points. Thus we take

$$M_j = \sum_{i=1}^{n} m_i(\Delta^2{}_{xij} + \Delta^2{}_{yij} + \Delta^2{}_{zij}) \tag{12.4}$$

and

$$E_j = \sum_{i=1}^{n} (X_i\Delta_{xij} + Y_i\Delta_{yij} + Z_i\Delta_{zij}) \tag{12.5}$$

where $\Delta_{xij}$ is the normalised deflection in the $x$ direction (at the $i$th point) in the $j$th mode, and similarly for $\Delta_{yij}$ and $\Delta_{zij}$. This method of representing the structure is known as 'semi-rigid representation' (see ref. 4). Provided that the mode shapes are well chosen, it can give results that are sufficiently accurate for most practical purposes (in the early stages of a design).

The loads $E_j$ and also the aerodynamic forces and moments $X_a$, $Y_a$, $Z_a$, $L_a$, $M_a$ and $N_a$ will depend on the deformation of the structure, as well as upon the velocity components of the aircraft, i.e. on $u$, $v$, $w$, $p$, $q$ and $r$. By analogy with Eqs. (2.30) - (2.35), we write

$$\begin{aligned} X_a = {} & \mathring{X}_u u + \mathring{X}_v v + \mathring{X}_{\dot{w}}\dot{w} + \mathring{X}_w w + \mathring{X}_p p + \mathring{X}_q q + \mathring{X}_r r \\ & + \sum_{i=1}^{n} (\mathring{X}_{\xi k}\xi_k + \mathring{X}_{\dot{\xi} k}\dot{\xi}_k) + \mathring{X}(t) \end{aligned} \tag{12.6}$$

and similarly for $Y_a$, $Z_a$, $L_a$, $M_a$, $N_a$ and $E_j$.

As in the case of a rigid aircraft (Chapter 2), provided that the aircraft is completely symmetrical about the plane $Oxz$ (including symmetry as regards the structural flexibility) and that the undisturbed steady state of flight is symmetric, then for small disturbances the equations of motion can be split up into two groups, longitudinal and lateral, and analysed separately.

## METHODS OF SOLUTION OF THE AEROELASTIC EQUATIONS

As shown above, the aeroelastic equations of motion for small disturbances can be reduced to a set of linear differential equations in the variables $u$, $v$, $w$, $\theta$, $\phi$, $\psi$ and $\xi_k$ and their derivatives with respect to $t$. A precise formulation of these equations for longitudinal symmetric motion is given in reference 3. For static problems (such as wing divergence or aileron reversal), no account is taken of the damping or inertia forces, and the equations reduce to simultaneous algebraic equations.

In the study of dynamic aeroelastic effects, damping and inertia terms must be retained (as with a rigid aircraft). In addition, the number of normal modes to be taken into consideration may sometimes need to be quite large to ensure a realistic representation of the deformations. However, several approximate techniques have been developed to simplify the problem.

Many aeroelastic problems (such as the effect of distortion of the fin or tailplane) can often be adequately treated as 'quasi-static', allowance being made for the deformations solely in terms of the static deflections of the aircraft (see ref. 5). In this method of solution, the linearized equations of motion (2.45) - (2.53) for a rigid aircraft are used, the influence of the elasticity of the structure being allowed for by modifying the values of the aerodynamic derivatives. Thus the elastic distortion due to a small change of incidence is used to determine the new values of $M_w$ and $Z_w$, and similarly for the other derivatives.

In other aeroelastic problems, an approximate solution can be found by considering only one dominant distortional coordinate $\xi$. Thus, for the short-period longitudinal oscillation of a flexible aircraft, the forward speed being taken to be constant, the motion is governed by the following set of equations:

$$(\hat{D} + z_w)\hat{w} - \hat{q} + z_\eta\eta' + (z_{\dot{\xi}}\hat{D} + z_\xi)\xi = 0, \tag{12.7}$$

$$(m_{\dot{w}}\hat{D} + m_w)\hat{w} + (\hat{D} + m_q)\hat{q} + m_\eta\eta' + (m_{\dot{\xi}}\hat{D} + m_\xi)\xi = 0, \tag{12.8}$$

$$(e_{\dot{w}}\hat{D} + e_w)\hat{w} + e_q\hat{q} + e_\eta\eta' + [\hat{D}^2 + e_{\dot{\xi}}\hat{D} + (\omega^2 + e_\xi)]\xi = 0, \tag{12.9}$$

where $\hat{D} = d/d\hat{t}$.

On comparing these equations with Eqs. (6.22) and (6.23), we see that the additional terms involve generalized inertia coefficients $e_{\dot{w}}$ and additional derivatives such as $z_{\dot{\xi}}$, $z_\xi$, etc. The characteristic equation (stick fixed) is of the fourth degree, the two additional roots (compared with the rigid aircraft) corresponding to a mode in which the elasticity of the aircraft plays an important part.

## EFFECTS OF AEROELASTICITY ON DYNAMIC STABILITY AND RESPONSE

The commonest aeroelastic effects on dynamic stability and response are associated with the deformation of the wings, fin and tailplane (reference 6). Wing distortion is most pronounced on thin highly swept wings of high aspect ratio. For a sweptback wing, upward (spanwise) bending of the wing due to aerodynamic loads reduces the incidence, and thus there is a forward movement of the aerodynamic centre which, if associated with a negative manoeuvre margin, may result in a divergence in pitch (as shown in Chapter 7).

If the elevator is rigid, nose-up twisting of the tailplane will reduce the effective elevator angle. Thus flexibility will alter both the tailplane lift and the elevator effectiveness. If the tailplane setting is such that down elevator is required to trim, distortion will have a stabilizing effect on the static margin; the reverse is true if up elevator is required. These effects are, of course, lessened by stiffening up the tailplane.

The aerodynamic loads on the tailplane will produce bending of the fuselage; this will reduce the tail setting angle (for an up load) and hence the tail lift (for a given incidence and elevator angle). A flexible fuselage will almost always reduce the static and dynamic stability. However, in the pull-out (under an increased load factor), inertia forces cause fuselage downward bending, which has a favourable effect on stability.

Loss, or reversal, of aileron control is one of the most important lateral distortion effects. The additional lift due to applying aileron can cause a nose-down moment about the wing flexural axis; thus the increase in lift due to applying ailerons is lessened, and the rolling power of the ailerons is reduced.

Just as the lift curve slope of a swept wing decreases due to aeroelastic distortion, so also the effectiveness of a fin is reduced. The aerodynamic loads on the fin will produce bending of the fuselage; this too will reduce the fin incidence and hence its effectiveness. A very flexible fuselage could lead to dangerous instability at high speeds, due to $N_v$ becoming very small (or even negative). This effect would be more pronounced at low altitudes (where the dynamic pressure is larger for a given speed).

## DYNAMIC COUPLING

As stated above, coupling between the longitudinal and lateral motions of an aircraft can occur in both a rapid rolling manoeuvre and in the spin. Such cases of dynamic coupling have been accentuated in recent years by the changes in configuration between subsonic and supersonic aircraft, the latter often having thin swept-back or delta wings of low aspect ratio combined with a long slender fuselage. More of the aircraft weight is concentrated in the fuselage, and this leads to an increase in the moments of inertia in pitch and in yaw, and to a decrease in the inertia in roll. As shown below, these changes can lead to a gyroscopically induced instability, which can take the form of a divergence in roll.

## EQUATIONS OF MOTION

In order to investigate the phenomenon of dynamic coupling, we have to return to the complete set of six non-linear equations of motion, (2.1) - (2.6). As in Chapter 2, these equations are referred to a set of body axes $Oxyz$ through the c.g. $O$ of the aircraft. We shall assume for simplicity that the equations are referred to principal axes. Then

$$I_{xy} = I_{yz} = I_{zx} = 0. \qquad (12.10)$$

Thus the equations of linear motion of the aircraft parallel to the axes $Ox$, $Oy$, $Oz$ respectively are, in the usual notation,

$$m(\dot{U} - rV + qW) = X_a + X_g, \tag{12.11}$$

$$m(\dot{V} - pW + rU) = Y_a + Y_g, \tag{12.12}$$

$$m(\dot{W} - qU + pV) = Z_a + Z_g. \tag{12.13}$$

The equations of angular motion about $Ox$, $Oy$, $Oz$ respectively are

$$I_x\dot{p} - (I_y - I_z)qr = L_a, \tag{12.14}$$

$$I_y\dot{q} - (I_z - I_x)rp = M_a, \tag{12.15}$$

$$I_z\dot{r} - (I_x - I_y)pq = N_a. \tag{12.16}$$

The solution of Eqs. (12.11) - (12.16) is a formidable task, even when modern computing equipment is available. It need hardly be stressed that a good knowledge of the aerodynamic data is essential. This is preferably obtained from flight test data on the given, or comparable, aircraft.

## THE LINEARIZED EQUATIONS OF MOTION OF AN AIRCRAFT IN A RAPID ROLL

To simplify the analysis, we assume that the forward speed $V_e$ of the aircraft is kept constant; this enables us to dispense with the first equation of motion (12.11), which is assumed to be automatically satisfied (by throttle control). This is a valid assumption if the aerodynamic derivatives do not change rapidly with Mach number at the flight speed considered.

A number of other simplifications can be made with little loss of accuracy. Thus it is shown in reference 7 that gravitational forces may be neglected in the fast rolling motion considered. In addition the aerodynamic derivatives $Y_r$, $Y_\xi$, $Z_{\dot{w}}$ and $Z_q$ are usually small and will be neglected.

We consider an aircraft slightly disturbed from steady forward flight in a rapid roll, the rate of roll $p_e$ being taken to be constant. Elevator and rudder are taken to be fixed in their trimmed positions. It is to be noted that the equations (12.11) - (12.16) are referred to principal axes, which in general are not wind axes. Thus we must write

$$W = W_e + w. \tag{12.17}$$

From Fig. 2.2, in the datum state,

$$U_e = V_e \cos \alpha_e$$

and $$W_e = V_e \sin \alpha_e$$

where $\alpha_e$ is the incidence of $Ox$ in the steady flight. $\alpha_e$ is small and we can write

$$\left.\begin{aligned} U_e &= V_e \\ \text{and} \quad W_e &= V_e\, \alpha_e. \end{aligned}\right\} \tag{12.18}$$

In the datum state the aircraft has zero angles of yaw and sideslip. As in the classical analysis, we shall take $v$, $w$, $q$ and $r$ to be small quantities of the first order compared with $U_e$ (or $p_e$) and we shall neglect terms of the second degree and higher in these quantities.

With the above assumptions, *the linearized equations of motion of an aircraft in a constant rapid roll* $p_e$ *at constant speed* $V_e$ are, from Eqs. (12.12), (12,13), (12.15) and (12.16),

$$m(\dot{v} - p_e W_e - p_e w + rV_e) = \mathring{Y}_v v + \mathring{Y}_p p_e, \tag{12.19}$$

$$m(\dot{w} - qV_e + p_e v) = \mathring{Z}_w w, \tag{12.20}$$

$$I_y \dot{q} - (I_z - I_x)p_e r = \mathring{M}_w w + \mathring{M}_{\dot{w}} \dot{w} + \mathring{M}_q q, \tag{12.21}$$

$$I_z \dot{r} - (I_x - I_y)p_e q = \mathring{N}_v v + \mathring{N}_r r + \mathring{N}_p p_e + \mathring{N}_\xi \xi, \tag{12.22}$$

where, from Eq. (12.14), since the rate of roll is constant, the aileron angle $\xi$ satisfies the equation

$$\mathring{L}_v v + \mathring{L}_p p_e + \mathring{L}_r r + \mathring{L}_\xi \xi = 0. \tag{12.23}$$

From Eqs. (12.22) and (12.23), eliminating $\xi$ and putting

$$f = \mathring{N}_\xi / \mathring{L}_\xi \;, \tag{12.24}$$

we obtain $I_z \dot{r} - (I_x - I_y)p_e q = (\mathring{N}_v - f\mathring{L}_v)v + (\mathring{N}_r - f\mathring{L}_r)r + (\mathring{N}_p - f\mathring{L}_p)p_e \;.$ (12.25)

Equations (12.19) and (12.20) are the equations of motion of the aircraft parallel to $Oy$ and $Oz$ respectively. Eqs. (12.21) and (12.25) are the equations of angular motion of the aircraft about $Oy$ and $Oz$ respectively (i.e. the motion in pitch and yaw). We see that these equations involve $v$, the velocity of sideslip, $w$ the increment in the velocity of $O$ along $Oz$, $q$ the rate of pitch and $r$ the rate of yaw, and their derivatives with respect to $t$. We see that the motion involves both symmetric and asymmetric disturbances; thus there is coupling between the longitudinal and lateral motions.

These equations can be expressed in terms of the concise derivatives defined in Chapter 2 by multiplying Eqs. (12.19) and (12.20) by $1/\frac{1}{2}\rho_e V_e{}^2 S$, Eq. (12.21) by $\mu_1/\frac{1}{2}\rho_e V_e{}^2 S\bar{\bar{c}} i_y$ and Eq. (12.25) by $\mu_2/\frac{1}{2}\rho_e V_e{}^2 Sbi_z$. Also we write

$$\hat{p}_e = \tau p_e, \tag{12.26}$$

where, as in Eq. (2.101), $\tau = m/\frac{1}{2}\rho_e V_e S$. (12.27)

For simplicity we write

$$\left.\begin{aligned} i_1 &= (I_z - I_x)/I_y \\ \text{and} \quad i_2 &= (I_y - I_x)/I_z. \end{aligned}\right\} \tag{12.28}$$

For typical high speed aircraft, $i_1$ and $i_2$ are both positive.

On simplifying and using Eq. (12.18) we obtain

$$(\hat{D} + y_v)\hat{v} - \hat{p}_e\hat{w} + \hat{r} = (\alpha_e - y_p)\hat{p}_e, \tag{12.29}$$

$$\hat{p}_e\hat{v} + (\hat{D} + z_w)\hat{w} - \hat{q} = 0, \tag{12.30}$$

$$(m_{\dot{w}}\hat{D} + m_w)\hat{w} + (\hat{D} + m_q)\hat{q} - i_1\hat{p}_e\hat{r} = 0, \tag{12.31}$$

$$n_v{}'\hat{v} + i_2\hat{p}_e\hat{q} + (\hat{D} + n_r{}')\hat{r} = -n_p{}'\hat{p}_e, \tag{12.32}$$

where $\hat{D} = d/d\hat{t}$

and
$$\left.\begin{aligned} n_v' &= n_v - fl_v = n_v - (n_\xi/l_\xi)l_v, \\ n_p' &= n_p - fl_p = n_p - (n_\xi/l_\xi)l_p, \\ n_r' &= n_r - fl_r = n_r - (n_\xi/l_\xi)l_r. \end{aligned}\right\} \tag{12.33}$$

The terms on the right hand sides of Eqs. (12.29) and (12.32) can be regarded as forcing functions of the system.

## THE STABILITY OF AN AIRCRAFT IN A RAPID ROLL AT CONSTANT SPEED

The solution of Eqs. (12.29) - (12.32) can be put in the form

$$\hat{v} = \hat{v}_0 + \sum_{n=1}^{4} \sigma_n e^{\lambda_n \hat{t}}$$

(and similar expressions for $\hat{w}$, $\hat{q}$ and $\hat{r}$), where $\hat{v}_0$ is a constant (it is the particular integral of the equations) and $\lambda_n$ are the four roots of the characteristic equation

$$\begin{vmatrix} \lambda + y_v & -\hat{p}_e & 0 & 1 \\ \hat{p}_e & \lambda + z_w & -1 & 0 \\ 0 & m_{\dot{w}}\lambda + m_w & \lambda + m_q & -i_1\hat{p}_e \\ n_v' & 0 & i_2\hat{p}_e & \lambda + n_r' \end{vmatrix} = 0. \tag{12.34}$$

This is a quartic equation in $\lambda$ and can be written in the form

$$\Delta(\lambda) = A\lambda^4 + B\lambda^3 + C\lambda^2 + D\lambda + E = 0. \quad (A > 0) \tag{12.35}$$

As shown in Chapter 6, the necessary and sufficient conditions for stability are that $B$, $D$, $E$ and $R$ should all be positive, where $R$ is given by

$$R = BCD - B^2E - AD^2.$$

It is shown in reference 8 that, for a typical high speed aircraft, Eq. (12.35) can be approximately factorized as

$$\Delta(\lambda) = \left(A\lambda^2 + \frac{BC-AD}{C}\lambda + C\right)\left(\lambda^2 + \frac{D}{C}\lambda + \frac{E}{C}\right). \tag{12.36}$$

The first factor has a pair of complex roots, which correspond to a damped short period oscillation; the second factor may have either a pair of complex roots (which correspond to a damped long period oscillation) or a pair of real roots, one of which is negative (corresponding to a subsidence) and the other may be positive (corresponding to a divergence) or negative.

## CRITICAL STABILITY CRITERION

It is shown in reference 8 that, for a typical high speed aircraft, with positive static stability ($M_w < 0$, $N_v > 0$) and positive damping, the only critical criterion which it is necessary to consider is that corresponding to $E = 0$. As shown in

Chapter 6, if $E$ is negative, but all the other coefficients of the characteristic equation are positive, the equation will have one real positive root, which corresponds to a divergence.

Expanding Eq. (12.34), we find

$$E = i_1 i_2 \hat{p}_e^4 + (m_q n_r' + i_1 n_v' - i_2 m_w + i_1 i_2 y_v z_w)\hat{p}_e^2 - \\ -(n_v' - y_v n_r')(m_w + z_w m_q). \tag{12.37}$$

The form of the coefficients in this equation leads us to consider the expression

$$E' = (i_1 \hat{p}_e^2 - m_w - z_w m_q)(i_2 \hat{p}_e^2 + n_v' - y_v n_r'). \tag{12.38}$$

On multiplying out these factors, we see that $E$ and $E'$ differ only in the coefficient of $\hat{p}_e^2$, in terms involving the damping terms $y_v$, $z_w$, $m_q$ and $n_r'$. In many cases, the contribution of these terms is small, and the divergence boundary can be taken as $E' = 0$.

Now, when $\hat{p}_e = 0$, from Eqs. (12.30) and (12.31), $(m_w + z_w m_q)$ is the square of the undamped non-dimensional frequency $\hat{\omega}_\theta$ of the pitching oscillation and, similarly, $(-n_v' + y_v n_r')$ is the square of the undamped non-dimensional frequency $\hat{\omega}_\psi$ of the yawing oscillation. We see that

$$\hat{\omega}_\theta = \sqrt{(m_w + z_w m_q)} = \omega_\theta \tau, \tag{12.39}$$

$$\hat{\omega}_\psi = \sqrt{(-n_v' + y_v n_r')} = \omega_\psi \tau, \tag{12.40}$$

where $\omega_\theta$ and $\omega_\psi$ are the undamped frequencies of the pitching and yawing oscillations of the aircraft in steady flight without rolling (allowing for the adverse yawing moment due to ailerons).

## STABILITY DIAGRAMS

From Eqs. (12.38) - (12.40), we see that the simplified divergence boundaries are given by

$$\left.\begin{aligned} \frac{p_e}{\omega_\theta} &= \frac{\hat{p}_e}{\hat{\omega}_\theta} = \sqrt{\frac{1}{i_1}} = \sqrt{\left(\frac{I_y}{I_z - I_x}\right)} \\ \text{and} \quad \frac{p_e}{\omega_\psi} &= \frac{\hat{p}_e}{\hat{\omega}_\psi} = \sqrt{\frac{1}{i_2}} = \sqrt{\left(\frac{I_z}{I_y - I_x}\right)} \end{aligned}\right\} \tag{12.41}$$

For typical high speed aircraft, $i_1 \simeq 1$ and $0 < i_2 < 1$. These simplified divergence boundaries are shown by broken lines in Fig. 12.1, in which they are plotted against $(\omega_\theta/p_e)^2$ and $(\omega_\psi/p_e)^2$. When the aerodynamic damping terms are included, the divergence boundary can be found from Eq. (12.37), and is shown in Fig. 12.1. It can be seen that, except in the region of the point $P$, the approximate divergence boundaries are in good agreement with the exact ones. For simplicity, we shall in general base the subsequent discussion on the approximate boundaries.

As shown in references 9, 10 and 11, for an aircraft with positive static stability (i.e. $M_w < 0$ and $N_v > 0$) in the motion without rolling, there will be four possible types of motion in the steady roll:

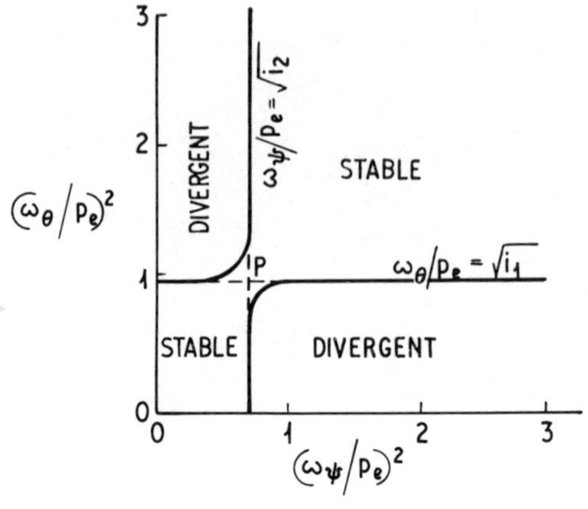


Fig. 12.1 Stability diagram for a rolling aircraft

(i) If $\omega_\theta/p_e > \sqrt{i_1}$ and $\omega_\psi/p_e > \sqrt{i_2}$, $E' > 0$,

and there will be two stable oscillatory modes, both involving coupling between pitch and yaw. In general, the frequency of one of these is more than the higher (longitudinal) frequency of the non-rolling aircraft and the frequency of the other is less than the lower (lateral) frequency of the non-rolling aircraft.

(ii) If $\omega_\theta/p_e > \sqrt{i_1}$ and $\omega_\psi/p_e < \sqrt{i_2}$, $E' < 0$,

and there will be one divergence, one subsidence and one damped oscillation.

(iii) If $\omega_\theta/p_e < \sqrt{i_1}$ and $\omega_\psi/p_e > \sqrt{i_2}$, $E' < 0$,

and there will be one divergence, one subsidence and one damped oscillation.

(iv) If $\omega_\theta/p_e < \sqrt{i_1}$ and $\omega_\psi/p_e < \sqrt{i_2}$, $E' > 0$,

and there will be two stable oscillatory modes. This condition can arise if the rate of roll $p_e$ is very high, or if $\omega_\theta$ and $\omega_\psi$ are both vanishingly small (i.e. if $M_w$ and $N_v$ are both numerically very small). As shown in reference 11, there will be periodic variation of incidence and sideslip, the principal axis remaining at a fixed attitude in space.

Figure 12.1 can be considered from another point of view. For a given aircraft at a given height and forward speed (and thus with given values of $\omega_\theta$ and $\omega_\psi$), the curve of $(\omega_\theta/p_e)^2$ against $(\omega_\psi/p_e)^2$, as $p_e$ varies, is a straight line through $O$ with slope $(m_w + z_w m_q)/(-n_v' + y_v n_r')$.

Consider two aircraft, aircraft $A$ with poor directional stability (small $N_v$) and aircraft $B$ with poor static longitudinal stability (numerically small $M_w$). The variation of $(\omega_\theta/p_e)^2$ with $(\omega_\psi/p_e)^2$ for these two aircraft is shown in Fig. 12.2.

We see that aircraft $A$ will be stable when

$$p_e < \frac{\omega_\psi}{\sqrt{i_2}} = \omega_\psi \sqrt{\left(\frac{I_z}{I_y - I_x}\right)}$$

For $\omega_\psi/\sqrt{i_2} < p_e < \omega_\theta/\sqrt{i_1}$, as stated above, the aircraft will be unstable, with a divergence (predominantly in yaw, due to the low $N_v$), while for higher rates of roll the aircraft will again be stable.

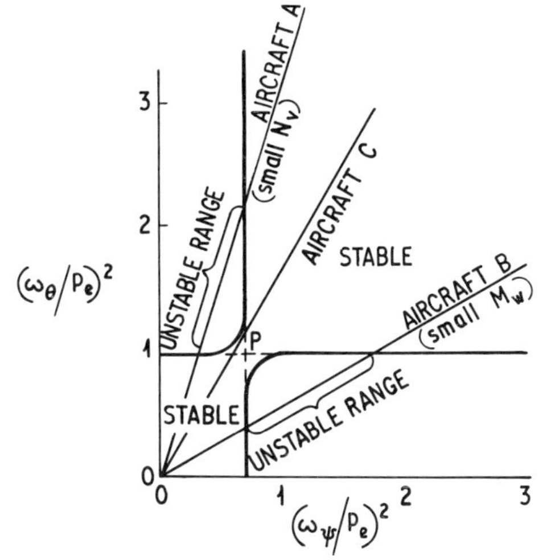


Fig. 12.2 Effect of $M_w$ and $N_v$ on the stability of a rolling aircraft. (Reproduced from ARC Current Paper 404 by W.J.G. Pinsker) (Crown copyright).

From Fig. 12.2 we see that aircraft $B$ will be stable when

$$p_e < \frac{\omega_\theta}{\sqrt{i_1}} = \omega_\theta \sqrt{\left(\frac{I_y}{I_z - I_x}\right)} .$$

For $\omega_\theta/\sqrt{i_1} < p_e < \omega_\psi/\sqrt{i_2}$, as stated above, the aircraft will be unstable, with a divergence (predominantly in pitch, due to the small $M_w$), while for still higher rates of roll the aircraft will again be stable.

Consider now the case of aircraft $C$ (Fig. 12.2), for which the values of $M_w$ and $N_v$ are such that the curve of $(\omega_\theta/p_e)^2$ against $(\omega_\psi/p_e)^2$ passes close to $P$, i.e. $(\omega_\theta/\omega_\psi)\sqrt{(i_2/i_1)}$ does not differ very much from unity. Using the exact expression for $E$, given by Eq. (12.37), we see, as in Fig. 12.2, that this aircraft will be stable for all values of $p_e$. However, as shown in reference 8, the margin of stability is so small for values of the parameters near to $P$ (i.e. for $p_e \simeq \omega_\theta/\sqrt{i_1} \simeq \omega_\psi/\sqrt{i_2}$) that large values of incidence and sideslip may occur in the transient motion.

## HIGH INCIDENCE AERODYNAMICS

In flight at high angles of incidence, the stalling characteristics of an aircraft (such as the abruptness of the stall, and the stall warning) determine the handling qualities and the ability of the pilot to prevent, or to recover from, a complete stall. Stability and control problems may well start before the true stall. Thus flow separation can occur on highly swept wings at moderate incidence. When the tail is in the separated flow from the wings or fuselage, there will be a loss of effectiveness of both the tail unit and elevator and rudder, and sudden loss of control can occur. Some high speed aircraft cannot be flown safely up to the wing stall due to lateral stability and control deficiencies. As shown in Chapter 10, if fin effectiveness diminishes, and dihedral effect is insufficient to compensate, instability can occur.

At low angles of incidence, before separation of the flow over the wing, the curves of lift and pitching moment are practically linear with incidence. When flow starts to separate (Fig. 12.3, incidence $A$), the lift curve slope decreases; the slope of the pitching moment curve may increase or decrease, depending on the spanwise position of the point of separation, and on the flow over the tailplane.

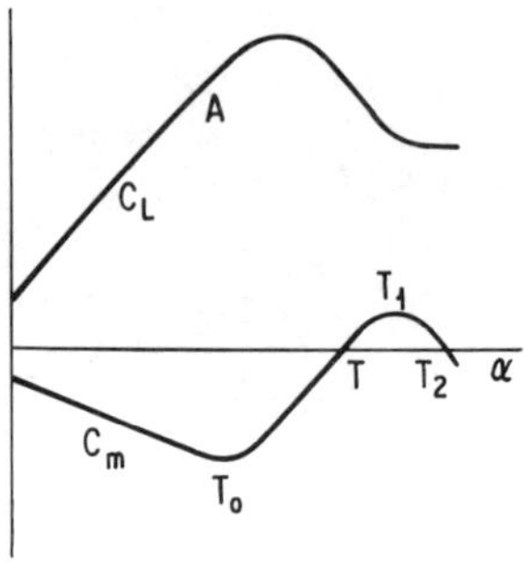


Fig. 12.3 Variation of $C_L$ and $C_m$ with incidence

For incidences below the stall, the lift increases with increase of incidence; the reverse is true for high angles of incidence. The nature of the stall and the stalling incidence vary considerably with the wing section and planform; the stalling incidence is of the order of 15° for an unswept wing, but may be 20°-30° for sweptback wings.

For aircraft with highly swept wings, $C_m$ may increase when flow separation begins on the outboard part of the span, making the aircraft unstable at incidences below the stall. This nose-up pitching moment gives rise to 'pitch-up'. As shown in reference 12, the aspect ratio and sweepback of the wing are especially important in determining whether pitch-up will occur at high angles of incidence; the tail-plane can augment this effect, especially if it is mounted high above the extended wing-chord plane, in a region of large downwash.

In many cases, the stall comes suddenly, due to asymmetric flow breakaway, in the form of uncommanded yaw or roll. As shown in Chapter 10, the damping in roll depends on $L_p$ which, in turn, depends on $dC_L/d\alpha$. The change in lift curve slope at the stall thus results in loss of damping in roll. In stalled flight, the aero-dynamic rolling moment on the wing due to the rate of roll will tend to increase the rate of roll, and the wing is said to autorotate. Roll stabilization may well be needed, particularly with low aspect ratio wings. Alternatively, the addition of sharp-edged strakes at the leading edge of the inboard portion of the wing has been shown (ref. 13) to postpone the stall and hence the loss of damping (but the aircraft drag will increase).

## LONGITUDINAL MOTION AT HIGH INCIDENCE

As shown above, non-linear aerodynamic effects are of considerable importance in flight at high incidence. The aerodynamic phenomena are generally extremely complicated; they include changes in the flow pattern over both wings and tail-plane (see ref. 14), and can involve large regions of stalled flow, strong vortex flows and aerodynamic interference between the various parts of the aircraft. The associated non-linearities may be difficult to predict quantitatively. We shall first confine our attention to longitudinal symmetric motion at constant speed and height (as in references 15 and 16).

Consider an aircraft with a single degree of freedom, in pitch. Such a symmetric motion is governed solely by Eq. (2.5), which reduces to

$$I_y\dot{q} = M. \tag{12.42}$$

The term on the right-hand side of this equation arises from the aerodynamic pitching moment which, as shown in Chapter 2, depends upon the aircraft speed, incidence $\alpha$, rate of pitch $q$ and elevator angle $\eta'$. Now, with the given assumptions, the change in incidence is equal to the angle of pitch, and hence $\dot{\alpha} = q$. Since the speed is taken to be constant, Eq. (12.42) can be written (to an acceptable degree of approximation) as

$$\ddot{\alpha} = F_1(\alpha,\eta') + F_2(\alpha)\dot{\alpha}, \tag{12.43}$$

where the term in $F_1$ is proportional to $C_m$.

Figure 12.3 shows a typical pitching moment curve for an aircraft with a high tail-plane; the aircraft is statically unstable at incidences between $T_0$ and $T_1$. We are here concerned with longitudinal motion at incidences close to the trim point $T(\alpha = \gamma_0)$.

Now, as shown in references 15 and 16, if $\alpha$ is close to $\gamma_0$, the functions $F_1$ and $F_2$ can be approximately expanded in the form

$$\left.\begin{aligned} -F_1(\alpha,\eta') &= c_0 + c_1\alpha + c_2\alpha^2 + d_0\eta' \\ \text{and}\quad -F_2(\alpha) &= b_0 + b_1\alpha. \end{aligned}\right\} \tag{12.44}$$

Thus Eq. (12.43) becomes

$$\ddot{\alpha} + (b_0 + b_1\alpha)\dot{\alpha} + c_0 + c_1\alpha + c_2\alpha^2 + d_0\eta' = 0. \tag{12.45}$$

## ANALYSIS WITH FIXED ELEVATOR

Suppose $\eta' = \eta_0$, a constant. From Eq. (12.45), the aircraft can be trimmed at incidence $\gamma$ given by

$$c_0 + c_1\gamma + c_2\gamma^2 + d_0\eta_0 = 0. \tag{12.46}$$

Now, for the T-tailed aircraft considered in reference 15, at high incidence, $c_0$, $c_2$ and $d_0$ are positive and $c_1$ is negative. Thus, if $c_1^2 > 4(c_0 + d_0\eta_0)c_2$, there are two positive values of incidence (both in the high incidence range) at which the aircraft could be trimmed for the given elevator setting (as shown in Fig. 12.3). Let $\gamma_0$ be the smaller of these values.

In the disturbed motion, put $\alpha = x + \gamma_0$. Then Eq. (12.45) becomes

$$\ddot{x} + (b_0 + b_1\gamma_0 + b_1x)\dot{x} + (c_1 + 2c_2\gamma_0)x + c_2x^2 = 0. \tag{12.47}$$

From Eq. (12.47) we see that the pitching motion satisfies an equation of the form

$$\ddot{x} + (D_1 + D_2x)\dot{x} + E_1x + E_2x^2 = 0 \tag{12.48}$$

$$\text{i.e.}\quad \left.\begin{aligned} \dot{x} &= q, \\ \dot{q} &= -(D_1 + D_2x)q - E_1x - E_2x^2, \end{aligned}\right\} \tag{12.49}$$

where the constant coefficients $D_1$, $D_2$, $E_1$ and $E_2$ are given by

$$D_1 = b_0 + b_1\gamma_0 = -F_2(\gamma_0),$$

$$D_2 = b_1 = -\mathrm{d}F_2/\mathrm{d}\alpha,$$

$$E_1 = c_1 + 2c_2\gamma_0 = -[\partial F_1/\partial\alpha]_{\alpha=\gamma_0},$$

$$E_2 = c_2 = -\tfrac{1}{2}\partial^2 F_1/\partial\alpha^2.$$

Figure 12.4 shows typical variations of $F_1$ and $F_2$ with incidence, from reference 15. We see that $D_1 > 0$, $D_2 < 0$, $E_1 < 0$ and $E_2 > 0$.

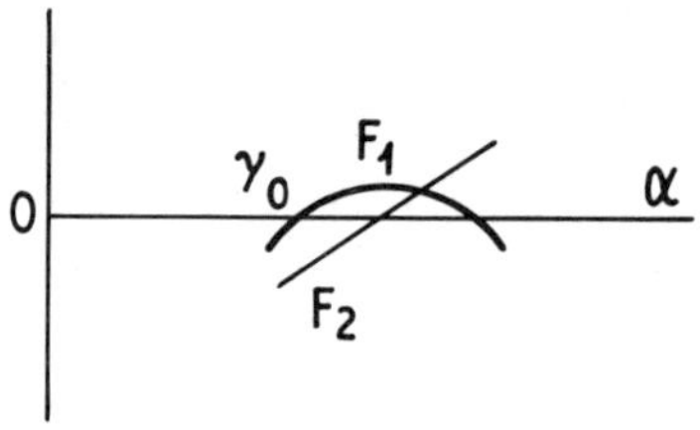


Fig. 12.4 Variation of aerodynamic parameters with incidence.

From Eq. (12.48), the characteristic equation (obtained from the linear terms) is

$$\lambda^2 + D_1\lambda + E_1 = 0 \tag{12.50}$$

which has one positive and one negative root. The origin $O$ ($x = 0$, $q = 0$) is thus a saddle point for the system (12.49), the slopes (at $O$) of the separatrices of the given system being given by the roots of Eq. (12.50). Fig. 12.5 shows the separatrices $AOB$, $COD$ and the trajectories of the system (12.49) for $D_1 = 0.4$, $D_2 = -1$, $E_1 = -0.6$, $E_2 = 2$. In this Figure, $x$ is the increase in incidence (in radians) above the trimmed value and $q$ is the rate of change of incidence (radians/sec); the arrows indicate the direction of movement along the trajectories.

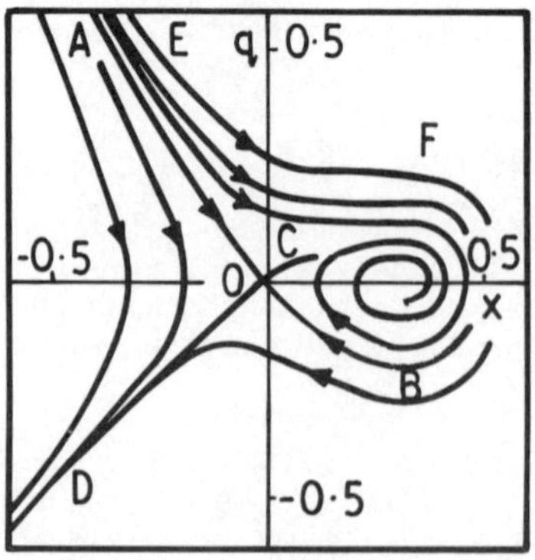


Fig. 12.5 $x$, $q$ trajectories for a non-linear system

We see that, if an aircraft has an incidence $\alpha$ and a rate of change of incidence $\dot{\alpha}$ ($= q$) which correspond to points to the right of the separatrix $AO$, it will develop a superstall (or deep-stall). Trajectories such as $EF$ correspond to a potentially dangerous manoeuvre, leading to extremely high angles of incidence, from which recovery is difficult or impossible (see refs. 15 and 17). However, if the trajectory is to the left of $AO$, the incidence will reach some maximum value ($< \gamma_0$) and then begin to decrease. The separatrix *AO* can therefore be taken as a 'safety' boundary for the aircraft to have a normal recovery from high incidence flight. We note that the aircraft response for large changes of incidence (from the trimmed condition) differs markedly from that for small changes; this is a typical phenomenon with non-linear systems. As stated above, wing strakes have been found to eliminate some of the non-linear effects, or to postpone them to a higher incidence.

The simplest method of preventing super-stalled (longitudinal symmetric) flight is to apply positive (down) elevator. This increases the nose-down pitching moment. However, because of the low speeds usually associated with the high incidence condition, the response to controls tends to be sluggish. If the elevator effectiveness is low, the control movement may have to be reinforced by some departure-prevention device, such as a feedback control relating $\eta'$, $\alpha$ and $\dot{\alpha}$ (see refs. 16 and 17). Thus one way of ensuring both manoeuvrability and safety is to design the aircraft to have enough basic stability to give good handling characteristics over the operational flight envelope (up to the maximum useful angle of incidence) and then to use the flight control system to prevent excursions outside this envelope (see refs. 18 and 19).

## AERODYNAMIC COUPLING AT HIGH INCIDENCE

At high angles of incidence, asymmetric flow phenomena (connected with flow separation) and low damping can lead to large amplitude wing rocking, or wing drop, with a large increase in drag; because of its sensitivity to small details in the aircraft geometry, wing drop is impossible to predict and difficult to produce faithfully in wind tunnel tests. The resulting changes in incidence and sideslip introduce aerodynamic coupling between the longitudinal and lateral motions of an aircraft (as compared with the primarily inertial coupling effects discussed above). Thus, at moderate angles of incidence and sweepback, $C_m$ decreases with increase of sideslip (i.e. there is a nose-down pitching moment due both to the loss of lift on the inboard part of the trailing wing and to the gain of lift at the tip of the leading wing). This effect can be reversed at a high incidence (say 16°-20°) due to tip stalling, which is more pronounced on the trailing wing.

At high incidence, the cross-flow round the fuselage on a sideslipping aircraft becomes more important. This in turn affects the flow over both the fin and tailplane, and is a further source of aerodynamic coupling. Asymmetric flow separation over the wing greatly alters the rolling and yawing moments, especially if there is asymmetric vortex shedding and vortex breakdown (or burst); these effects are very sensitive to small variations in both incidence and sideslip. Wing strakes can have a beneficial effect by ensuring symmetric shedding of vortices.

When separation occurs from the fuselage, that part of the fin and rudder above the fuselage tends to be within the separated flow and hence to lose its effectiveness, and directional stability may become borderline. It has long been recognized that the rudder is the most important control in the recovery from a spin, and it is essential that it should be shielded (by fuselage or tailplane) as little as possible. Thus any portion of the rudder below the fuselage (or other surface) is beneficial.

When increasing incidence and sideslip both cause further loss of directional stability and dihedral effect ($-L_v$), and longitudinal control is not effective (or is not applied), the aircraft will start an oscillatory spin, in which both aerodynamic and inertial coupling are of importance.

In the subsequent analysis, we shall concentrate out attention on the effects of aerodynamic coupling. Our aim is to derive simple design criteria for the dynamic stability of an aircraft at high incidence and moderate angles of sideslip. The analysis is based on that of Kalviste (ref. 20).

## EQUATIONS OF ANGULAR MOTION

The full set of non-linear equations of motion, referred to principal axes, are given by Eqs. (12.11) - (12.16). As in the case of dynamic coupling, some generalized stability criteria can be obtained by linearizing these equations. The aircraft is assumed to be slightly disturbed from horizontal flight. For simplicity we shall take the aircraft speed to be constant in magnitude and direction, and we shall consider only the rotary motion. This is valid as a first approximation since, in high incidence motion (and also in the spin), the most important aerodynamic coupling effects are those due to the rolling, pitching and yawing moments. As in the classical theory, the angular velocities of the aircraft are assumed to be small quantities of the first order.

On linearizing the equations of angular motion, they become (referred to principal axes)

$$I_x\dot{p} = L_a, \tag{12.51}$$

$$I_y\dot{q} = M_a, \tag{12.52}$$

$$I_z\dot{r} = N_a. \tag{12.53}$$

In the steady state, the aircraft is assumed to be trimmed and to have no angular rotation, and to be moving with uniform velocity, with *constant* angles of incidence and sideslip. The aerodynamic moments $L_a$, $M_a$ and $N_a$ will depend on both incidence and sideslip.

### Angles of incidence and sideslip

We shall now determine expressions for $p$, $q$ and $r$ in terms of the rates of change of incidence $\alpha$, sideslip $\beta$ and bank angle $\gamma$. In Fig. 12.6, $Oa$ (parallel to the aircraft drag) is the projection of the aircraft velocity vector $Oc$ on the $Oxz$ plane (the plane of symmetry of the aircraft). $Ob$ (the direction of the aircraft lift) is perpendicular to both $Oa$ and $Oy$ (and thus lies in the plane $Oxz$). The

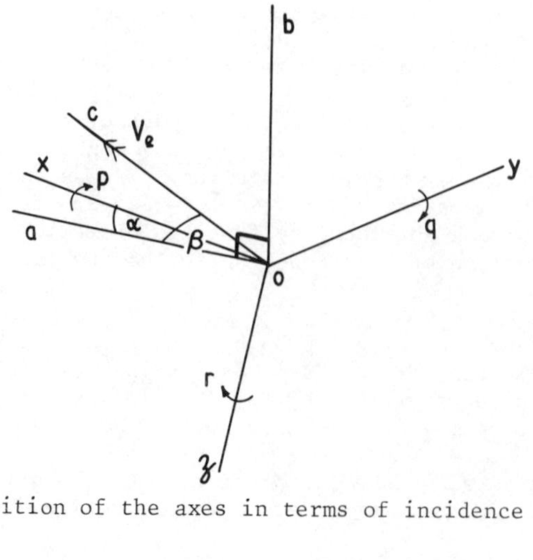


Fig. 12.6 Position of the axes in terms of incidence and sideslip

angle of incidence $\alpha$ (or angle of attack) is defined to be the angle between $Ox$ and $Oa$; the angle of sideslip $\beta$ is the angle between $Oa$ and $Oc$, the direction of the aircraft velocity vector. The bank angle $\gamma$ refers to rotation about $Oc$, and is equal to the inclination of $Ob$ to the vertical.

Consider rotation relative to the velocity vector. The frame $Oxyz$ can be considered to have angular velocities $\dot{\alpha}$ about $Oy$, $\dot{\beta}$ about $Ob$ and $\dot{\gamma}$ about $Oc$. Resolving these angular velocities about $Ox$, $Oy$ and $Oz$ we find

$$p = \dot{\gamma}\cos\beta\cos\alpha + \dot{\beta}\sin\alpha, \tag{12.54}$$

$$q = \dot{\gamma}\sin\beta + \dot{\alpha}, \tag{12.55}$$

$$r = \dot{\gamma}\cos\beta\sin\alpha - \dot{\beta}\cos\alpha. \tag{12.56}$$

Thus

$$\dot{\alpha} = q - (p\cos\alpha + r\sin\alpha)\tan\beta, \tag{12.57}$$

$$\dot{\beta} = p\sin\alpha - r\cos\alpha \tag{12.58}$$

and

$$\dot{\gamma} = (p\cos\alpha + r\sin\alpha)\sec\beta. \tag{12.59}$$

On differentiating Eqs.(12.57) and (12.58), and omitting second order terms such as $p\dot{\alpha}$, $p\dot{\beta}$, etc., we obtain

$$\ddot{\alpha} = \dot{q} - (\dot{p}\cos\alpha + \dot{r}\sin\alpha)\tan\beta, \tag{12.60}$$

$$\ddot{\beta} = \dot{p}\sin\alpha - \dot{r}\cos\alpha. \tag{12.61}$$

Combining these equations with Eqs.(12.51) - (12.53), we find, in the notation of reference 20,

$$\ddot{\alpha} = m_{DYN} = (M_a/I_y) - [(L_a/I_x)\cos\alpha + (N_a/I_z)\sin\alpha]\tan\beta, \tag{12.62}$$

$$\ddot{\beta} = -n_{DYN} = -(N_a/I_z)\cos\alpha + (L_a/I_x)\sin\alpha. \tag{12.63}$$

Here $m_{DYN}$ is the pitching acceleration which causes a change in incidence, and $(-n_{DYN})$ is the yawing acceleration which causes a change in sideslip.

## Stability analysis at non-zero angle of sideslip

Following the analysis of Kalviste (ref. 20), we shall obtain a way of presenting the stability characteristics of an aircraft at non-zero angle of sideslip in the datum state. For simplicity we shall consider only the static contributions to $m_{DYN}$ and $n_{DYN}$ (due to small changes in incidence $\alpha$ and sideslip $\beta$). Diagrams showing the quantitative nature of these effects are given by Kalviste. We also consider controls to be kept in the trimmed position. Thus we write

$$\begin{aligned} \Delta\alpha &= \alpha - \alpha_e, \\ \Delta\beta &= \beta - \beta_e, \end{aligned} \tag{12.64}$$

where the suffix $e$ denotes the datum value.

Then

$$\begin{aligned} D^2(\Delta\alpha) &= m_{DYN} = m_{\alpha DYN}\,\Delta\alpha + m_{\beta DYN}\,\Delta\beta, \\ -D^2(\Delta\beta) &= n_{DYN} = n_{\alpha DYN}\,\Delta\alpha + n_{\beta DYN}\,\Delta\beta, \end{aligned} \tag{12.65}$$

where the operator $D = d/dt$, $m_{\alpha DYN} = \partial m_{DYN}/\partial d$ and similarly for $m_{\beta DYN}$, $n_{\alpha DYN}$ and $n_{\beta DYN}$.

The constant coefficients $m_{\alpha DYN}$, $m_{\beta DYN}$, $n_{\alpha DYN}$ and $n_{\beta DYN}$ are to be evaluated at the datum state (in which the incidence is $\alpha_e$ and the angle of sideslip $\beta_e$). They can be expressed in terms of $\partial L_a/\partial\alpha$, $\partial M_a/\partial\alpha$, etc., by differentiating the right-hand sides of Eqs. (12.62) and (12.63). We note that the terms $m_{\beta DYN}$ and $n_{\alpha DYN}$ occur because $\beta_e$ is not zero.

The stability of the motion is determined from the roots of the characteristic equation derived from Eq. (12.65), that is

$$\begin{vmatrix} \lambda^2 - m_{\alpha DYN} & -m_{\beta DYN} \\ n_{\alpha DYN} & \lambda^2 + n_{\beta DYN} \end{vmatrix} = 0 \tag{12.66}$$

or
$$\lambda^4 + A\lambda^2 + B = 0, \tag{12.67}$$

where
$$A = n_{\beta DYN} - m_{\alpha DYN} \tag{12.68}$$

and
$$B = n_{\alpha DYN} m_{\beta DYN} - n_{\beta DYN} m_{\alpha DYN}. \tag{12.69}$$

We see that, since we have neglected the aerodynamic damping terms, there are no terms in $\lambda$ or $\lambda^3$.

The roots of Eq. (12.67) are of the form $\lambda = \pm\lambda_r$ $(r = 1, 2)$, where $\lambda_r$ may be real, purely imaginary or complex. Thus the motion may be composed of at least one divergence or an increasing oscillation unless the roots are purely imaginary (or zero), i.e. $\lambda_r^2 \leq 0$ $(r = 1, 2)$. The former case, which corresponds to simple harmonic motion, will occur if

$$A > 0 \quad \text{and} \quad A^2 \geq 4B > 0. \tag{12.70}$$

We see that

$$\begin{aligned} A^2 - 4B &= n_{\beta DYN}^2 + m_{\alpha DYN}^2 + 2n_{\beta DYN} m_{\alpha DYN} - 4n_{\alpha DYN} m_{\beta DYN} \\ &= (n_{\beta DYN} + m_{\alpha DYN})^2 - 4n_{\alpha DYN} m_{\beta DYN} . \end{aligned}$$

Thus a large positive value of $n_{\alpha DYN} m_{\beta DYN}$ can make $A^2 - 4B < 0$ and can cause instability, a new type of coupled pitch-yaw unstable oscillation occurring. A large negative value of $n_{\alpha DYN} m_{\beta DYN}$ can make $B$ negative, and again produce instability. The coupling term $n_{\alpha DYN} m_{\beta DYN}$ will be of special importance if both $n_{\beta DYN}$ and $m_{\alpha DYN}$ are numerically small, i.e. for an aircraft with borderline stability at zero sideslip.

If $n_{\alpha DYN}$ and $m_{\beta DYN}$ are both zero, the longitudinal and lateral modes are uncoupled; $n_{\beta DYN}$ is then equal to the square of the Dutch roll frequency, and $(-m_{\alpha DYN})$ is equal to the square of the frequency of the short period pitching oscillation.

In the uncoupled motion, Eq. (12.66) reduces to

$$(\lambda^2 + n_{\beta DYN})(\lambda^2 - m_{\alpha DYN}) = 0. \tag{12.71}$$

By analogy with this, if $A^2 \geq 4B$, Eq. (12.67) can be factorized in the form

$$(\lambda^2 + n_{\beta COP})(\lambda^2 - m_{\alpha COP}) = 0, \tag{12.72}$$

where
$$\begin{aligned} n_{\beta COP} &= \tfrac{1}{2}[A + C\sqrt{(A^2 - 4B)}], \\ m_{\alpha COP} &= \tfrac{1}{2}[-A + C\sqrt{(A^2 - 4B)}] \end{aligned}$$

and $C = \text{sign}\,(n_{\beta DYN} + m_{\alpha DYN})$.

Thus the aircraft will be unstable unless

$$n_{\beta COP} > 0, \quad m_{\alpha COP} < 0 \quad \text{and} \quad A^2 \geq 4B. \tag{12.73}$$

The corresponding stability criteria for an aircraft in a symmetric flow in the datum state (with zero sideslip) are, from the classical theory given in Parts II and III,

$$N_v > 0, \quad M_w < 0.$$

From Eqs. (12.62) and (12.63), we see that the new stability criteria involve rolling, pitching and yawing moments, all to be evaluated at non-zero angles of sideslip. Thus a considerable amount of wind tunnel testing, together with correlation with flight test results, is needed to provide adequate aerodynamic data. As shown in reference 21, non-linear effects can also be of importance.

## REFERENCES

1. COLLAR, A.R. The expanding domain of aeroelasticity. *J. Roy. Aeronaut. Soc.*, 50, 428 (1946).

2. MILNE, R.D. Dynamics of the deformable aeroplane. R. & M. 3345 (1964).

3. TAYLOR, A.S. and WOODCOCK, D.L. Mathematical approach to the dynamics of deformable aircraft. R. & M. 3776 (1976).

4. DUNCAN, W.J. Introductory survey. *AGARD Manual on Aeroelasticity*, Vol. 1 (1959).

5. LYON, H.M. A method of estimating the effect of aeroelastic distortion of a sweptback wing on stability and control derivatives. R. & M. 2331 (1949).

6. RUNYAN, H.L., PRATT, K.G. and BENNETT, F.V. Effects of aeroelasticity on the stability and control characteristics of airplanes. AGARD Report 348 (1961).

7. RHOADS, D.W. and SCHULER, J.M. A theoretical and experimental study of airplane dynamics in large-disturbance manoeuvres. *J. Aeronaut. Sci.*, 24, 507 (1957).

8. STERNFIELD, L. A simplified method for approximating the transient motion in angles of attack and sideslip during a constant rolling manoeuvre. NACA Report 1344 (1958).

9. PHILLIPS, W.H. Effect of steady rolling on longitudinal and directional stability. NACA Tech. Note 1627 (1948).

10. PINSKER, W.J.G. Critical flight conditions and loads resulting from inertia cross-coupling and aerodynamic stability deficiencies. ARC Current Paper 404 (1958).

11. PINSKER, W.J.G. Charts of peak amplitudes in incidence and sideslip in rolling manoeuvres due to inertia cross-coupling. R. & M. 3293 (1962).

12. SHORTAL, J.A. and MAGGIN, B. Effect of sweepback and aspect ratio on longitudinal stability characteristics of wings at low speeds. NACA Tech. Note 1093 (1946).

13. High angle of attack aerodynamics. AGARD Conf. Proc. No. 247 (1979).

14. HANCOCK, G.J. Problems of aircraft behaviour at high angles of attack. AGARDograph 136 (1969).

15. THOMAS, H.H.B.M. and COLLINGBOURNE, J. Longitudinal motions of aircraft involving high angles of attack. R. & M. 3753 (1974).

16. BABISTER, A.W. Aircraft longitudinal motion at high incidence. *Aero. J.*, 83, 230 (1979).

17. STENGEL, R.F. and BERRY, P.W. Stability and control of manoeuvring high performance aircraft. NASA CR 2788 (1977).

18. CHAMBERS, J.R. and GRAFTON, S.B. Aerodynamic characteristics of airplanes at high angles of attack. NASA TM 74097 (1977).

19. Stall/spin problems of military aircraft. AGARD Conf. Proc. No. 199 (1976).

20. Dynamic stability parameters. AGARD Conf. Proc. No. 235 (1978).

21. BABISTER, A.W. Aircraft stability at high incidence. *Aero. J.*, 84 (February, 1980).

# Part V

# STABILITY AND DESIGN

# Chapter 13

# ESTIMATION OF DYNAMIC STABILITY CHARACTERISTICS

## INTRODUCTION

In this chapter we shall show how to estimate the aerodynamic derivatives, and hence the dynamic stability characteristics, of a typical (fictitious) fighter aircraft. The analysis is based on the theory given in Parts I - III. In particular, the analysis shows the sources for obtaining the numerical values of the aerodynamic derivatives.

It must be emphasized that it is based only on existing (and, in some cases, inadequate) information on the numerical values of the aerodynamic parameters. The estimates given are, in many cases, based on the Engineering Sciences Data Sheets; these data sheets are amended, and their layout altered, from time to time, as the results of both theoretical and experimental work are extended to cater for new aircraft configurations. In addition, the estimate given here has been based on information given in unclassified reports. For a particular aircraft, there may well be much relevant classified information.

An estimate of this kind is often carried out at an early stage in the design of an aircraft. At a subsequent stage, when wind tunnel and flight test results become available for the particular aircraft configuration, the estimate should be amended accordingly; only then will we be able to have confidence in our predictions.

## DETAILS OF THE AIRCRAFT CONSIDERED

A three-view general arrangement of the aircraft is shown in Fig. 13.1. The aircraft is single-engined, with a sweptback wing and tail. Further details are given below:

| | | |
|---|---|---|
| | Aircraft mass $m$ | 18,000 kg |
| Wing | Gross wing area $S$ | 52 m$^2$ |
| | Wing loading $W/S = mg/S$ | 3,400 N/m$^2$ |
| | Span $b$ | 14.8 m |
| | Semi-span $s$ | 7.4 m |
| | Sweepback of quarter chord | 30° |
| | Root chord $c_0$ | 5.0 m |
| | Tip chord $c_t$ | 2.0 m |

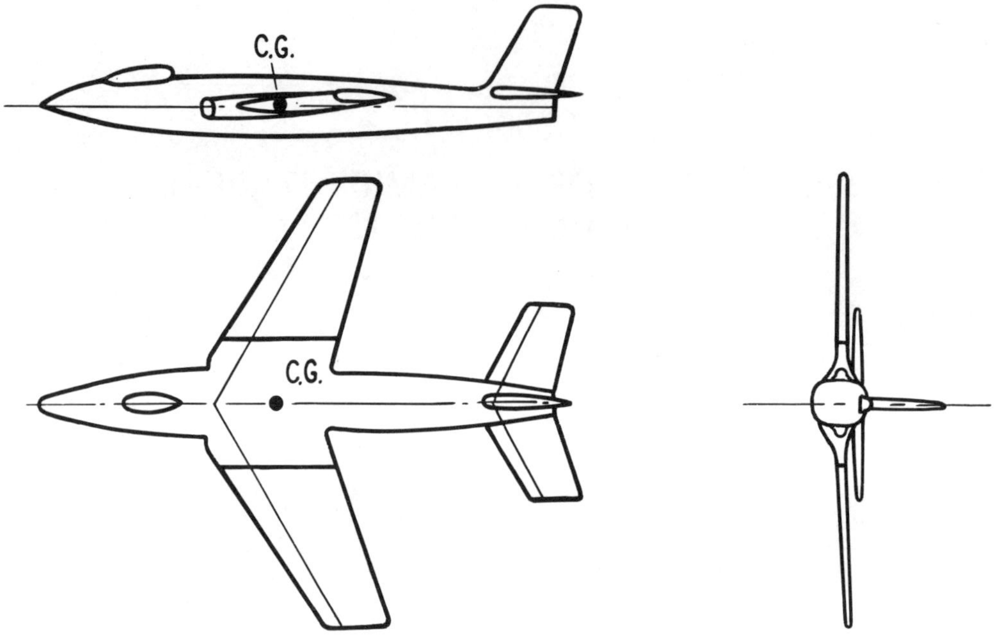


Fig. 13.1 A three-view general arrangement of the aircraft

| | | |
|---|---|---|
| | Taper ratio $\lambda$ | 0.4 |
| | Mean aerodynamic chord $\bar{\bar{c}}$ | 3.7 m |
| | Aspect ratio | 4.2 |
| | Aerofoil section parallel to line of flight | NACA 65A009 |
| | Thickness/chord ratio | 9% |
| | Dihedral | 1° from 0.3s to tip |
| | Wash-out at tips | 3° |
| Tailplane | Gross area $S_T$ | 14.3 m$^2$ |
| | Span | 6.5 m |
| | Sweepback of quarter chord | 25° |
| | Root chord | 2.6 m |
| | Tip chord | 1.8 m |
| | Taper ratio | 0.7 |
| | Mean aerodynamic chord | 2.2 m |
| | Aspect ratio | 3.0 |
| | Aerofoil section parallel to line of flight | NACA 65A006 |
| | Thickness/chord ratio | 6% |
| | Distance of aerodynamic centre of tailplane aft of c.g. of aircraft $l_T$ | 8.1 m |
| | Tailplane volume ratio $\bar{V}_T$ | 0.60 |
| Fin | Gross area $S_F$ | 8.4 m$^2$ |
| | Sweepback of quarter chord | 25° |
| | Aerofoil section parallel to line of flight | NACA 65A006 |

| | | | |
|---|---|---|---|
| | Thickness/chord ratio | | 6% |
| | Distance of aerodynamic centre of fin aft of c.g. of aircraft | $l_F$ | 8.3 m |
| | Fin volume ratio $\bar{V}_F$ | | 0.091 |
| Fuselage | Overall length $l_B$ | | 18 m |
| | Distance of aircraft c.g. aft of nose of fuselage | $l_{BF}$ | 8.3 m |
| | Maximum height $h$ | | 2.0 m |
| | Maximum width | | 2.0 m |
| | Side area of fuselage | $S_B$ | 28 $m^2$ |
| | Side area of fuselage forward of c.g. of aircraft | $S_{BF}$ | 13 $m^2$ |

The aerodynamic characteristics will be estimated for low speed sea level conditions, $C_L = 0.8$ ($V = 83$ m/s = 161 knots).

## AERODYNAMIC DATA

### Lift curve slope for wing

Aspect ratio 4.2, taper ratio 0.4, sweepback of quarter chord 30°.

The lift curve slope for swept wings of various plan-forms is given in reference 1, the effects of thickness being neglected.

From reference 1,

$$\frac{a(\text{given wing})}{a(\text{unswept wing of same aspect ratio and taper})} = \frac{0.062}{0.065} = 0.95.$$

We now allow for the effect of thickness. The aerofoil section NACA 65A009 has a trailing edge angle of 12°. Hence we have, from Eng. Sci. Data Sheets (Wings 01.01.01 and 01.01.05),

$$a(\text{unswept wing of aspect ratio 4.2, taper ratio 0.4}) = 3.84.$$

Thus, for the given wing,

$$a = 3.84 \times 0.95 = 3.65.$$

Wing incidence (measured from zero lift line)

$$= (C_L/a) \times 57.3 = (0.8/3.65) \times 57.3 = 12.5°.$$

### Lift curve slope for tailplane

Aspect ratio 3, taper ratio 0.7, sweepback of quarter chord 25°.

From reference 1,

$$\frac{a_1(\text{given tailplane})}{a_1(\text{unswept tailplane of same aspect ratio and taper})} = \frac{0.053}{0.055} = 0.96.$$

From Eng. Sci. Data Sheets (Wings 01.01.01 and 01.01.05), with the trailing edge angle of the tailplane of 8°,

$a_1$(unswept tailplane of aspect ratio 3, taper ratio 0.7) = 3.20.

The lift curve slope will be decreased slightly due to the fuselage. For the given aircraft, the local fuselage width at the tailplane is small compared with the tailplane span. From reference 2, we take the tailplane efficiency as 0.95. Thus for the given tailplane,

$$a_1 = 0.95 \times 0.96 \times 3.20 = 2.92.$$

## Lift curve slope for the fin

In estimating the lift curve slope for the fin, we have to find (i) the effective area of the fin, (ii) its effective aspects ratio, allowing for the tailplane, and (iii) the effect of the fuselage.

The trailing edge angle of the fin is 8°.
The height of the fin including the body depth = $h$ = 4.0 m.
The distance from the tailplane to the top of fin = $h_1$ = 3.0 m.
The body depth at one-quarter chord behind the fin leading edge = $d$ = 1.0 m.
The effective area of the fin including the body contribution = $S_F$ = 8.4 m$^2$.
The aspect ratio of the fin = $h^2/S_F$ = 1.90.

From Eng. Sci. Data Sheets (Controls 01.01.01), with $h_1/h$ = 0.75, the effective aspect ratio of the fin = 1.05 × 1.90 = 2.00.

For an unswept fin of this aspect ratio and trailing edge angle, $a_1$ = 2.70. From reference 1, we see that the effect of sweepback will reduce this to 2.65.

Allowing for the effect of the fuselage, with $d/h$ = 0.25, and using Eng. Sci. Data Sheets we find the fin efficiency is 0.83.

Hence $a_1 = 2.65 \times 0.83 = 2.20.$

# AIRCRAFT DRAG

## Wing profile drag

$$\text{Flight Reynolds Number} = \frac{V\bar{\bar{c}}}{\nu} = \frac{83 \times 3.7}{1.4607} \times 10^5 = 21.0 \times 10^6.$$

For the aerofoil section NACA 65A009 at zero incidence at this Reynolds number, $C_{D_0}$ = 0.0055.

To allow for the effect of incidence and roughness and for the increase of drag on a sweptback wing, we shall take $C_{D_0}$ = 0.010.

## Wing induced drag

For the given wing, from reference 3, at $C_L$ = 0.8,

$$C_{D_i} = 1.01 \frac{C_L^2}{\pi A} = 0.05.$$

Fuselage drag

Fuselage surface area = 73 $m^2$.
Fuselage surface area / wing area = 73/52 = 1.40.
Length of fuselage $l_B$ = 18 m.
Fore-body length = 7 m.

$$\text{Reynolds number} = \frac{Vl_B}{\nu} = \frac{83 \times 18}{1.4607} \times 10^5 = 1.02 \times 10^8 .$$

From Eng. Sci. Data Sheets (77028 and 78019), for a streamlined fuselage with transition at the nose, at this Reynolds number,

$C_D$ (based on fuselage surface area) = 0.0023.

Thus $C_D$ (based on wing area) = 0.0032.

To allow for the cockpit and for the intake and jet pipe effects, this figure is increased by 30% (a nominal figure, due to lack of available data).

We take $C_D$(fuselage) = 0.0042.

Drag of tailplane and fin

For simplicity, the profile drag of the tail unit is taken to be

$$C_{D_0}(\text{wing}) \times \frac{\text{tail unit area}}{\text{wing area}} = 0.010 \times \frac{14.3 + 6.0}{52} = 0.004 .$$

Therefore the total drag coefficient of the aircraft is

$$C_D = 0.068 .$$

Separating out the profile drag and the induced drag,

$$C_D = 0.018 + 0.077\, C_L^2 .$$

## INCIDENCE OF ROOT CHORD WITH RESPECT TO ZERO-LIFT LINE OF THE WING

We now have to determine the position of the zero-lift line of the wing relative to some known line in the aircraft.

The wing section is symmetric, but the wing itself has a wash-out of 3° linearly distributed across the span.

From reference 1, the angle of incidence of the root chord with respect to the mean zero-lift line of the wing, for a wing of aspect ratio 4.2, taper ratio 0.4, sweepback 30° is

$$0.39 \times (\text{twist in degrees}) = 1.2° .$$

## QUARTER-CHORD POINT OF THE MEAN AERODYNAMIC CHORD OF THE WING

From Eng. Sci. Data Sheet 76003, the quarter-chord point of the mean aerodynamic chord of the wing is 0.61 $c_0$ = 3.05 m aft of the wing apex, i.e. 7.9 m aft of the nose of the fuselage. The length of the mean aerodynamic chord is 3.7 m.

## AERODYNAMIC CENTRE OF THE AIRCRAFT LESS TAIL

For the section NACA 65A009, the section aerodynamic centre is at $0.25c$. From Eng. Sci. Data Sheet 70011, the aerodynamic centre of the wing is at $0.26\bar{\bar{c}}$ aft of the leading edge of the mean aerodynamic chord.

From reference 4 it can be seen that the effect of the fuselage is to shift the aerodynamic centre forward by about $0.01\bar{\bar{c}}$. In the absence of wind tunnel data, we take the aerodynamic centre of the aircraft less tail to be given by

$$h_0 = 0.25.$$

## QUARTER-CHORD POINT OF THE MEAN AERODYNAMIC CHORD OF THE TAILPLANE

From Eng. Sci. Data Sheet 76003, the quarter-chord point of the mean aerodynamic chord of the tailplane is $0.53c_{OT}$ = 1.4 m aft of the tailplane apex, i.e. 16.4 m aft of the nose of the fuselage, i.e. 8.5 m aft of the quarter-chord point of the mean aerodynamic chord of the wing.

## DOWNWASH GRADIENT

We next find the rate of change of downwash with incidence. For the given wing, from reference 3, at the line of the wing tip vortices, $d\varepsilon/d\alpha = 0.71$. The height of the tailplane above the extended wing root chord = 1.5 m. Allowing for this, we find $d\varepsilon/d\alpha = 0.9 \times 0.71 = 0.64$.

## STICK FIXED LONGITUDINAL STATIC STABILITY

### Position of the aerodynamic centre of the whole aircraft

From Eq. (1.13),

$$h_n = h_0 + \bar{V}\frac{a_1}{a}\left(1 - \frac{d\varepsilon}{d\alpha}\right);$$

where $$\bar{V} = \frac{S_T l}{S\bar{\bar{c}}} = \frac{14.3 \times 8.5}{52 \times 3.7} = 0.63.$$

Therefore $$h_n = 0.25 + 0.63 \times \frac{2.92}{3.65} \times 0.36 = 0.43.$$

### Static margin (stick fixed)

The c.g. of the aircraft is 8.3 m aft of the nose of the fuselage, i.e. 0.4 m aft of the quarter-chord point of the mean aerodynamic chord of the wing.

Thus $$h = 0.25 + (0.4/3.7) = 0.36,$$

and the static margin (stick fixed) $K_n = h_n - h = 0.07$.

AERODYNAMIC DERIVATIVES (LONGITUDINAL)

We consider horizontal flight, $C_L = 0.8$, at sea level.

$X$ Force component derivatives

If the variation of thrust with speed is neglected,

$$X_u = -2C_D = -0.136.$$

$$X_w = C_L - dC_D/d\alpha = C_L - (dC_D/dC_L).(dC_L/d\alpha).$$

$$C_D = 0.018 + 0.077\ C_L^2 .$$

$$dC_D/dC_L = 0.154\ C_L = 0.12.$$

$$X_w = 0.8 - 0.12 \times 3.65 = 0.36.$$

$Z$ Force component derivatives

$$Z_u = -2C_L = -1.6.$$

$$Z_w = -(C_D + dC_L/d\alpha) = -(0.068 + 3.65) = -3.72.$$

$$Z_q \simeq Z_q(\text{tail}) = -a_1\bar{V}_T = -2.92 \times 0.60 = -1.75.$$

$$Z_{\dot{w}} = Z_q(\text{tail})\ d\varepsilon/d\alpha = -1.75 \times 0.64 = -1.12.$$

Pitching moment derivatives

At low speeds, $M_u = 0$.

$$M_w = -(dC_L/d\alpha)\ K_n = -3.65 \times 0.07 = -0.26.$$

The main contribution to $M_q$ is from the tailplane.

$$M_q(\text{tail}) = (l_T/\bar{\bar{c}})\ Z_q(\text{tail}) = -\frac{8.1}{3.7} \times 1.75 = -3.8.$$

The contribution from the wing is found from reference 5.

$$C_{m_q} = -0.68.$$

Thus $\quad M_q(\text{wing}) = \tfrac{1}{2}C_{m_q} = -0.34,$

and, for the complete aircraft, $M_q = -4.1$.

$$M_{\dot{w}} = M_q(\text{tail})\ d\varepsilon/d\alpha = -3.8 \times 0.64 = -2.43.$$

AERODYNAMIC DERIVATIVES (LATERAL)

Horizontal flight, $C_L = 0.8$, at sea level.

Rolling moment derivative due to sideslip $L_v$

*Contribution due to wing dihedral*

Wing dihedral angle 1° from 0.3s to tip. From Eng. Sci. Data Sheets (Aircraft

06.01.03 and 06.01.10), for the given wing,

$$(L_v)_\Gamma = -0.008.$$

*Contribution due to wing sweepback* (independent of the dihedral effect)

From reference 6, for the given wing,

$$L_v = -0.20C_L = -0.16.$$

*Contribution due to the fuselage*

The given aircraft has a mid-wing arrangement, and there is no contribution to $L_v$.

*Contribution due to the fin*

We take the aerodynamic centre of the fin at 1.8 m above the fuselage centre line. The distance of this point above the wind axis $Ox$ is $h_F \simeq 0$. Thus, from Eq. (4.14),

$$L_v(\text{fin}) = -a_1\bar{V}_F \frac{h_F}{l_F} = 0.$$

Thus, for the complete aircraft, $L_v = -0.008 - 0.16 = -0.168$.

Rolling moment derivative due to rate of roll $L_p$

*Contribution due to the wing*

From Eng. Sci. Data Sheet (Aircraft 06.01.01), for the given wing,

$$L_p = -0.016.$$

The contributions from the fuselage and fin are negligible.

Rolling moment derivative due to rate of yaw $L_r$

*Contribution due to the wing*

From Eng. Sci. Data Sheet. 72021, for the given wing,

$$L_r = 0.151\ C_L = 0.121.$$

*Contribution due to the fin*

From Eq. (4.34),

$$L_r(\text{fin}) = a_1\bar{V}_F \frac{h_F}{b} = 0.$$

Hence, for the complete aircraft, $L_r = 0.121$.

Yawing moment derivative due to sideslip $N_v$

*Contribution due to the wing*

From reference 5, for the given wing,

$$N_v = 0.04\ C_L{}^2 = 0.026.$$

*Contribution due to the fuselage*

For the given fuselage, $l_B = 18$ m, $l_{BF} = 8.3$ m, $h = 2.0$ m,
$S_B = 28$ m$^2$, $S_{BF} = 13$ m$^2$.

Thus $h^2/S_B = 0.143$, $(S_{BF}l_{BF}/S_Bl_B)^{\frac{1}{2}} = 0.49$, $S_Bl_B/Sb = 0.585$.

From Eng. Sci. Data Sheet (Aircraft 07.01.01), for a circular fuselage with a low or high wing,

$$N_v(\text{fuselage}) = -0.10(S_Bl_B/Sb) = -0.059.$$

This is increased by 20% due to the mid-wing arrangement, and is reduced by 5% due to the elliptic section of the fuselage.

Thus $\quad N_v(\text{fuselage}) = -0.068.$

*Contribution due to the fin*

From Eq. (4.19), $N_v(\text{fin}) = a_1\bar{V}_F = 2.20 \times 0.091 = 0.200.$

Hence, for the complete aircraft,

$$N_v = 0.026 - 0.068 + 0.200 = 0.158.$$

Yawing moment due to rate of roll $N_p$

*Contribution due to the wing*

From reference 7, for the given wing, with $\partial C_{D_0}/\partial\alpha = 0$,

$$C_{n_p} = -0.09C_L = -0.072.$$

Thus $\quad N_p = \frac{1}{2}C_{n_p} = -0.036.$

This will be reduced by wash-out. We take $N_p = -0.03$.

*Contribution due to the fin*

For the given aircraft, with $h_F$ zero, the contribution due to the fin is negligible.

Yawing moment due to rate of yaw $N_r$

*Contribution due to the wing*

From Eng. Sci. Data Sheet 71017, for the given wing,

$$N_r = -0.0083.$$

*Contribution due to the fin*

From Eq. (4.39), $N_r(\text{fin}) = -\frac{l_F}{b} N_v(\text{fin}) = -\frac{8.3}{14.8} \times 0.200 = -0.112.$

Hence, for the complete aircraft, $N_r = -0.120$.

Side force derivative due to sideslip $Y_v$

*Contribution due to the fuselage*

From reference 8, for a circular section fuselage of the same general shape,

$$C_{Y_\beta} = -57.3 \times 0.004\ S_B/S = -0.23 \times 28/52 = -0.124.$$

We increase this by 20% to allow for the given shape of fuselage. Thus

$$Y_v(\text{fuselage}) = C_{Y_\beta} = -0.15.$$

*Contribution due to the fin*

From Eq. (4.23), $Y_v(\text{fin}) = -\frac{S_F}{S} a_1 = -\frac{8.4}{52} \times 2.20 = -0.36.$

Thus, for the complete aircraft, $Y_v = -0.51$.

## DYNAMIC STABILITY CHARACTERISTICS

We consider horizontal flight, $\Theta_e = 0$.

$$\tau = m/\tfrac{1}{2}\rho_e V_e S = 6.8,$$

$$\mu_1 = m/\tfrac{1}{2}\rho_e S\bar{\bar{c}} = 153, \quad \mu_2 = m/\tfrac{1}{2}\rho_e Sb = 38.$$

We take

$$i_x = I_x/mb^2 = 0.05,$$

$$i_y = I_y/m\bar{\bar{c}}^2 = 1.75,$$

$$i_z = I_z/mb^2 = 0.15,$$

$$i_{zx} = I_{zx}/mb^2 = -0.02.$$

$$\hat{g}_1 = C_L = 0.8, \quad \hat{g}_2 = C_L \tan\Theta_e = 0.$$

Longitudinal dynamic stability

From Eq. (2.111), the concise derivatives have the following values:

$x_u = -X_u = 0.136$, $x_w = -X_w = -0.36$, $x_{\dot{w}} = x_q = 0$.

$z_u = -Z_u = 1.6$, $z_w = -Z_w = 3.72$, $z_{\dot{w}} = -Z_{\dot{w}}/\mu_1 = 0.007$,

$z_q = -Z_q/\mu_1 = 0.011$, $m_u = 0$, $m_w = -\mu_1 M_w/i_y = 23$,

$m_{\dot{w}} = -M_{\dot{w}}/i_y = 1.39$, $m_q = -M_q/i_y = 2.34$.

Thus

$$x_u z_w - x_w z_u = 1.08,$$

$$x_u(1 - z_q) = 0.135,$$

and

$$\hat{g}_1 z_u = 1.28.$$

From Chapter 6, the coefficients of the characteristic equation for longitudinal motion are given by:

$$A_1 = 1 + z_{\dot{w}} = 1.01,$$

$$\begin{aligned} B_1 &= [x_u(1 + z_{\dot{w}}) + z_w - x_{\dot{w}} z_u] + (1 + z_{\dot{w}})m_q + (1 - z_q)m_{\dot{w}} \\ &= [0.136 \times 1.01 + 3.72] + 1.01 \times 2.34 + 0.99 \times 1.39 \\ &= 3.86 + 2.36 + 1.38 = 7.60, \end{aligned}$$

$$\begin{aligned} C_1 &= (x_u z_w - x_w z_u) + [x_u(1 + z_{\dot{w}}) + z_w - x_{\dot{w}} z_u]m_q + \\ &\quad + [x_u(1 - z_q) + x_q z_u - \hat{g}_2]m_{\dot{w}} + (1 - z_q)m_w - \\ &\quad - [x_{\dot{w}}(1 - z_q) + x_q(1 + z_{\dot{w}})]m_u \\ &= 1.08 + 3.86 \times 2.34 + 0.135 \times 1.39 + 0.989 \times 23 \\ &= 1.08 + 9.03 + 0.19 + 22.75 = 33.1, \end{aligned}$$

$$\begin{aligned} D_1 &= (x_u z_w - x_w z_u)m_q + (\hat{g}_1 z_u - \hat{g}_2 x_u)m_{\dot{w}} + \\ &\quad + [x_u(1 - z_q) + x_q z_u - \hat{g}_2]m_w - \\ &\quad - [x_w(1 - z_q) + x_q z_w + \hat{g}_1(1 + z_{\dot{w}}) - \hat{g}_2 x_{\dot{w}}]m_u \\ &= 1.08 \times 2.34 + 1.28 \times 1.39 + 0.135 \times 23 \\ &= 2.53 + 1.78 + 3.11 = 7.42, \end{aligned}$$

$$\begin{aligned} E_1 &= (\hat{g}_1 z_u - \hat{g}_2 x_u)m_w - (\hat{g}_1 z_w - \hat{g}_2 x_w)m_u \\ &= 1.28 \times 23 = 29.4 \end{aligned}$$

The characteristic equation for longitudinal motion is

$$\Delta(\lambda) = A_1\lambda^4 + B_1\lambda^3 + C_1\lambda^2 + D_1\lambda + E_1 = 0,$$

i.e. $\Delta(\lambda) = 1.01\lambda^4 + 7.60\lambda^3 + 33.1\lambda^2 + 7.42\lambda + 29.4 = 0.$

We see that $D_1$ and $E_1$ are small compared respectively with $C_1$ and $C_1{}^2$. Thus, from Appendix 2, the approximate factors of $\Delta(\lambda)$ are

$$\Delta(\lambda) = (1.01\lambda^2 + 7.60\lambda + 33.1)(\lambda^2 + \gamma_1\lambda + \delta_1),$$

where $\gamma_1 = \dfrac{C_1 D_1 - B_1 E_1}{C_1^2} = 0.021$

and $\delta_1 = \dfrac{E_1}{C_1} = 0.888.$

Using the iterative method of Appendix 2, we find the exact factors are

$$\Delta(\lambda) = (1.01\lambda^2 + 7.59\lambda + 32.1)(\lambda^2 + 0.0145\lambda + 0.917) = 0$$

with roots $\lambda = -3.76 \pm 4.20i, \quad -0.0073 \pm 0.958i.$

We see that the characteristic equation has two pairs of complex roots, both pairs having negative real parts. Thus the aircraft is stable in longitudinal motion.

## Period and damping of longitudinal motion

The first pair of roots corresponds to the highly damped short period motion. The time $t_{\frac{1}{2}}$ to half-amplitude is

$$t_{\frac{1}{2}} = \frac{\log_e 2}{3.76}\tau = \frac{0.693}{3.76} \times 6.8 = 1.25 \text{ sec.}$$

The period $T$ is

$$T = \frac{2\pi}{4.20}\tau = \frac{2\pi}{4.20} \times 6.8 = 10.2 \text{ sec.}$$

The second pair of roots corresponds to the lightly damped long period oscillation (the phugoid oscillation). The time $t_{\frac{1}{2}}$ to half-amplitude is

$$t_{\frac{1}{2}} = \frac{\log_e 2}{0.0073}\tau = \frac{0.693}{0.0073} \times 6.8 = 646 \text{ sec.}$$

The period $T$ is

$$T = \frac{2\pi}{0.958}\tau = \frac{2\pi}{0.958} \times 6.8 = 44.6 \text{ sec.}$$

As shown in Chapter 7, the damping of the phugoid oscillation could be improved by using an automatic control.

## LATERAL DYNAMIC STABILITY

From Eq. (2.119), the concise derivatives have the following values:

$y_v = -Y_v = 0.51,$ $\quad y_p = y_r = 0,$

$l_v = -\mu_2 L_v/i_x = 127,$ $\quad l_p = -L_p/i_x = 3.2,$ $\quad l_r = -L_r/i_x = -2.4,$

$n_v = -\mu_2 N_v/i_z = -40,$ $\quad n_p = -N_p/i_z = 0.2,$ $\quad n_r = -N_r/i_z = 0.8,$

$e_x = -i_{zx}/i_x = 0.4,$ $\quad e_z = -i_{zx}/i_z = 0.133.$

Thus $\quad l_p n_r - l_r n_p = 3.04$

and $\quad l_v n_r - l_r n_v = 5.6.$

From Chapter 10, the coefficients of the characteristic equation for lateral motion are given by:

$$A_2 = 1 - e_x e_z = 0.95,$$

$$\begin{aligned} B_2 &= (l_p + n_r - e_x n_p - e_z l_r) + (1 - e_x e_z) y_v \\ &= (3.2 + 0.8 - 0.08 + 0.318) + 0.95 \times 0.51 \\ &= 4.24 + 0.49 = 4.73, \end{aligned}$$

$$\begin{aligned} C_2 &= (l_p n_r - l_r n_p) + (l_p + n_r - e_x n_p - e_z l_r) y_v + \\ &\quad + [e_z(1 + y_r) - y_p] l_v - [1 + y_r - e_x y_p] n_v \\ &= 3.04 + 4.24 \times 0.51 + 0.133 \times 127 + 40 \\ &= 3.04 + 2.16 + 16.9 + 40 = 62.1, \end{aligned}$$

$$\begin{aligned} D_2 &= (l_p n_r - l_r n_p) y_v + [n_p(1 + y_r) - n_r y_p + \hat{g}_1 - e_z \hat{g}_2] l_v - \\ &\quad - [l_p(1 + y_r) - l_r y_p - \hat{g}_2 + e_x \hat{g}_1] n_v \\ &= 3.04 \times 0.51 + 1.0 \times 127 + 3.52 \times 40 \\ &= 1.55 + 127 + 140.8 = 269.4, \end{aligned}$$

$$\begin{aligned} E_2 &= \hat{g}_1(n_r l_v - l_r n_v) - \hat{g}_2(n_p l_v - l_p n_v) \\ &= 0.8 \times 5.6 = 4.5. \end{aligned}$$

The characteristic equation for lateral motion is

$$\Delta(\lambda) = A_2\lambda^4 + B_2\lambda^3 + C_2\lambda^2 + D_2\lambda + E_2 = 0,$$

i.e. $$\Delta(\lambda) = 0.95\lambda^4 + 4.73\lambda^3 + 62.1\lambda^2 + 269.4\lambda + 4.5 = 0.$$

We see that $E_2$ is small compared with $D_2$. Thus, from Appendix 2, the approximate value of the small root of the characteristic equation is $(-E_2/D_2) = -0.017$. There is also a large root, approximately equal to $(-B_2/A_2) = -5.0$.

Using the methods of Appendix 2, we find the exact factors of $\Delta(\lambda)$ are

$$\Delta(\lambda) = 0.95(\lambda + 0.0168)(\lambda + 4.47)(\lambda^2 + 0.49 \quad + 63.1) = 0$$

with roots $\lambda = -0.0168, \quad -4.47, \quad -0.245 \pm 7.49i.$

We see that the characteristic equation has two real roots and a pair of complex roots, all the roots having a negative real part. Thus the aircraft is stable in lateral motion.

Period and damping of lateral motion

The large negative root corresponds to the heavily damped rolling subsidence. The time $t_{\frac{1}{2}}$ to half-amplitude is

$$t_{\frac{1}{2}} = \frac{\log_e 2}{4.47}\,\tau = \frac{0.693}{4.47} \times 6.8 = 1.05 \text{ sec.}$$

The small negative root corresponds to the lightly damped spiral subsidence. The time $t_{\frac{1}{2}}$ to half-amplitude is

$$t_{\frac{1}{2}} = \frac{\log_e 2}{0.0168}\,\tau = \frac{0.693}{0.0168} \times 6.8 = 280 \text{ sec.}$$

The pair of complex roots corresponds to the lateral oscillation. The time $t_{\frac{1}{2}}$ to half-amplitude is

$$t_{\frac{1}{2}} = \frac{\log_e 2}{0.245}\,\tau = \frac{0.693}{0.245} \times 6.8 = 19.2 \text{ sec.}$$

The period $T$ is

$$T = \frac{2\pi}{7.94}\,\tau = \frac{2\pi}{7.94} \times 6.8 = 5.38 \text{ sec.}$$

As shown in Chapter 11, the damping could be improved by using a yaw damper.

REFERENCES

1. DE YOUNG, J. and HARPER, C.W. Theoretical symmetric span loading at subsonic speeds for wings having arbitrary plan form. NACA Report 921 (1948).

2. LYONS, D.J. and BISGOOD, P.L. An analysis of the lift curve slope of aerofoils of small aspect ratio, including fins, with design charts for aerofoils and control surfaces. R. & M. 2308 (1945).

3. WOLOWICZ, C.G. and YANCEY, R.B. Longitudinal aerodynamic characteristics of light, twin-engine, propeller-driven airplanes. NASA TN D-6800 (1972).

4. SCHLICHTING, H. Calculation of the influence of a body on the position of the aerodynamic centre of aircraft with sweptback wings. R. & M. 2582 (1952).

5. TOLL, T.A. and QUEIJO, M.J. Approximate relations and charts for low speed stability derivatives of swept wings. NACA Tech. Note 1581 (1948).

6. WOLOWICZ, C.H. and YANCEY, R.B. Lateral-directional aerodynamic characteristics of light, twin-engine, propeller-driven airplanes. NASA TN D-6946 (1972).

7. CAMPBELL, J.P. and McKINNEY, M.O. Summary of methods for calculating dynamic lateral stability and response and for estimating lateral stability derivatives. NACA Report 1098 (1952).

8. QUEIJO, M.J. and WOLHART, W.D. Experimental investigation of fuselage shape and length on the static lateral stability characteristics of a model with 45° sweptback wing and tail surfaces. NACA Report 1049 (1951).

# APPENDICES

# Appendix 1

# THE EQUATIONS OF MOTION OF A RIGID BODY

The dynamical equations of motion of an aircraft considered as a rigid body are given in Chapter 2. We shall show here how they can be determined from first principles. We shall find it convenient to refer the equations to axes fixed in the body (body axes) but moving in space as the body moves.

## MOVING AXES

Consider a point $P(x,y,z)$ referred to a rectangular frame $Oxyz$ through a fixed point $O$ (Fig. A.1.1). The frame moves about $O$ so that at the instant considered

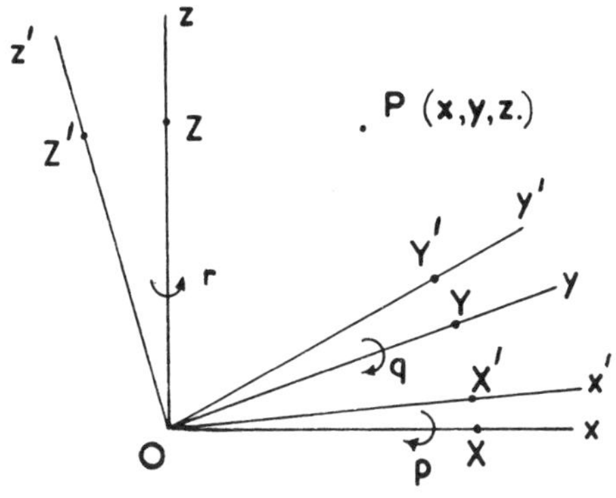


Fig. A1.1 Moving rectangular frame of axes

(time $t$) it has components of angular velocity $p$, $q$, $r$ about the instantaneous positions of $Ox$, $Oy$, $Oz$ respectively. The positive senses of $p$, $q$, $r$ are taken to be clockwise with respect to $Ox$, $Oy$, $Oz$. Consider points $X$, $Y$, $Z$ at *unit* distance from $O$ along these axes. Then at time $t + \mathrm{d}t$, $X$, $Y$, $Z$ are at $X'$, $Y'$, $Z'$ on the frame $Ox'y'z'$. Considering the small rotations about the axes $Ox$, $Oy$, $Oz$ we find the coordinates of $X'$ are $(1,\ r\mathrm{d}t,\ -q\mathrm{d}t)$ with respect to the frame $Oxyz$, those of $Y'$ are $(-r\mathrm{d}t,\ 1,\ p\mathrm{d}t)$ and those of $Z'$ $(q\mathrm{d}t,\ -p\mathrm{d}t,\ 1)$, where second order terms have been neglected. Now since $OX'$, $OY'$, $OZ'$ are of unit length, these coordinates are also the direction cosines of $Ox'$, $Oy'$, $Oz'$ with respect to $Ox$, $Oy$, $Oz$, the positions of the axes at time $t$.

## COMPONENTS OF VELOCITY AND ACCELERATION REFERRED TO MOVING AXES

At time $t$ the coordinates of $P$ are $(x, y, z)$ referred to $Oxyz$; at time $t + dt$, the coordinates of $P$ are $(x + \dot{x}dt, y + \dot{y}dt, z + \dot{z}dt)$ referred to the frame at time $t + dt$, i.e. to $Ox'y'z'$.

The displacement of $P$ parallel to $Ox$ in time $dt$ is (using the direction cosines obtained above)

$$(x + \dot{x}dt)\cdot 1 + (y + \dot{y}dt)\cdot(-rdt) + (z + \dot{z}dt)\cdot(qdt) - x = (\dot{x} - ry + qz)dt,$$

where second order terms have been neglected.

But if $u$ is the velocity component of $P$ parallel to $Ox$, the displacement of $P$ parallel to $Ox$ in time $dt$ is $udt$.

Thus $$u = \dot{x} - ry + qz. \quad \text{(A1.1)}$$

Similarly, if $v$ and $w$ are the velocity components of $P$ parallel to $Oy$ and $Oz$ respectively,

$$v = \dot{y} - pz + rx \quad \text{(A1.2)}$$
and $$w = \dot{z} - qx + py. \quad \text{(A1.3)}$$

If the origin $O$ has velocity components $(U, V, W)$ at time $t$, parallel to the instantaneous positions of $Ox$, $Oy$, $Oz$, the velocity components of $P$ are

$$u = U + \dot{x} - ry + qz, \quad \text{(A1.4)}$$
$$v = V + \dot{y} - pz + rx \quad \text{(A1.5)}$$
and $$w = W + \dot{z} - qx + py. \quad \text{(A1.6)}$$

At time $t$, the velocity components of $P$ are $(u, v, w)$ referred to $Oxyz$; at time $t + dt$, the velocity components of $P$ are $(u + \dot{u}dt, v + \dot{v}dt, w + \dot{w}dt)$ referred to $Ox'y'z'$. Hence, by a precisely similar method to that given above, the components of acceleration of $P$ parallel to $Ox$, $Oy$, $Oz$ are $a_x$, $a_y$, $a_z$ respectively, where

$$a_x = \dot{u} - rv + qw, \quad \text{(A1.7)}$$
$$a_y = \dot{v} - pw + ru, \quad \text{(A1.8)}$$
$$a_z = \dot{w} - qu + pv. \quad \text{(A1.9)}$$

## COMPONENTS OF VELOCITY AND ACCELERATION FOR A POINT FIXED IN A MOVING BODY REFERRED TO MOVING AXES

If the point $P$ is fixed in the body, the coordinates $(x, y, z)$ are constants and we have

$$u = U - ry + qz, \quad \text{(A1.10)}$$
$$v = V - pz + rx \quad \text{(A1.11)}$$
and $$w = W - qx + py. \quad \text{(A1.12)}$$

From Eqs. (A1.7) - (A1.12), if $P$ is fixed in the body, the components of acceleration of $P$ parallel to $Ox$, $Oy$, $Oz$ are given by

$$a_x = \dot{U} - rV + qW - (q^2 + r^2)x + (qp - \dot{r})y + (rp + \dot{q})z, \quad \text{(A1.13)}$$
$$a_y = \dot{V} - pW + rU - (r^2 + p^2)y + (rq - \dot{p})z + (pq + \dot{r})x \quad \text{(A1.14)}$$
and $$a_z = \dot{W} - qU + pV - (p^2 + q^2)z + (pr - \dot{q})x + (qr + \dot{p})y. \quad \text{(A1.15)}$$

## D'ALEMBERT'S PRINCIPLE

When the mass is constant, from Newton's laws of motion, the product of the mass of a particle and its resolved acceleration in a given direction equals the force acting on the particle in that direction. The *inertia force* of a particle is defined to be the product of the *reversed* acceleration and the mass. Thus a particle is in equilibrium under the action of the given forces together with the inertia forces.

Now a rigid body may be considered as a large number of particles; thus the whole system of forces acting on the body (including inertia forces) must be in equilibrium. The body may be acted upon by external forces and internal forces; the internal forces are due to the actions of the particles of the body on one another (e.g. internal tensile and compressive forces) and occur in equal and opposite pairs, since, by Newton's third law, actions and reactions are equal and opposite. We see that the internal forces of the body cancel one another; thus the body is in equilibrium under the action of the external forces and the inertia forces.

From the above we see that:

(i) *The sum of the resolved parts in any direction of the inertia forces and the external forces is zero*, and

(ii) *The sum of the moments about any axis due to the inertia forces and the external forces is zero*,

*the summations in* (i) *and* (ii) *being taken over the whole body*. This is *d'Alembert's principle*.

## EQUATIONS OF MOTION FOR A RIGID BODY REFERRED TO BODY AXES THROUGH THE CENTRE OF GRAVITY

We refer the equations to a set of rectangular axes $Oxyz$ through the centre of gravity $O$, the axes being fixed in the body and moving with the body. The body is considered to be made up of particles such as that at $P(x,y,z)$ of mass $\delta m$, acted upon by external forces $X_m$, $Y_m$, $Z_m$ and having components of acceleration $a_x$, $a_y$, $a_z$ parallel to the instantaneous position of the axes at time $t$. Figure A1.2 shows the external and inertia forces acting on the mass $\delta m$.

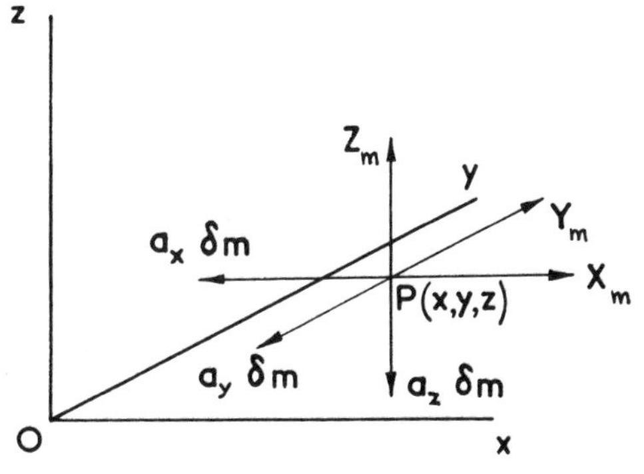


Fig. A1.2 External and inertia forces acting on a mass $\delta m$.

Applying d'Alembert's principle to the resolved parts of the forces parallel to $Ox$, $Oy$, $Oz$ respectively, we obtain

$$\Sigma(X_m - a_x\delta m) = 0, \tag{A1.16}$$

$$\Sigma(Y_m - a_y\delta m) = 0 \tag{A1.17}$$

and

$$\Sigma(Z_m - a_z\delta m) = 0, \tag{A1.18}$$

the summations being taken over the whole body.

Similarly, for the moments about $Ox$, $Oy$, $Oz$ respectively,

$$\Sigma[y(Z_m - a_z\delta m) - z(Y_m - a_y\delta m)] = 0, \tag{A1.19}$$

$$\Sigma[z(X_m - a_x\delta m) - x(Z_m - a_z\delta m)] = 0, \tag{A1.20}$$

$$\Sigma[x(Y_m - a_y\delta m) - y(X_m - a_x\delta m)] = 0. \tag{A1.21}$$

The whole system of external forces acting on the body can be reduced to the forces $X$, $Y$, $Z$ acting at $O$ parallel to the axes, together with the couples $L$, $M$, $N$ about $Ox$, $Oy$, $Oz$ respectively.

From Eqs. (A1.16) - (A.1.21),

$$\Sigma a_x\delta m = \Sigma X_m = X, \tag{A1.22}$$

$$\Sigma a_y\delta m = \Sigma Y_m = Y, \tag{A1.23}$$

$$\Sigma a_z\delta m = \Sigma Z_m = Z, \tag{A1.24}$$

$$\Sigma(ya_z - za_y)\delta m = \Sigma(yZ_m - zY_m) = L, \tag{A1.25}$$

$$\Sigma(za_x - xa_z)\delta m = \Sigma(zX_m - xZ_m) = M, \tag{A1.26}$$

$$\Sigma(xa_y - ya_x)\delta m = \Sigma(xY_m - yX_m) = N. \tag{A1.27}$$

Now $O$ is the centre of gravity of the body.

Thus

$$\Sigma x\delta m = \Sigma y\delta m = \Sigma z\delta m = 0. \tag{A1.28}$$

We define the following quantities:

$$m = \Sigma\delta m = \text{total mass of the body}, \tag{A1.29}$$

$$I_x = \Sigma(y^2 + z^2)\delta m = \text{moment of inertia about } Ox, \tag{A1.30}$$

$$I_y = \Sigma(z^2 + x^2)\delta m = \text{moment of inertia about } Oy, \tag{A1.31}$$

$$I_z = \Sigma(x^2 + y^2)\delta m = \text{moment of inertia about } Oz, \tag{A1.32}$$

$$I_{yz} = \Sigma yz\delta m = \text{product of inertia about } Oy \text{ and } Oz, \tag{A1.33}$$

$$I_{zx} = \Sigma zx\delta m = \text{product of inertia about } Oz \text{ and } Ox, \tag{A1.34}$$

$$I_{xy} = \Sigma xy\delta m = \text{product of inertia about } Ox \text{ and } Oy. \tag{A1.35}$$

From Eqs. (A1.13) - (A1.15) and (A1.22) - (A1.29), the *equations of motion* parallel to the axes $Ox$, $Oy$, $Oz$ respectively become

$$m(\dot{U} - rV + qW) = X, \tag{A1.36}$$

$$m(\dot{V} - pW + rU) = Y, \tag{A1.37}$$

$$m(\dot{W} - qU + pV) = Z. \tag{A1.38}$$

We see that these equations are the same as those for a particle of mass $m$ at $O$ acted upon by forces equal to the external forces acting on the body.

Consider next the moments about $Ox$, $Oy$, $Oz$ given by Eqs. (A1.25) - (A1.27). From Eqs. (A1.14) and (A1.15), using (A1.28) - (A1.35),

$$\begin{aligned}\Sigma(ya_z - za_y)\delta m &= (\dot{W} - qU + pV)\Sigma y\delta m - (p^2 + q^2)\Sigma yz\delta m + \\ &+ (pr - \dot{q})\Sigma xy\delta m + (qr + \dot{p})\Sigma y^2\delta m - \\ &- (\dot{V} - pW + rU)\Sigma z\delta m + (r^2 + p^2)\Sigma yz\delta m - \\ &- (rq - \dot{p})\Sigma z^2\delta m - (pq + \dot{r})\Sigma zx\delta m \\ &= \dot{p}\Sigma(y^2 + z^2)\delta m - qr\Sigma(z^2 - y^2)\delta m - I_{yz}(q^2 - r^2) - \\ &- I_{zx}(\dot{r} + pq) - I_{xy}(\dot{q} - rp).\end{aligned}$$

Thus Eq. (A1.25) becomes

$$I_x\dot{p} - (I_y - I_z)qr - I_{yz}(q^2 - r^2) - I_{zx}(\dot{r} + pq) - I_{xy}(\dot{q} - rp) = L. \tag{A1.39}$$

Similarly, from Eq. (A1.26),

$$I_y\dot{q} - (I_z - I_x)rp - I_{zx}(r^2 - p^2) - I_{xy}(\dot{p} + qr) - I_{yz}(\dot{r} - pq) = M. \tag{A1.40}$$

and from Eq. (A1.27),

$$I_z\dot{r} - (I_x - I_y)pq - I_{xy}(p^2 - q^2) - I_{yz}(\dot{q} + rp) - I_{zx}(\dot{p} - qr) = N. \tag{A1.41}$$

Equations (A1.39) - (A1.41) are the *equations of angular motion* of the body about $Ox$, $Oy$, $Oz$ respectively, body axes through the centre of gravity $O$.

# Appendix 2

# METHODS OF SOLVING THE STABILITY QUARTIC AND DETERMINATION OF DYNAMIC STABILITY CRITERIA

## INTRODUCTION

As shown in Parts II and III, for both the longitudinal and lateral stability of an aircraft considered as a rigid body, with controls fixed, the characteristic equation can be put in the form

$$\Delta(\lambda) = A\lambda^4 + B\lambda^3 + C\lambda^2 + D\lambda + E = 0, \tag{A2.1}$$

(with $A > 0$) where $B$, $C$, $D$ and $E$ are constants involving the aerodynamic derivatives of the aircraft. In this Appendix we summarize various methods of finding the roots of this equation. We shall also derive the dynamic stability criteria given in Parts II and III.

## LONGITUDINAL STABILITY

As stated in Part II, Chapter 6, for conventional aircraft the coefficients $D$ and $E$ in the characteristic equation (A2.1) are usually small compared respectively with $C$ and $C^2$, and we can factorize the equation in the form

$$\Delta(\lambda) = (a_1\lambda^2 + b_1\lambda + c_1)(\lambda^2 + \gamma_1\lambda + \delta_1), \tag{A2.2}$$

where $\gamma_1$ and $\delta_1$ are small compared with $b_1$ and $c_1$. Equating coefficients of powers of $\lambda$ we find

$$\left.\begin{aligned} a_1 &= A, \\ b_1 + a_1\gamma_1 &= B, \\ c_1 + b_1\gamma_1 + a_1\delta_1 &= C, \\ b_1\delta_1 + c_1\gamma_1 &= D, \\ c_1\delta_1 &= E. \end{aligned}\right\} \tag{A2.3}$$

Thus, as $\gamma_1$ and $\delta_1$ are small compared with $b_1$ and $c_1$, we may take as a first approximation

$$\left.\begin{aligned} b_1 &= B, \\ c_1 &= C, \\ \delta_1 &= \frac{E}{c_1}, \\ \gamma_1 &= \frac{c_1 D - b_1 E}{c_1^2} \end{aligned}\right\} \qquad (A2.4)$$

We can then write the approximate factors of $\Delta(\lambda)$ as

$$\Delta(\lambda) = (A\lambda^2 + B\lambda + C)\left(\lambda^2 + \frac{CD - BE}{C^2}\lambda + \frac{E}{C}\right). \qquad (A2.5)$$

The roots of the two quadratic factors can easily be found. In general, for a conventional aircraft, the equation

$$A\lambda^2 + B\lambda + C = 0$$

will have a pair of complex roots, corresponding to the highly damped short period oscillation.

The equation

$$\lambda^2 + \frac{CD - BE}{C^2}\lambda + \frac{E}{C} = 0$$

will, in general, have a pair of complex roots corresponding to the lightly damped long period oscillation (phugoid oscillation).

## Exact solution

Having found the approximate values of the roots from Eq. (A2.5), we can find the exact solution by using an iterative process on equations (A2.3), substituting the values of $b_1$, $c_1$, $\gamma_1$, $\delta_1$ to find second approximations $b_2$, $c_2$, $\gamma_2$, $\delta_2$, given by

$$\begin{aligned} b_2 &= B - A\gamma_1, \\ c_2 &= C - b_1\gamma_1 - A\delta_1, \\ \gamma_2 &= \frac{c_2 D - b_2 E}{c_2^2}, \\ \delta_2 &= \frac{E}{c_2}, \end{aligned}$$

and so on for higher approximations.

## Example

To find the roots of the equation

$$\Delta(\lambda) = \lambda^4 + 5\lambda^3 + 7\lambda^2 + 0.5\lambda + 0.2 = 0.$$

Here $A = 1$, $B = 5$, $C = 7$, $D = 0.5$, $E = 0.2$.

We see that $D$ and $E$ are small compared respectively with $C$ and $C^2$ and thus we can use the above method.

*First approximation*

$$CD - BE = 2.5,$$

$$\gamma_1 = \frac{CD - BE}{C^2} = 0.0510,$$

$$\delta_1 = \frac{E}{C} = 0.0286.$$

Therefore $\Delta(\lambda) \simeq (\lambda^2 + 5\lambda + 7)(\lambda^2 + 0.0510\lambda + 0.0286) = 0,$

having roots $\lambda = -2.5 \pm 0.866i, \quad -0.0255 \pm 0.167\, i.$

*Second approximation*

$$b_2 = B - A\gamma_1 = 4.949,$$
$$c_2 = C - \gamma_1 b_1 - A\delta_1 = 6.716,$$
$$c_2 D - B_2 E = 2.368,$$

$$\gamma_2 = \frac{c_2 D - b_2 E}{c_2{}^2} = 0.05250,$$

$$\delta_2 = \frac{E}{c_2} = 0.0298.$$

Therefore $\Delta(\lambda) \simeq (\lambda^2 + 4.949\lambda + 6.716)(\lambda^2 + 0.05250\lambda + 0.0298),$

having roots $\lambda = -2.475 \pm 0.770i, \quad -0.0263 \pm 0.172i.$

*Third approximation*

$$b_3 = B - A\gamma_2 = 4.948,$$
$$c_3 = C - \gamma_2 b_2 - A\delta_2 = 6.703,$$
$$c_3 D - b_3 E = 2.364,$$

$$\gamma_3 = \frac{c_3 D - b_3 E}{c_3{}^2} = 0.05254$$

$$\delta_3 = \frac{E}{c_3} = 0.02982.$$

Therefore $\Delta(\lambda) \simeq (\lambda^2 + 4.948\lambda + 6.708)(\lambda^2 + 0.05254\lambda + 0.02982),$

having roots $\lambda = -2.474 \pm 0.766i, \quad -0.02627 \pm 0.1707i.$

Comparing the second and third approximations, we see that the method gives rapid convergence and that the roots are correct to at least three significant figures.

Alternative method when the static margin is very small

There is an alternative method when the coefficient $E$ (proportional to the static margin) is very small compared with $D$. Considering small values of $\lambda$ we see that the characteristic equation will have an approximate root

$$\lambda = -\frac{E}{D}.$$

We note that (if $D$ is positive) the corresponding motion will be a subsidence if $E > 0$, and a divergence if $E < 0$.

LATERAL STABILITY

As stated in Part III, Chapter 10, for conventional aircraft the coefficient $A$ in the characteristic equation (A2.1) is approximately equal to 1, $B$ is usually much greater than unity, and the coefficient $E$ is much smaller than $D$. $E$ may be negative. Considering very small values of $\lambda$, we see that the characteristic equation for lateral stability has an approximate root

$$\lambda = -E/D.$$

Considering large values of $\lambda$, we see that the characteristic equation for lateral stability has an approximate root

$$\lambda = -B/A \simeq -B.$$

Thus, in general, for conventional aircraft, the characteristic equation for lateral stability has (i) a small root $\lambda \simeq -E/D$, corresponding to a slow spiral divergence ($E < 0$) or subsidence ($E > 0$), (ii) a large root $\lambda \simeq -B$, corresponding to the damped rolling subsidence, and (iii) a pair of complex roots corresponding to an oscillation.

Exact solution

We first determine the approximate value of the small root, improving the approximation as shown below. Taking out this root, we are left with a cubic, which has an approximate large root $\lambda \simeq -B$, and we find the exact solution by a similar method. Finally, we can solve the remaining quadratic factor.

*Example:* $\Delta(\lambda) = \lambda^4 + 13\lambda^3 + 12\lambda^2 + 10\lambda + 0.8 = 0.$

We see that $B$ is much greater than unity and $E$ is small compared with $D$ and thus we can use the above method.

The approximate value of the small root is $-E/D = -0.08$.

We find $\Delta(\lambda) = (\lambda + 0.08)(\lambda^3 + 12.92\lambda^2 + 10.97\lambda + 9.12) + 0.070.$

For the second approximation we take $\lambda = -\dfrac{E}{9.12} = -0.088.$

Then $\Delta(\lambda) = (\lambda + 0.088)(\lambda^3 + 12.91\lambda^2 + 10.86\lambda + 9.04) + 0.0045.$

For the third approximation we take $\lambda = -\dfrac{E}{9.04} = -0.0885.$

Then $\Delta(\lambda) = (\lambda + 0.0885)(\lambda^3 + 12.91\lambda^2 + 10.86\lambda + 9.039) + 0.00005.$

Thus the small root is -0.0885 to three significant figures.

For the remaining cubic, $F(\lambda) = \lambda^3 + 12.91\lambda^2 + 10.86\lambda + 9.039$, we write

$$\lambda = -12.91 - \frac{10.86}{\lambda} - \frac{9.039}{\lambda^2} + R,$$

where $R$ is zero when $F(\lambda) = 0$.

The first approximation to the large root is -12.91. A better approximation can be found either by direct substitution of values of $\lambda$ in $F(\lambda)$ to find where the zero occurs or, if $D/B^2$ is small, by continued iteration as shown below.

The second approximation is then

$$\lambda = -12.91 + \frac{10.86}{12.91} - \frac{9.039}{166.7} = -12.12.$$

The third approximation is given by

$$\lambda = -12.91 + \frac{10.86}{12.12} - \frac{9.039}{146.9} = -12.07.$$

Therefore $F(\lambda) = (\lambda + 12.07)(\lambda^2 + 0.838\lambda + 0.747)$.

Thus the large root is −12.07 and the complex roots are $-0.419 \pm 0.756i$.

## FERRARI'S METHOD (REDUCING CUBIC METHOD)

The above methods are applicable when the given relations hold between the various coefficients. There is, however, a general analytical solution of the quartic equation due to Ferrari (see ref. 1). This is the classical method first published in 1579. It contrasts with more modern methods in that it gives an *exact algebraic method* of reducing the solution of any quartic equation to that of a cubic. It thus has the virtue of not requiring any initial guess at the values of the roots. It is particularly useful when we suspect that the given quartic has no real roots and is not of the standard type.

The quartic equation

$$\Delta(\lambda) = A\lambda^4 + B\lambda^3 + C\lambda^2 + D\lambda + E = 0 \qquad \text{(A2.6)}$$

can always be expressed as the product of two quadratic factors

$$\Delta(\lambda) = A(\lambda^2 + p\lambda + r)(\lambda^2 + q\lambda + s), \qquad \text{(A2.7)}$$

where $p$, $q$, $r$ and $s$ are real.

Equating coefficients of powers of $\lambda$ in Eqs. (A2.6) and (A2.7), we obtain

$$A(p + q) = B, \qquad \text{(A2.8)}$$

$$A(pq + r + s) = C, \qquad \text{(A2.9)}$$

$$A(ps + qr) = D, \qquad \text{(A2.10)}$$

$$Ars = E. \qquad \text{(A2.11)}$$

Multiplying Eq. (A2.9) by $p$ and subtracting Eq. (A2.10),

$$A(p - q)r = p(C - Apq) - D. \qquad \text{(A2.12)}$$

Multiplying Eq. (A2.9) by $q$ and subtracting Eq. (A2.10),

$$A(q - p)s = q(C - Apq) - D. \qquad \text{(A2.13)}$$

Multiplying Eqs. (A2.12) and (A2.13), and using Eq. (A2.11),

$$-A^2(p-q)^2E = A[p(C-Apq) - D][q(C-Apq) - D],$$

i.e. $$-A^2E[(p+q)^2 - 4pq] = Apq(C-Apq)^2 - A(C-Apq)D(p+q) + AD^2.$$

Using Eq. (A2.8) and writing

$$Apq = \mu, \qquad \text{(A2.14)}$$

We have $-B^2E + 4AE\mu = \mu[C^2 - 2C\mu + \mu^2] - BCD + BD\mu + AD^2,$

i.e. $\mu^3 - 2C\mu^2 + S\mu - R = 0,$ (A2.15)

where $S = BD + C^2 - 4AE$

and $R = BCD - B^2E - AD^2.$

Equation (A2.15) is the reducing cubic corresponding to the quartic equation (A2.6).

We note that $R$ is the familiar Routh's discriminant for a quartic. Now $p$ and $q$ are real, and, from Eq. (A2.8),

$$\mu = Apq = \tfrac{1}{4}A\,[(p+q)^2 - (p-q)^2] \leq B^2/4A.$$

Thus the cubic equation (A2.15) has at least one real root,

$$\mu = Apq \leq B^2/4A. \quad \text{(A2.16)}$$

We therefore solve Eq. (A2.15) for this root. This can easily be done by an iterative process as shown below. Then, from Eqs. (A2.8) and (A2.16), knowing $pq$ and $p+q$, we can find $p$ and $q$ and hence, from Eqs. (A2.9) and (A2.10) or (A2.11), we can find $r$ and $s$. Thus we can completely determine the quadratic factors in Eq. (A2.7) and hence the roots of the quartic equation (A2.6).

Example

$$\Delta(\lambda) = \lambda^4 + \lambda^3 + 12\lambda^2 + 10\lambda + 25 = 0. \quad \text{(A2.17)}$$

We see that $D$ is not small compared with the other coefficients. We use Ferrari's method.

$A = 1,\quad B = 1,\quad C = 12,\quad D = 10,\quad E = 25,$

$BD = 10,\quad C^2 = 144,\quad 4AE = 100,$

$BCD = 120,\quad AD^2 = 100,\quad B^2E = 25,$

$2C = 24,\quad S = 54,\quad R = -5.$

In this example $B$, $D$ and $E$ are positive, but $R$ is negative. Thus the corresponding dynamical system is unstable.

The reducing cubic given by Eq. (A2.15) is

$$f(\mu) = \mu^3 - 24\mu^2 + 54\mu + 5 = 0, \quad \text{(A2.18)}$$

and we have to look for a real root $\mu \leq B^2/4A = 0.25$. We see that the constant term in Eq. (A.2.18) is much smaller than the coefficient of $\mu$, and thus, by similar reasoning to that given above, Eq. (A2.18) has an approximate small root

$$\mu = -\frac{5}{54} \simeq -0.09.$$

We find
$$f(\mu) = (\mu + 0.09)(\mu^2 - 24.1\mu + 56.2) - 0.058.$$

For the second approximation we take

$$\mu = -\frac{5}{56.2} = -0.089.$$

Then
$$f(\mu) = (\mu + 0.089)(\mu^2 - 24.09 \quad + 56.14) - 0.004.$$

For the third approximation we take

$$\mu = -\frac{5}{56.14} = -0.0891.$$

Then $$f(\mu) = (\mu + 0.0891)(\mu^2 - 24.09 \quad + 56.15) + 0.003.$$

Thus
$$Apq = \mu = -0.0891,$$
$$A(p+q) = B = 1, \quad \text{and } A = 1.$$
$$p - q = \surd[(p+q)^2 - 4pq] = 1.1647.$$

Thus $p = 1.0824, \quad q = -0.0824.$

Hence $A(r+s) = C - Apq = 12.089, \quad$ i.e. $\quad r + s = 12.089$

and $A(ps + qr) = D,$

i.e. $1.0824s - 0.0824r = 10,$

i.e. $-s + 0.0761r = 9.239.$

Thus $r = 2.648, \quad s = 9.441,$

and from Eq. (A2.7),

$$\Delta(\lambda) = (\lambda^2 + 1.0824\lambda + 2.648)(\lambda^2 - 0.0824\lambda + 9.441).$$

$$\left[\begin{array}{l}\text{Check: multiplying out, we find} \\ \Delta(\lambda) = \lambda^4 + 1.0000\lambda^3 + 11.9998\lambda^2 + 10.0007\lambda + 24.9998\end{array}\right].$$

Finally, solving for the roots of the two quadratic factors, we find that the roots of Eq. (A2.17) are given by

$$\lambda = -0.5412 \pm 1.535i, \qquad 0.0412 \pm 3.072i.$$

The first pair of roots corresponds to a damped oscillation, the second pair to an increasing oscillation.

## DYNAMIC STABILITY CRITERIA

We shall now derive the necessary and sufficient conditions for the stability of the dynamic system with characteristic equation (A2.1). We write

$$\begin{aligned}\Delta(\lambda) &= A\lambda^4 + B\lambda^3 + C\lambda^2 + D\lambda + E \\ &= A(\lambda^2 + p\lambda + r)(\lambda^2 + q\lambda + s) = 0,\end{aligned} \tag{A2.19}$$

where $A > 0$ and $p$, $q$, $r$ and $s$ are real.

Consider the quadratic equation

$$\lambda^2 + p\lambda + r = 0. \tag{A2.20}$$

Figure A2.1 shows how the nature of the roots of Eq. (A2.20) varies as we vary $p$ and $r$. Eq.(A.2.20) will have a pair of imaginary roots if $p^2 < 4r$. If, in addition, $p > 0$, they correspond to a damped oscillation, while, if $p < 0$, they correspond to an increasing oscillation. If $p^2 > 4r$, Eq. (A2.20) will have a pair of real roots. These will both be negative, corresponding to two subsidences, if and only if $p$ and $r$ are both positive. From Fig. A2.1 we see that the necessary and sufficient conditions that the equation

$$\lambda^2 + p\lambda + r = 0$$

should have no real positive roots, and no complex roots with positive real parts, are that $p > 0$, $r > 0$.

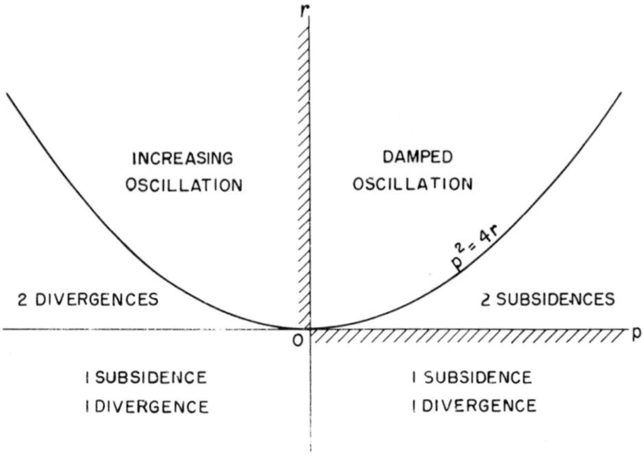


Fig. A2.1 Stability boundaries for the quadratic equation $\lambda^2 + p\lambda + r = 0$ (the boundaries are shaded on their unstable sides).

Thus, in Eq. (A2.19), the necessary and sufficient conditions for stability are

$$p > 0, \quad q > 0, \quad r > 0, \quad s > 0. \tag{A2.21}$$

We shall prove that the dynamic stability criteria given in Parts II and III are equivalent to Eq. (A2.21).

From Eq. (A2.19), equating coefficients of powers of $\lambda$, we find that

$$\left.\begin{aligned} B &= A(p+q), \\ C &= A(pq+r+s), \\ D &= A(ps+qr), \\ E &= Ars. \end{aligned}\right\} \tag{A2.22}$$

Then, in the notation of Part I (Chapter 6), the test functions $T_2$ and $T_3$ are given by

$$\begin{aligned} T_2 = BC - AD &= A^2[(p+q)(pq+r+s) - (ps+qr)] \\ &= A^2[(p+q)pq + pr + qs], \end{aligned} \tag{A2.23}$$

$$\begin{aligned} R = T_3 &= DT_2 - B^2E \\ &= A^3(ps+qr)[(p+q)pq+pr+qs] - A^3(p+q)^2rs \\ &= A^3pq[(p+q)(ps+qr) + (r-s)^2]. \end{aligned} \tag{A2.24}$$

If Eq. (A2.21) is satisfied we see from Eqs. (A2.22) and (A2.24) that (with $A > 0$)

$$B > 0, \quad D > 0, \quad E > 0 \text{ and } R > 0. \tag{A2.25}$$

Thus the conditions given by Eq. (A2.25) are *necessary* for stability; we shall now show they are sufficient.

Consider a quartic equation in the form of Eq. (A2.19) with real quadratic factors, and suppose that the conditions given by Eq. (A2.25) are satisfied.

Now Eq. (A2.24) can be put in the form

$$R = Apq[BD + A^2(r-s)^2]. \tag{A2.26}$$

From Eqs. (A2.25) and (A2.26) we see that (with $A > 0$), $pq > 0$. Hence, as $B = A(p+q) > 0$ and $pq > 0$, with $p$ and $q$ both real,

$$p > 0, \quad q > 0. \tag{A2.27}$$

Also $A(ps + qr) = D > 0$
and $Apqrs = pqE > 0.$

Therefore, as $p$, $q$, $r$ and $s$ are real,

$$ps > 0, \quad qr > 0,$$

and hence, from Eq. (A2.27),

$$r > 0, \quad s > 0.$$

Thus Eqs. (A2.21) are satisfied and hence the system is stable. Thus the *necessary and sufficient conditions* that the dynamical system with the characteristic equation

$$A\lambda^4 + B\lambda^3 + C\lambda^2 + D\lambda + E = 0$$

(with $A > 0$) should be stable are

$$B > 0, \quad D > 0, \quad E > 0, \quad R > 0,$$

where $R = BCD - AD^2 - B^2E.$

If Eq. (A2.19) has a pair of equal and opposite roots, $\lambda = \pm\beta$, where $\beta$ may be real or totally imaginary, then one quadratic factor will be

$$\lambda^2 - \beta^2.$$

Then either $p$ or $q$ is zero and hence, from Eq. (A2.24), $R = 0$.

Conversely, if $B$ and $D$ are of the same sign, and if $R = 0$, from Eq. (A2.26), either $p = 0$ or $q = 0$, and the quartic equation has a factor $(\lambda^2 - \beta^2)$. Taking $p = 0$, we find

$$Aq = B,$$
$$Aqr = D.$$

Thus $r = -\beta^2 = D/B > 0$
and $As = C - Ar = C - (AD/B).$

Eq. (A2.19) then has quadratic factors

$$\Delta(\lambda) = \left(\lambda^2 + \frac{D}{B}\right)\left(A\lambda^2 + B\lambda + C - \frac{AD}{B}\right).$$

Finally, the necessary and sufficient condition for the quartic Eq. (A2.19) to have a zero root is $E = 0$.

## REFERENCES

1. TURNBULL, H.W. *Theory of Equations*. Oliver & Boyd (1946).

# INDEX